Mégers

Poultry Production

By

Leslie E. Card, Ph.D.

Professor of Animal Science, Emeritus, University of Illinois, Urbana, Illinois

and

Malden C. Nesheim, Ph.D.

*Associate Professor of Animal Nutrition, Cornell University,
Ithaca, New York*

Tenth Edition, Thoroughly Revised

With 195 Illustrations and 4 Plates, 2 in Color

LEA & FEBIGER

PHILADELPHIA

SBN–8121–0031–X

Printed in the United States of America

Library of Congress Catalog Card Number 66–23239

Preface to the Tenth Edition

TECHNOLOGICAL changes in poultry and egg production and processing have been so extensive that the poultry industry of 1966 is completely different from what it was ten or fifteen years ago. Practices in all phases of poultry production—breeding, feeding, management, housing and marketing—have become so highly specialized that they cannot be covered in complete detail in a book such as this. Instead of trying to develop a comprehensive manual for poultry raising, we have stressed the fundamental principles underlying successful poultry and egg production, thereby providing a base on which to build a working knowledge of poultry science.

The organization of the book has not been changed from that of the ninth edition, but Chapters 1, 7, 8, 9, 10 and 14 have been almost completely rewritten. We have continued to stress the results of research and the interpretation of new findings as they apply to poultry practice. Recent statistical data on the poultry industry have been included.

Our colleagues at Cornell University and at the University of Illinois have offered many helpful suggestions, and for these we are particularly grateful.

Dr. Bradley M. Patten and The Blakiston Division, McGraw-Hill Book Co., Inc., permitted the use of four illustrations from the fourth edition of "Early Embryology of the Chick," and The Company of Biologists, Ltd., Cambridge, England, granted permission to reproduce from the *Journal of Experimental Biology* the illustrations used in Plate II.

Credit for the use of illustrations made available to us by various other organizations and individuals has been indicated in the legends.

L. E. C.
M. C. N.

August, 1966

Contents

Chapter 1

The Poultry Industry

Of the 2.4 million commercial farms in the United States in 1959, only 103,000 were classified as poultry farms, that is, farms which realized 50 per cent or more of their total sales from poultry and poultry products. But these farms provided 80 per cent of the total value of poultry products from all commercial farms in the country. This is in sharp contrast to conditions thirty years earlier when 85 per cent of all farms reported chickens and 62 per cent reported sales of eggs averaging 505 dozens per farm. In the five years from 1954 to 1959, the number of farms reporting chickens declined by 1.3 million to half as many as in 1949.

Clearly the business of producing poultry and eggs, like many other phases of commercial farm production, is concentrating in fewer hands. The shift has been accelerated in recent years by increasing and prolonged cost-price pressures which in turn have provided the incentive for many technological developments in the industry.

There has been geographical concentration also. Nearly half of the nation's poultry farms in 1959 were found in seven states with from five to ten thousand each (see Table 1–1). More than half of the commercial broilers produced in 1964 were raised in the four states of Georgia, Arkansas, Alabama and North Carolina, with about one-fourth of them coming from the ten leading counties. Poultry farms accounted for 39 per cent of all commercial farms in Delaware in 1959, and 31 per cent in New Jersey. They were among the three leading farm types in the six New England States as well as in New York, Pennsylvania, West Virginia and Georgia.

Poultry production exists as an industry because poultry and eggs are prized as human food. Chickens are often raised as a hobby, feathers are put to many different uses, and great quantities of eggs are used in the preparation of therapeutic vaccines, but all these things are distinctly secondary to the use of poultry and eggs as human food. Furthermore, the business of producing, processing, transporting, storing, financing, and serving food gives employment to more persons in this country than do all other businesses combined. Poultry meat and eggs are important commodities in the food business.

Changes in population can have significant effects on the poultry business. In 1930 California shipped more eggs to New York, Chicago and Philadelphia than it did to either of its own markets,

San Francisco and Los Angeles. Since 1950 it has shipped almost no eggs east, and its own poultry industry has greatly expanded in order to meet the needs of its rapidly growing population. In 1959 California surpassed Iowa to become the leading state in total number of eggs produced. By 1963 California was producing as many eggs as the next two states combined.

Table 1–1.—The Ten Leading States in Number of Poultry Farms* and in Total Value of Poultry Products Sold, 1959. (From the U. S. Census of Agriculture, 1959.)

Rank	State	Number of poultry farms	Rank	State	Poultry products sold (millions)
1	Georgia	9,923	1	California	$210
2	California	7,023	2	Georgia	166
3	Pennsylvania	6,920	3	Pennsylvania	115
4	North Carolina	6,209	4	Texas	101
5	Texas	5,394	5	Minnesota	100
6	Alabama	5,378	6	North Carolina	99
7	Arkansas	5,018	7	Iowa	98
8	New York	3,693	8	Alabama	95
9	New Jersey	3,593	9	Arkansas	94
10	Indiana	3,162	10	Indiana	76
Ten-State Total		56,313	Ten-State Total		$1,154
United States (50)		103,279	United States (50)		$2,257

* A poultry farm, as defined by the Census, is one on which 50 per cent or more of total sales was realized from poultry products.

Table 1–2.—The Ten Leading States in Gross Poultry Income from Broilers, Other Chickens and Eggs, 1964. Based on Estimates by the U. S. Department of Agriculture.

		Millions of Dollars			
Rank	State	Broilers	Other Chickens	Eggs	Total
1	Georgia	174.2	8.2	112.4	294.8
2	California	34.8	7.0	204.8	246.6
3	Arkansas	126.4	3.2	69.7	199.3
4	Alabama	111.4	5.2	73.5	190.1
5	North Carolina	101.5	7.3	77.2	186.0
6	Texas	66.2	4.0	77.5	147.7
7	Mississippi	68.9	2.8	72.9	144.6
8	Pennsylvania	24.5	6.9	95.9	127.3
9	Iowa	1.6	4.0	80.5	86.1
10	Maryland	75.6	0.6	9.1	85.3
United States*		1,069.0	105.6	1,805.9	2,980.5

* Alaska and Hawaii not included

Table 1–3.—The Rank of the First Ten States in Percentage of Total Farm Cash Receipts Derived from Poultry and Eggs, 1964, with Comparisons for Earlier Years. (Data from the U. S. Department of Agriculture.)

Rank	State	1964	1959	1949	1939	1929
1	Delaware	61	54	71	57	33
2	Maine	35	39	26	14	12
3	Georgia	33	28	13	5	5
4	Alabama	30	23	7	5	3
5	New Hampshire	30	41	47	33	27
6	Maryland	29	26	30	18	18
7	Connecticut	27	29	31	23	18
8	Arkansas	24	15	9	6	4
9	West Virginia	21	25	31	18	20
10	New Jersey	21	29	39	23	23
	United States (50)	9	9	11	11	10

Table 1–4.—The Ten Leading Counties in Chickens and Eggs Sold in 1959, with Comparisons for 1954 and 1949. (From U. S. Census Reports.)

Chickens Sold				Eggs Sold			
County	Rank			County	Rank		
	1959	1954	1949		1959	1954	1949
Sussex, Del.	1	1	1	San Bernardino, Calif.	1	3	6
Scott, Miss.	2	5	49	Lancaster, Pa.	2	6	5
Washington, Ark.	3	2	4	San Diego, Calif.	3	8	11
Benton, Ark.	4	3	3	Orange, Calif.	4	9	26
Wicomico, Md.	5	4	7	Sonoma, Calif.	5	4	1
Worcester, Md.	6	8	2	Monmouth, N. J.	6	2	3
Cullman, Ala.	7	24	74	Los Angeles, Calif.	7	1	2
Hall, Ga.	8	6	12	Cumberland, N. J.	8	7	8
Cherokee, Ga.	9	7	5	Ocean, N. J.	9	5	4
Forsyth, Ga.	10	10	13	Stanislaus, Calif.	10	14	27

GROWTH OF THE INDUSTRY

The poultry industry has shown a tremendous growth in the last twenty-five years, largely because of a complete and fundamental change in viewpoint. Instead of keeping chickens as a hobby or a sideline, for pleasure and some incidental profit, thousands of flock owners have come to look upon the poultry enterprise on their farms as an economic unit, a means of livelihood, a source of income by which to raise and educate a family and acquire a certain degree of economic independence. Instead of keeping chickens, they have made the chickens keep them.

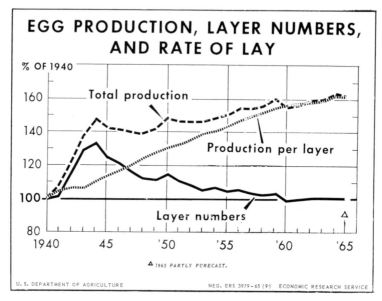

FIG. 1–1.—Annual rate of lay has been increasing steadily for 25 years, so that total production has increased in spite of fewer layers. (Data from U. S. Department of Agriculture.)

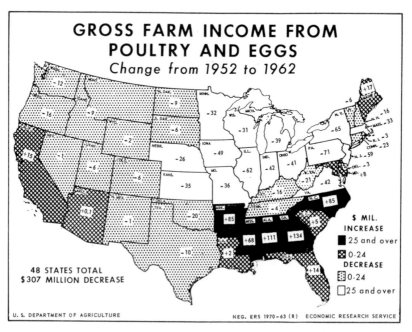

FIG. 1–2.—Gross farm income from poultry and eggs has been increasing in the Southeastern States and declining in the North Central and Middle Atlantic regions. (Data from U. S. Department of Agriculture.)

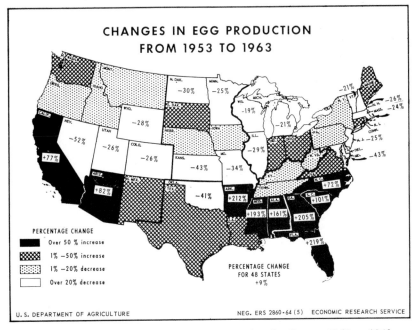

FIG. 1–3.—Percentage change in egg production, by States, 1953 to 1963. (Data from U. S. Department of Agriculture.)

In January, 1925, the U. S. Department of Agriculture began reporting the number of eggs produced each month for each 100 layers on farms. For twelve years the annual total ranged a little above or below 120 eggs for each hen and pullet in farm flocks. Then in 1937 there began a steady and almost continuous rise in production which brought the 1964 figure to 216, 80 per cent above the average for the first twelve years of record.

There are several reasons for this spectacular rise, and the increased production has, in turn, been responsible for many other marked changes in the poultry industry. In 1928, about 43 per cent of the chickens raised on farms were hatched under hens, and only 23 per cent were bought as baby chicks. By 1938, 66 per cent of the chickens raised were purchased as baby chicks. In 1959, this figure had risen to 96 per cent and, in addition, commercial hatcheries produced over 1,800 million chicks for the commercial broiler trade. This change has enabled producers to start their chicks earlier than is usually possible when all must be hatched on the farm where they are grown. The pullets raised from these early chicks are ready to lay in September or October instead of in November or December.

Early hatching by commercial operators meant that breeding flocks had to be in production well in advance of the usual hatching season. This was accomplished in part by the early hatching of a previous year, in part by better feeding and management methods, and in part by selection and breeding for the ability to lay well. These methods will be discussed in some detail in later chapters.

The increase of 80 per cent in annual production per layer from 1937 to 1964 was gained chiefly by improved performance in the months of September through February. The increase in these six months added nearly six dozen eggs to the annual average, whereas the increase during the other six months added only two dozen (see Table 1–6).

Table 1–5.—States in Which Total Egg Production Increased by as Much as 49 Per Cent in 1963 over 1953, or Decreased by as Much as 25 Per Cent. Based on Estimates by the U. S. Department of Agriculture.

Increases		*Decreases*	
State	*Per cent change*	*State*	*Per cent change*
Florida	219	Nevada	52
Arkansas	212	Kansas	43
Georgia	205	Maryland	43
Mississippi	193	Oklahoma	41
Alabama	161	Missouri	34
South Carolina	101	North Dakota	30
Arizona	82	Illinois	29
California	77	Wyoming	28
North Carolina	72	New Hampshire	26
New Mexico	50	Colorado	26
Maine	49	Utah	26
U. S. Total*	9	New Jersey	25

* Alaska and Hawaii not included

Table 1–6.—Egg Production per Layer, by Months, for Indicated Years. (Data from U. S. Department of Agriculture.)

Month	*1929*	*1939*	*1949*	*1959*	*1964**
January	5.9	8.1	12.8	16.8	17.5
February	7.5	9.7	13.6	16.1	17.2
March	13.6	14.9	17.5	19.1	19.2
April	16.7	17.0	18.1	19.1	19.1
May	16.5	17.0	18.2	19.6	19.7
June	14.0	14.6	16.2	18.3	18.7
July	12.7	13.2	15.0	18.0	18.6
August	11.1	11.7	13.6	17.0	17.9
September	8.7	9.3	11.8	15.6	16.9
October	6.3	7.4	11.2	15.8	17.3
November	4.1	6.1	10.9	15.4	16.8
December	4.1	6.8	12.2	16.6	17.6
Totals	121.2	135.8	171.1	207.4	216.5

* Preliminary

The longtime upward trend in egg production per layer is shown also in the records of official egg-laying tests. The following tabulation is for the Storrs (Connecticut) Test which was operated continuously from 1911 to 1961.

Test	Year	Average number of eggs per layer
1st	1911–12	154
5th	1915–16	162
10th	1920–21	160
15th	1925–26	162
20th	1930–31	183
25th	1935–36	192
30th	1940–41	209
35th	1945–46	215*
40th	1950–51	230†
45th	1955–56	231†
50th	1960–61	259†

* 51 weeks
† 50 weeks

Prior to 1937, egg consumption per person in the United States was about 300 eggs a year. With increased production per layer, more eggs of better quality became available, and the American public responded by increasing consumption till it reached a maximum of 403 in 1945. In the last twenty years there has been a gradual decline to about 75 per cent of that figure.

With increased production, fresh eggs are available to more people throughout the year. From 1925, the first year of record, through 1939 (see Table 1–6) there were six months of the year when the average number of eggs per hen was fewer than 10, but by 1949 it was better than 10 in all twelve months, and in 1964 it was 17 or more in all twelve months. This leveling out of production has tended to level out the price. The peak monthly price is much closer to the springtime average price than it was even twenty years ago. Because of more uniform production, fewer shell eggs go into storage. Peak holdings in 1959 were only 10 per cent of what they were thirty years earlier.

Coincidental with the nation-wide increase in average egg production was an even more spectacular rise in the production of commercial broilers. Broilers were being grown on a fairly extensive scale in the Delmarva section (adjoining counties in Delaware, Maryland and Virginia) in the late twenties. In 1934, when the U. S. Department of Agriculture began reporting commercial broilers separately from farm-raised chickens, the U. S. total was 34 million, about 4 per cent of the total chicken meat supply. Broiler production increased, by successive 5-year intervals, to 106 million in 1939, 274 million in 1944, 513 million in 1949, 1,048 million in 1954, and 1,731 million in 1959. In 1964 broilers accounted for 88 per cent of all chicken meat consumption, and 15 per cent of the combined total of chicken, turkey and red meat.

This rapid expansion has been possible largely because of the nation-wide increase in average egg production. Since fewer hens were needed to produce the nation's eggs, fewer farm-raised chickens were grown relative to human food needs, and about one-third of the crop consisted of pullets instead of straight-run chicks of both sexes. This left a gap to be filled by commercial broilers.

But production alone was not enough. New methods of processing, packaging and distribution, especially the retailing of fresh-killed and frozen ready-to-cook broilers, and the fact that such

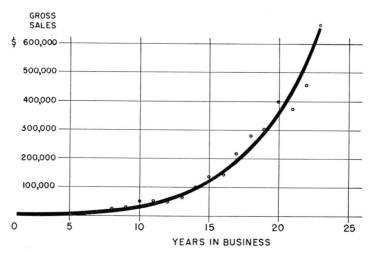

Fig.1–4.—Developing a successful business takes years of hard work, but after twenty-three years this breeder-hatchery was doing better than a half-million-dollar business annually.

broilers were widely available at a favorable price when compared with other meats, favored an increase in consumption. During the five years from 1935 through 1939, chicken meat consumption, converted to a ready-to-cook basis, averaged 13.8 pounds per person per year. Ten years later, during 1945–1949, it had risen to 19.4 pounds, an increase of 41 per cent. Most of the increase was broilers. This increase has continued. The average for 1955–1959 was 25.7 pounds, and the 1964 figure reached an all-time high of 40 pounds.

Since broiler production has been concentrated in new areas, as contrasted with the production of farm-raised chickens, many new processing plants have been built in the broiler areas, even when other well-equipped plants in areas of farm production had to be shut down and devoted to other purposes because of an inadequate local volume of poultry. Similarly, large tonnages of manufactured feeds have moved in new directions to accommodate broiler growers. The same kinds of changes have occurred in respect to baby chicks, equipment for growing chickens, and services of various kinds. As the broiler business became firmly established, many bankers have come to look upon "chicken paper" as among their best risks.

This brief review of developments should be sufficient to indicate the many opportunities for employment in the various phases of the poultry industry. A profitable exercise for any group of poultry students is to make a list of the many kinds of jobs which must be done in order to keep the industry operating efficiently.

THE NATURE OF POULTRY AND EGG PRODUCTION

There are many ways of measuring both the size and the significance of the poultry industry. Several different charts and tables are therefore included in this chapter to give the reader some conception of the nature of the poultry business as an important part of American agriculture. No single ranking of the states will tell the whole story of their relative importance. Georgia now leads in total gross poultry income and in number of commercial broilers raised, but Delaware outranks all other states in the per cent of total farm income realized from poultry products. California produces more eggs than any other state, but is not among the first ten in either eggs produced per person or eggs produced per square mile of land area.

Largely because of the many technological problems involved, the industry is fairly well concentrated in certain geographical areas. The ten leading states, as listed in Tables 1–7, 1–8, 1–9 and 1–10, accounted for 72 per cent of all the chicks hatched, 52 per cent of the farm-raised chickens, 51 per cent of the eggs produced, and 82 per cent of the commercial broilers raised in 1964.

Table 1–7.—The Ten Leading States in Numbers of Chicks Hatched by Commercial Hatcheries, 1964 and 1959. Based on Estimates by the U. S. Department of Agriculture.

Rank	State	Chicks hatched (millions) 1964	Rank	State	Chicks hatched (millions) 1959
1	Georgia	439	1	Georgia	345
2	Arkansas	313	2	Alabama	156
3	Alabama	273	3	Arkansas	154
4	North Carolina	240	4	North Carolina	145
5	Texas	171	5	Texas	134
6	Mississippi	167	6	California	114
7	Maryland	143	7	Mississippi	114
8	California	129	8	Maryland	106
9	Pennsylvania	78	9	Indiana	92
10	Maine	74	10	Missouri	87
United States*		2,830	United States*		2,385

* Alaska and Hawaii not included

Fig. 1–5.—The poultry industry holds several important trade conventions and conferences each year. This is a view of the exhibit hall at the 1966 Fact Finding Conference in Kansas City. (Courtesy of the Institute of American Poultry Industries.)

Table 1–8.—The Ten Leading States in Number of Non-broiler Chicks Raised in 1965 and 1959. Based on Estimates by the U. S. Department of Agriculture.

Rank	State	Number raised (millions) 1965	Rank	State	Number raised (millions) 1959
1	California	30.6	1	California	31.5
2	Georgia	20.3	2	Iowa	28.6
3	Iowa	15.7	3	Minnesota	20.8
4	North Carolina	14.3	4	Pennsylvania	20.3
5	Texas	13.0	5	Georgia	17.5
6	Alabama	12.9	6	North Carolina	16.6
7	Mississippi	12.1	7	Missouri	15.5
8	Pennsylvania	12.1	8	Texas	15.3
9	Indiana	11.2	9	Illinois	14.6
10	Minnesota	11.0	10	Indiana	14.5
United States (50)		296.0	United States*		398.7

* Alaska and Hawaii not included

Table 1–9.—The Ten Leading States in Numbers of Eggs Produced, 1964 and 1959. Based on Estimates by the U. S. Department of Agriculture.

Rank	State	Number of eggs (millions) 1964	Rank	State	Number of eggs (millions) 1959
1	California	7,801	1	California	5,236
2	Iowa	3,818	2	Iowa	5,042
3	Georgia	3,299	3	Minnesota	3,803
4	Pennsylvania	3,143	4	Pennsylvania	3,625
5	Minnesota	2,791	5	Illinois	2,970
6	Texas	2,592	6	Ohio	2,463
7	Ohio	2,424	7	Indiana	2,410
8	North Carolina	2,388	8	Wisconsin	2,401
9	Arkansas	2,242	9	Texas	2,384
10	Indiana	2,182	10	New Jersey	2,379
	United States (50)	64,546		United States*	62,401

* Alaska and Hawaii not included

Table 1–10.—The Ten Leading States in Numbers of Commercial Broilers Raised, 1964 and 1959. Based on Estimates by the U. S. Department of Agriculture.

Rank	State	Number raised (millions) 1964	Rank	State	Number raised (millions) 1959
1	Georgia	374	1	Georgia	303
2	Arkansas	286	2	Arkansas	164
3	Alabama	243	3	Alabama	158
4	North Carolina	213	4	North Carolina	137
5	Mississippi	157	5	Texas	115
6	Texas	139	6	Mississippi	108
7	Maryland	129	7	Maryland	93
8	Delaware	109	8	Delaware	85
9	Maine	68	9	Maine	58
10	California	57	10	Virginia	54
	United States (50)	2,161		United States*	1,731

* Alaska and Hawaii not included

Over one-half of all the farms reporting chickens in 1930, and again in 1940, had flocks of fewer than 50 each, and the average for these 3,000,000 farms was 23 chickens per flock. It was also true in 1960 that about half of all farms reporting chickens had fewer than 50 each, but there were only about one-third as many of them. Most of these farms were in the South, and very few of them sold any eggs in 1959. Furthermore, of the 1.1 million farms that did sell eggs in 1959, 598,000, or 54 per cent, sold fewer than 800 dozens and accounted for less than 4 per cent of all eggs sold.

2

At the other end of the scale were 31,000 farms selling 20,000 or more dozens. They made up less than 3 per cent of all farms selling eggs but accounted for 52 per cent of all eggs sold. And at the very top were 12,000 among these 31,000 farms that sold 50,000 or more dozens in 1959 and accounted for 36 per cent of all eggs sold that year. Perhaps even more indicative of the extent of large-scale egg farming is the fact that 2400 farms, a mere 0.2 per cent of all farms selling eggs in 1959, sold 100,000 or more dozens each and accounted for 16 per cent of the total egg crop.

Large production units have also become the rule in the broiler business. Farms selling 60,000 or more broilers a year increased from 1,687 in 1954 to 6,102 in 1959 and accounted for almost half of all broilers sold in the latter year. Some 2200 commercial broiler farms sold 100,000 or more in 1959 and accounted for 28 per cent of total sales. Half of these farms were located in the 6 states of Arkansas, Georgia, Mississippi, Alabama, Maryland and North Carolina.

Census reports show that when size is measured by dollar value of sales there were 2,000 commercial poultry farms reporting gross sales in 1959 of $100,000 or more. Three-fourths of these farms were located in 17 states. Those in Georgia, Mississippi and Delaware were primarily broiler farms. California led in number of egg farms, while Minnesota, California, Virginia, Iowa and Wisconsin had the most turkey farms.

The same kind of change has occurred in the hatchery phase of the business. From 10,000 chick hatcheries in 1943 the number of hatcheries has declined to about 2,400 in 1965 with very little reduction in total capacity. In 1965 there were 252 chick hatcheries with an egg capacity of 500,000 or more, and they represented 45 per cent of the total hatching capacity of the industry. And there are breeder-hatcheries, in which a farm and a hatchery are combined, with gross annual incomes well in excess of $500,000. The production of poultry and eggs is truly big business.

OTHER PHASES OF THE POULTRY INDUSTRY

This book is concerned primarily with those things that have to do directly with production, and other phases of the industry can be given but brief mention. It is important to remember, however, that the poultry industry as it exists today involves a great deal more than the farm production of poultry and eggs for food or other purposes.

The business of producing chicks for sale began in a small way but has enjoyed a remarkable growth since March 15, 1918, when shipments of day-old chicks were first admitted to the mails. The appearance, in 1922, of room-type mammoth incubators of large capacity gave added impetus to the business and made rapid expansion an easy matter. Most hatcheries today operate on a year-round basis, and weekly placements of broiler chicks in the 22 important broiler-producing states averaged about 40 million in

1964–65. The incubating of eggs and the hatching of chicks have literally been taken off the farm, and this change has had marked effects on many other practices in the industry.

More than 30 million breeding hens are tested annually for pullorum disease, and comparable numbers of chickens must be vaccinated for the prevention of such diseases as fowl pox, laryngotracheitis and Newcastle disease.

A necessary accompaniment of commercial hatching is artificial brooding. Without modern brooding equipment it would have been impossible for the industry to reach anything like its present size.

Adequate rations are essential to such expansion, and in this direction the industry has made such strides that more is known about the nutritional requirements of the chicken than about those of any other farm animal. This, and the fact that several different nutrients can now be produced synthetically at low cost, makes it possible to produce a tremendous tonnage of feed which is vastly superior to the most carefully prepared mixtures of a few years ago. Of the 56 million tons of manufactured feeds, including supplements, produced in 1964, about 49 per cent were poultry feeds.

FIG. 1–6.—A view of the trading floor on the Chicago Mercantile Exchange.

Both changing poultry practices and increased production call for new equipment beyond the ordinary replacement needs of the industry. Incubators, brooders, feeding equipment, egg cases, chick boxes and many other articles must be made in increasing numbers as the industry grows. Leg bands, time clocks, battery brooders, laying batteries, egg cartons, glass substitutes, hardware cloth, insulating boards and automatic feeders have been needed to meet changing practices. Many new kinds of labor-saving equipment have been introduced into poultry and egg processing plants. Refrigerator units are needed by thousands of retail stores offering pan-ready poultry for sale. New demands take the place of old needs as new ideas develop and older practices are discarded.

Table 1–11.—The Ten Leading States in Egg Production per Person and per Square Mile of Land Area, 1964. Based on Production Estimates by the U. S. Department of Agriculture and Population Estimates for July 1, 1964 by the Bureau of the Census.

Rank	State	Eggs per person	Rank	State	Eggs per square mile (Thousands)
1	South Dakota	1974	1	New Jersey	250
2	Iowa	1382	2	Connecticut	158
3	Arkansas	1157	3	Massachusetts	77
4	Maine	963	4	Rhode Island	75
5	Nebraska	951	5	Pennsylvania	70
6	Mississippi	941	6	Iowa	68
7	Minnestoa	792	7	Delaware	64
8	Georgia	768	8	Indiana	60
9	Alabama	635	9	Ohio	59
10	North Dakota	596	10	Georgia	56
	United States (50)	337		United States (50)	18

Table 1–12.—The Ten Leading States in Broiler Production per Person and per Square Mile of Land Area, 1964. Based on Production Estimates by the U. S. Department of Agriculture and Population Estimates for July 1, 1964 by the Bureau of the Census.

Rank	State	Broilers per person	Rank	State	Broilers per square mile (Thousands)
1	Delaware	221	1	Delaware	54.6
2	Arkansas	147	2	Maryland	13.1
3	Georgia	87	3	Georgia	6.4
4	Alabama	71	4	Arkansas	5.5
5	Maine	68	5	Alabama	4.8
6	Mississippi	68	6	North Carolina	4.3
7	North Carolina	44	7	Mississippi	3.3
8	Maryland	38	8	Connecticut	2.5
9	Texas	13	9	Maine	2.2
10	Virginia	11	10	Virginia	1.2
	United States	11		United States	0.6

Allied Interests

It is easy to see that feed, equipment and supplies must be manufactured to meet production needs. Just as important, though perhaps not so readily apparent, are the needs for processing equipment, cold storage warehouse facilities, trucks for the bulk handling of feed and for the transportation of live and dressed poultry and eggs, laboratories for the production of embryo-propagated vaccines, and facilities for getting information about poultry and eggs to the consuming public by way of the press, radio and television.

The Chicago Mercantile Exchange, at 110 North Franklin Street, provides a trading floor where buyers and sellers can meet each business day to trade in eggs, tom and hen turkeys, butter and other commodities. This provides a futures market which is necessary for hedging operations, and which automatically indicates from day to day the combined judgment of a large group of buyers and sellers as to the value of the various commodities traded. Because of the limitations surrounding trading in futures, the overall effect is a highly desirable stabilizing of the market. The maximum daily price range for eggs, for example, is 2 cents a dozen above or below the previous day's settling price. The New York Mercantile Exchange provides similar trading facilities in that city.

THE BREEDS OF CHICKENS

Of the nearly 200 varieties of chickens listed in the American Standard of Perfection, not more than five were of commercial importance in 1950, and only two—the White Leghorn and the White Plymouth Rock—could so qualify in 1960. New Hampshires accounted for about 100,000 breeders in NPIP flocks in their home state and in Indiana, and Rhode Island Reds accounted for over 90,000 in Massachusetts in 1958–59. Nowhere else did they represent a significant number on a statewide basis.

FIG. 1–7.—Single Comb White Leghorns (Mediterranean).
(Courtesy of Poultry Tribune.)

Table 1-13.—The More Important Characteristics of Some Representative Breeds of Chickens

Breed	Standard weight, pounds		Type of comb	Color of earlobe	Color of skin	Color of shank	Shanks feathered?	Color of egg
	Cock	Hen						
American Breeds:								
Plymouth Rock	9½	7½	Single	Red	Yellow	Yellow	No	Brown
Wyandotte	8½	6½	Rose	Red	Yellow	Yellow	No	Brown
Rhode Island Red	8½	6½	Single and rose	Red	Yellow	Yellow	No	Brown
Jersey Black Giant	13	10	Single	Red	Yellow	Black	No	Brown
New Hampshire	8½	6½	Single	Red	Yellow	Yellow	No	Brown
Asiatic Breeds:								
Brahma (Light)	12	9½	Pea	Red	Yellow	Yellow	Yes	Brown
Cochin	11	8½	Single	Red	Yellow	Yellow	Yes	Brown
Langshan (Black)	9½	7½	Single	Red	White	Bluish-black	Yes	Brown
English Breeds:								
Australorp	8½	6½	Single	Red	White	Dark slate	No	Brown
Cornish (Dark)	10	7½	Pea	Red	Yellow	Yellow	No	Brown
Dorking (Silver-gray)	9	7	Single	Red	White	White	No	White
Orpington (Buff and White)	10	8	Single	Red	White	White	No	Brown
Sussex	9	7	Single	Red	White	White	No	Brown
Mediterranean Breeds:								
Leghorn	6	4½	Single and rose	White	Yellow	Yellow	No	White
Minorca (S. C. Black)	9	7½	Single	White	White	Dark slate	No	White
Ancona	6	4½	Single and rose	White	Yellow	Yellow	No	White
Andalusian (Blue)	7	5½	Single	White	White	Slaty blue	No	White

FIG. 1–8.—Barred Plymouth Rocks (American). (Courtesy of Poultry Tribune.)

FIG. 1–9.—White Plymouth Rocks (American). (Courtesy of Poultry Tribune.)

FIG. 1–10.—Rose Comb Rhode Island Reds (American).
(Courtesy of Poultry Tribune.)

FIG. 1–11.—New Hampshires (American).   (Courtesy of Poultry Tribune.)

FIG. 1–12.—Dark Cornish (English).   The Cornish is often crossed with other breeds to produce a desirable meat type chicken.   (Courtesy of Poultry Tribune.)

Fig. 1–13.—A popular meat-type male used in broiler breeding flocks. (Courtesy of Brown's Ledbrest, Inc., Springdale, Arkansas.)

Fig. 1–14.—A popular meat-type female used in broiler breeding flocks. (Courtesy of Pilch's Poultry Breeding Farms, Inc., Hazardville, Connecticut.)

FIG. 1-15.—A popular egg-type female of the sort used on many commercial egg farms. (From an artist's painting, courtesy of DeKalb Agricultural Association, Inc., DeKalb, Illinois.)

On the other hand, cross-mated flocks, which accounted for only 2 per cent of the 11 million head of breeding stock in NPIP hatchery supply flocks in 1941–42, increased gradually to 16 per cent of 34 million head in 1952–53, and then rapidly to 64 per cent of the 40 million head in these flocks in 1958–59.

With increased emphasis being placed on performance—whether it be growth or egg production—poultrymen have become less and less concerned about the supposed "purity" of the breeds with which they work. If dominant white plumage and early feathering are needed in White Plymouth Rocks, they do not object to introducing these characters by the use of White Leghorns if necessary, in spite of the rigorous selection which must follow the original introduction. They are not disturbed by a few black feathers in a white fowl, by an extra point on a single comb, or by a little down

FIG. 1–16.—An egg-type White Leghorn as she would appear in the laying house. (Courtesy of Kimber Farms, Inc., Fremont, California.)

between the toes, *provided* growth and egg production are satisfactory. This change in attitude, like the growing interest in cross
breeding and in the production of hybrid chickens, has developed as
a part of present-day commercial poultry and egg production.

Table 1–14.—Chickens in National Poultry Improvement Plan
Hatchery Supply Flocks and Their Distribution by Varieties and
Regions. As Reported by the U. S. Department of Agriculture.

	North Atlantic	East North Central	West North Central	South Atlantic	South Central	Western
			Per Cent			
New Hampshire:						
1949–50	49	26	21	68	44	39
1958–59	2	4	2	1	2	4
1963–64	0.4	2.5	1.3	0.1	0.5	1.1
White Leghorn:						
1949–50	15	24	32	6	15	42
1958–59	10	25	25	5	6	29
1963–64	24	28	25	4	6	24
White Plymouth Rock:						
1949-50	3	23	13	1	11	2
1958–59	16	15	4	7	10	6
1963–64	11	11	5	5	5	4
Barred Plymouth Rock:						
1949–50	15	8	2	2	7	1
1958–59	2	1	–	–	–	–
1963–64	1.4	0.6	0.3	–	0.1	0.1
Rhode Island Red:						
1949–50	10	2	2	2	3	5
1958–59	2	1	1	1	–	1
1963–64	1.6	0.9	1.1	0.4	0.2	0.5
Cross Mated:						
1949–50	7	12	25	18	15	9
1958–59	57	40	48	85	75	53
1963–64	56	30	44	89	85	61
Incross Mated:						
1949–50	–	–	–	–	–	–
1958–59	2	12	17	1	4	6
1963–64	5	24	21	2	4	9
Other:						
1949–50	1	5	5	3	5	2
1958–59	1	2	2	–	2	–
1963–64	0.5	2.2	2.5	0.2	0.2	0.4
			Millions			
Total Number:						
1949–50	7.6	8.6	9.0	5.8	2.6	2.6
1958–59	7.6	5.9	7.0	11.5	6.0	1.9
1963–64	4.6	2.9	3.4	14.2	9.4	1.3

Chapter 2

The Structure of the Chicken and the Formation of the Egg

THE FOWL AS A LIVING ORGANISM

In comparison with most other animals, birds are often spoken of as fast-living creatures. Structurally, too, they are among the most highly specialized of vertebrates, many of their modifications being in the nature of adaptations for flight. Their coating of feathers is sufficient to set them apart from all other forms, but they are also characterized by being warm-blooded, by having a high metabolic rate, and by the fact that development of the young takes place, for the most part, outside the body of the mother.

The body temperature of the fowl is higher than that of other domestic animals, and because of a more or less regular diurnal variation the recorded temperatures show a greater range than is found in other farm animals. The reported temperatures range from a minimum of 105° to a maximum of 109.4° F., depending upon the time of day the observations were made. The average noon figure is about 107° F. The minimum temperature during each twenty-four hour period occurs between 10 P.M. and midnight, whereas the maximum occurs some time during the afternoon.

The fowl is a rapid breather and its pulse rate is high. Records taken of the heart-beat of the chick embryo indicate that the pulse rate rises rapidly from about 130 to about 230 beats per minute, during the first nine days of incubation. It then rises but little during the next two or three days, and remains remarkably uniform during the remainder of the incubation period.

The heart rate again rises sharply during and immediately after hatching, and by the end of twelve hours it is about 300 beats per minute, where it remains reasonably constant. This rate is also characteristic of the adult fowl.

There is a definite relationship between body weight and heart rate. Small fowls such as Leghorn females have a resting heart rate of about 330 beats per minute, while large fowls such as Rhode Island Red males average below 250. There is also a regular diurnal variation in the normal heart rate, associated with the normal diurnal variation in temperature. Any excitement will cause an immediate and pronounced acceleration in heart rate. Dropping a day-old chick has been shown to cause the heart rate to increase from 300 to 560 beats per minute.

Feathers

Feathers help to protect the bird from physical injury, and are also of a great deal of aid in keeping the body warm. The wing feathers are, of course, essential to flight. The annual renewal of the feather coat constitutes a considerable physiological expense to the fowl, since the feathers make up from 4 to 9 per cent of the empty live weight, depending on the age and sex of the individual.

Though the body surface of most birds is almost entirely covered by feathers, there are only a very few species in which the feathers

Fig. 2–1.—Different types of feathers. (*A*) Primary of Pigeon—an important flight feather with a stiff vane. (*B*) Under wing covert of a Great Blue Heron; downy portion overlapped by an adjoining feather. (*C*) Wing covert of Owl; the downy edge makes possible the all-important noiseless flight of this bird. (*D*) Feather of Ostrich; the power of flight has been lost, and the entire vane is downy. (Beebe; *The Bird*, courtesy of Henry Holt and Company.)

actually grow from the entire surface of the skin. In most species, including the fowl, the feathers are arranged in definite areas or feather tracts. Several of these tracts, or *pterylae*, are paired, as may be seen readily by examining a picked carcass.

The parts of a typical body feather are the quill, which is continued throughout the vane of the feather as the shaft or rachis; the barbs, branching from the shaft; the barbules, branching from the barbs; and the barbicels, branching from the barbules. Except for size differences, most of the variation in the form and structure of feathers is due to differences in the mode of structure of the barbules and their branches.

The order of formation of the shaft of the feather is strictly apicobasal, and the order of age of the barbs is naturally the same. Similarly, in each barb, the apex at the margin of the feather is the first formed, and the central end attached to the shaft is the last. Thus there are two time gradients in each feather: from the apex to the base along the shaft, and from margin to center along the barbs.

The rate of growth of the shaft is approximately uniform throughout its length, at least during the formation of the vane of the feather. The rate of growth of the barbs, on the other hand, diminishes from the apex to the base of each, that is, from the margin of the feather to the shaft. This form of growth plays a large part in determining the pigmentation and general pattern of the feather. The time required to form the vane of a breast feather is approximately twenty days from the time of plucking an old feather.

The large feathers of the wings and tail are definite in number, and are molted and replaced, as a rule, in a regular order. As will be pointed out in the discussion of judging fowls for egg production, this fact can be used as a basis of estimating the length of time that certain birds have been out of production.

There are well-known differences between the sexes in the appearance of feathers in the neck, back, saddle, and tail sections. These are among the secondary sexual differences that are characteristic of birds. In certain "hen-feathered" breeds the feathers in these sections are essentially alike in both sexes. The Campine and the Sebright Bantam are examples.

The Skin

A description of the skin and its specialized development in the form of comb, wattles and ear lobes, and the scales on the shanks and toes might easily be developed into an extended discussion. It is sufficient here to point out that there is a close relation between gonad development and activity, and the size and appearance of the comb and wattles. The practical application of this fact will be pointed out in the discussion of judging fowls for egg production.

The several different shank colors found in fowls result from different combinations of pigments in the upper and lower layers of skin.

Yellow shanks are due to the presence of carotenoid pigment in the epidermis, with the absence of melanic pigment. Black and its variations depend upon the presence of melanic pigment in the epidermis. It is probable that the darkest type of shank occurs when melanic pigment is present in both the dermis and the epidermis. Yellow in the dermis is obscured by black in the epidermis.

Blue, or slaty blue shanks occur when melanic pigment is present in the dermis, and neither type of pigment is present in the epidermis. With black in the dermis and yellow in the overlying epidermis, the shank appears willow green in color. White shanks are the result of complete absence of both types of pigment.

The Skeleton

The skeleton of the fowl is compact, light in weight, and very strong. Many of the long bones are hollow, which helps to make them light; and many of them are fused together forming very strong structures to which the large muscles used in flight are attached. The keeled sternum is characteristic of the superorder *Neognathae,* to which the domestic fowl belongs.

Questions are often asked about the rumpless fowls that sometimes are found in flocks of otherwise normal specimens. This condition may be either hereditary or accidental. In either case it is due to the absence of the last few vertebrae, including the pygostyle.

The Muscles

The particular point of interest about the muscular system of the bird is the special development of the large muscles of the breast region. The greater part of this muscle group appears to be on the body proper because of the extensive attachment to the sternum. The muscles in this region weigh about as much as do all the rest of the muscles together, and make up about one-twelfth of the weight of the entire body.

The Respiratory System

The respiratory system of birds is quite different from that of mammals. The lungs are firmly attached to the thoracic wall, and the active part of respiration is expiration. In mammals the more vigorous part of breathing is inspiration.

Connected with the lungs are four pairs of air sacs placed on either side of the body, and ranging in position from the neck to the abdomen, with a single median sac located in the cavity of the thorax. Besides opening into the lungs, these sacs communicate directly with the cavities of most of the bones of the body, with the exception of those of the forearm and hand of the wing and those below the hock-joint of the leg.

The voice of the fowl is produced in the syrinx, or lower larynx, located where the trachea divides into the two bronchi. The syrinx is the only part of the respiratory tract that is capable of producing

3

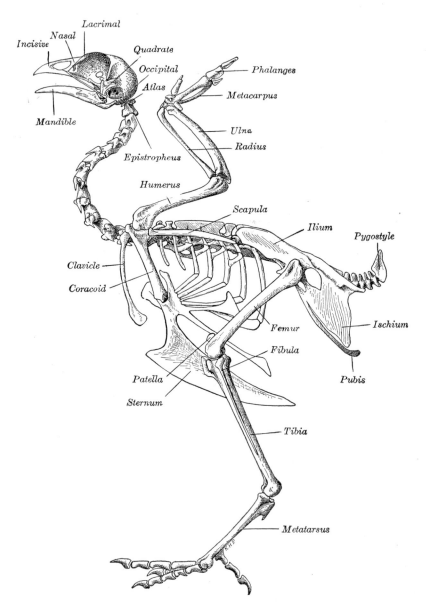

FIG. 2–2.—The skeleton of a fowl.

sound, the upper larynx serving only to modulate the voice. The syrinx is essentially the same in both male and female. The normal hen does not crow because she lacks the psychological incentive to do so. If this incentive is provided experimentally, by suitable injections of the male sex hormone, hens so treated will crow.

The Digestive System

The digestive system is the passage connecting the outside environment to the metabolic world of an animal. The development and anatomy of the alimentary tract largely determine the type of food that is nutritionally useful for a particular species. Carnivores have very short digestive tracts whereas in herbivores the alimentary canal is relatively long. The relationship of length of body to length of digestive tract of the cat is 1:4, the dog 1:6, but in the sheep the ratio is 1:27. The chicken has a ratio of body length to length of intestinal tract of about 1:4. The types of food most useful to chickens resemble those that are also most useful to cats and dogs, rather than to cattle and sheep.

Mouth, Esophagus and Crop.—The distinctive character of the mouth of a bird is the absence of lips and teeth. These parts are replaced by a horny mandible on each jaw forming the beak. The tongue in fowls and turkeys is shaped like the barbed head of an arrow with the point directed forward. The barb-like projections at the back of the tongue serve to force food toward the esophagus when the tongue is moved from back to front. Salivary glands are present which secrete a mucous saliva that lubricates the food as it passes down the esophagus.

The crop is a pouch formed as a specialized area of the esophagus. Little digestion occurs in the crop and its chief function is as a storage organ. The stomach of the fowl has relatively little storage capacity.

Glandular Stomach.—The true stomach (proventriculus) of a bird appears as little more than an enlargement at the end of the esophagus. Hydrochloric acid and an enzyme (pepsin) aiding in protein digestion are secreted by the wall of the proventriculus. Because the time spent by food in the proventriculus is very short, digestion taking place here is probably of relatively little importance.

Gizzard.—The gizzard is oval in shape, with two openings on its upper side, one from the proventriculus and the other opening to the duodenum. It is composed of two pairs of red thick powerful muscles covered internally with a thick horny epithelium.

The chief function of the gizzard is to grind or crush coarse feed. This process is normally aided by the presence of grit or gravel taken in through the mouth. With uniformly ground rations, grinding in the gizzard is probably relatively unimportant for good digestion. With whole grains, however, grinding in the gizzard is essential before they can be properly digested. The constant action of the gizzard may be heard by holding a little chick, which has been supplied with grit, to the ear.

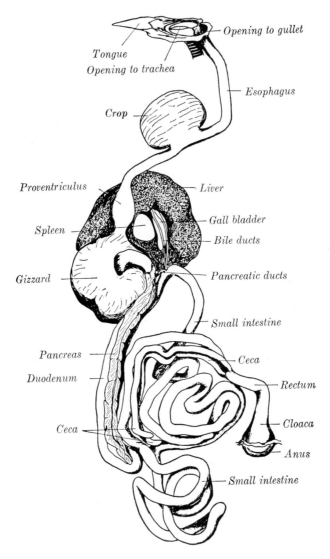

Tongue
Opening to trachea
Opening to gullet
Esophagus
Crop
Proventriculus
Liver
Spleen
Gall bladder
Bile ducts
Gizzard
Pancreatic ducts
Small intestine
Pancreas
Ceca
Duodenum
Rectum
Ceca
Cloaca
Anus
Small intestine

FIG. 2–3.—The digestive system of the fowl. (Courtesy of F. B. Adamstone.)

Pancreas.—Immediately after its attachment to the gizzard, the intestine is folded in a loop called the duodenum, the sides of which are parallel and enclose the pancreas. The pancreas secretes pancreatic juice into the lower end of the duodenum through the pancreatic ducts. Pancreatic juice is slightly alkaline, and neutralizes the acid secretion of the proventriculus. The pancreatic secretion contains enzymes that hydrolyze proteins, starches and fats. In the absence of pancreatic juice, little digestion of these substances occurs.

Liver.—Bile is necessary for proper absorption of fats from the small intestine. The bile is produced in the liver and is conveyed to the lower end of the duodenum by two bile ducts. The one from the right lobe of the liver is enlarged to form the gallbladder in which the bile is stored and concentrated. The presence of food in the duodenum causes the gallbladder to contract and empty its bile into the intestine. The duct from the left lobe does not have an enlargement but goes directly to the small intestine, where the bile ducts enter together.

Small Intestine.—The small intestine is normally considered to have two distinct parts, the duodenum and the lower small intestine. Enzymes present in the pancreatic juice act on starches, fats and proteins while enzymes produced in the intestinal wall complete the digestive process by breaking down small fragments of protein molecules (peptides) to amino acids and by splitting disaccharides such as sucrose and maltose into simple sugars which can be absorbed. Since there is no specialized area in the digestive tract for bacterial action to aid the breakdown of foodstuffs, only feed materials that can be digested by the enzymes secreted by the chicken are useful as food.

The epithelium lining the small intestine has tremendous surface area to make possible rapid absorption of nutrients. Nearly all the nutrients needed by an animal must be absorbed by the small intestine. The digestive and absorptive processes in the small intestine are extremely rapid; a chicken can digest and absorb a full meal in less than three hours.

Ceca.—At the juncture of the lower small intestine and the rectum are two blind pouches given off from either side, called ceca. These are usually 4 to 6 inches in length and are usually filled with fecal matter. With the usual modern highly digestible rations fed to poultry the ceca have little function in digestion. In adult birds fed highly fibrous rations, some digestion of fiber may take place in the ceca by action of microorganisms.

Rectum and Cloaca.—The large intestine is very short, and consists of a short rectum leading to the cloaca. The rectum of an adult chicken is usually not more than 3 or 4 inches long. The cloaca is a chamber common to the digestive, urinary and reproductive passages, which opens externally at the vent. The urine is discharged into the cloaca and excreted with the feces. White pasty material in chicken droppings is largely uric acid that has precipitated from urine. Birds excrete waste nitrogen as uric acid, a very insoluble compound, whereas in mammals urinary nitrogen is excreted as urea.

THE ENDOCRINE GLANDS

Both the appearance and functioning of the fowl are profoundly affected by the secretions of the endocrine glands. These glands, together with the nervous system, form the major regulatory system of the body. The nervous system normally reacts very quickly to

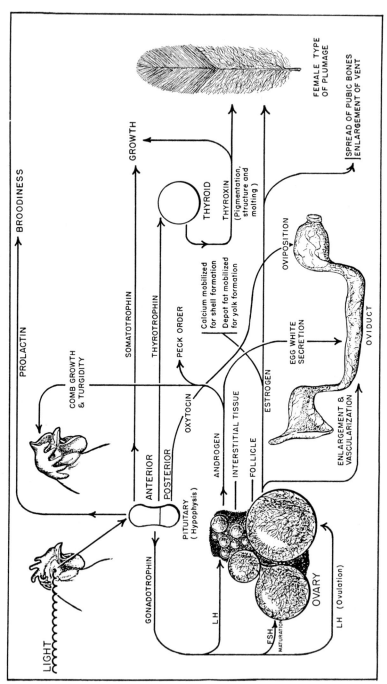

FIG. 2–4.—Diagram showing the principal effects of endocrine secretions, and their inter-relationships, in the female fowl. For adrenal effects, see Figure 2–5.

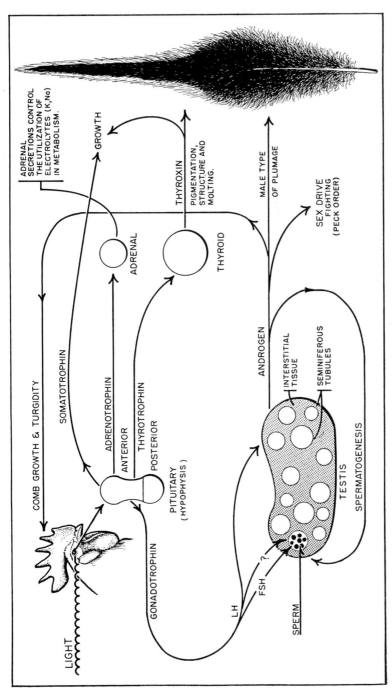

Fig. 2–5.—Diagram showing the principal effects of endocrine secretions, and their inter-relationships, in the male fowl.

a stimulus, whereas the endocrine system responds somewhat more slowly. They are described as endocrine, or glands of internal secretion, because the products of their cells are not carried away through a duct, but are disseminated in the blood stream to all parts of the body. The different secretions of specific glands have their own names but the term *hormone* (meaning rousing, or setting in motion) is commonly used for any endocrine secretion and is applicable to all of them.

The endocrine glands include the testes, the ovary, the thyroid, the parathyroids, the pituitary, the adrenal, the pineal and the islets of Langerhans of the pancreas. Hormones are also produced in the duodenum and the brain. The duodenal hormones regulate digestive secretions of the pancreas, contraction of the gallbladder and perhaps passage of food through the intestinal tract.

The anterior portion of the pituitary gland produces hormones that regulate the secretion of many other endocrine glands. These hormones include thyrotrophin, adrenotrophin, gonadotrophins that affect the thyroid, adrenal, and sex glands, and somatotrophin that regulates the growth of the whole animal.

The nervous system and the endocrine system are not independent, but act together to regulate body functions. A particularly important relationship exists between an area of the brain called the hypothalamus and the pituitary gland. There is good experimental evidence indicating that the release of the regulating hormones of the pituitary is controlled by hormone-releasing factors produced in nervous tissue of the hypothalamus and released by appropriate nervous stimuli. In addition, two hormones are produced in the hypothalamus that are then stored in the posterior pituitary prior to their release. There are numerous environmental stimuli that affect the endocrine system through the nervous system. One of the most important as far as chickens are concerned is the effect of light on reproduction.

Hormone Control of Egg Production.

There are very few endocrine effects which result from the simple and direct action of a single hormone. Instead, the physiological and psychological activity of the chicken, particularly the female, is dependent upon a very complex interrelation of glandular effects.

A good example is the complex hormonal control of ovulation and egg formation. A follicle-stimulating hormone (commonly abbreviated FSH) from the anterior lobe of the pituitary gland causes the growth of the ovarian follicles with their contained ova. When a follicle has reached ovulatory size, another hormone from the pituitary gland (luteinizing hormone or LH) is released and causes ovulation.

The oviduct also is under hormone control and it is stimulated, at exactly the right time, to pick up or engulf the released ovum.

Hormone secretions from the ovarian follicle are responsible for the enlargement of the oviduct to functioning size, for the spread of the pubic bones and enlargement of the vent, and for the mobilization of depot fat for yolk formation and of calcium for shell formation. Egg white secretion is apparently under the control of a hormone secreted by the ovarian interstitial tissue.

Formation of the egg shell is at least partially under the control of hormones secreted by the parathyroid glands and here also, timing—both as to the beginning and end of shell formation—is remarkably exact. And finally, a hormone stored in the posterior pituitary but secreted by specialized cells of the hypothalamus

Fig. 2–6.—Sex dimorphism in structure of feathers. From left to right the paired male and female feathers are from the wing bow, neck and saddle regions. The male feathers (on the right in each pair) appear more pointed and lacier because of the large areas free from barbules toward the tip of the feathers. (Photo by Dr. W. F. Lamoreaux, Cornell University.)

probably comes into play to cause the fully formed egg to be laid. The interrelationships are shown diagrammatically in Figure 2–4.

Normal functioning of the whole process of egg production is completely dependent upon extremely fine adjustment and synchronization of all the foregoing events. If any gland begins to function "on its own," without awaiting the proper signal, such freaks as yolkless eggs, soft-shell eggs, and eggs within eggs are likely to result.

A striking example of the extent to which physiological activity is subject to endocrine control has been provided by workers at Illinois. Leghorn hens placed in individual cages without food but with water always available were injected daily with 2 milligrams of crude chicken pituitary extract. They continued to lay for a period of eight to ten days, literally because they could not help it, drawing on body tissues for both maintenance and the formation of eggs, and losing about a pound each in body weight during that time.

Not all of the known endocrine effects in the fowl are shown in Figures 2–4 and 2–5. The thyroid gland, for example, in addition to influencing body growth and feather formation, is partially responsible for more or less regular seasonal changes in egg production, body weight, and egg weight. The stimulus for this latter effect comes,

a   *b*   *c*

Fig. 2–7.—Effects of thyroxin on color and structure of saddle feathers in Brown Leghorn males. *a*, Is normal; *b*, was injected with 1.0 mg. of thyroxin every seventh day; *c*, was injected with 1.5 mg. of thyroxin every sixth day. Extension of the black is accompanied by formation of barbules in the affected areas. (After Lillie and Juhn in Physiol. Zoöl., Vol. 5.)

presumably, from the varying amount of light to which hens are subjected with the changing seasons, although the picture is complicated by the unfavorable effect of high air temperature on egg size.

One should also remember that not all of the postulated endocrine effects can be ascribed solely to a particular hormone. Oxytocin, shown in Figure 2–4 as the hormone responsible for oviposition, is probably not the only factor involved in stimulating the actual laying of the egg. The time of laying of a particular egg will be delayed one or more days if the follicle from which its yolk came is surgically removed shortly after ovulation. Removal of other parts of the ovary has no such effect. The follicle probably plays a role in oviposition but the manner in which it does is not at all clear at present.

Time of oviposition may also be affected by external influences. The mere handling of hens shortly before normal laying would have occurred may delay oviposition long enough for a second egg to be forming in the oviduct before the preceding one is laid.

Stimulation and growth of the ovary result in increased production of the ovarian hormones which, strangely enough, include both a male and a female sex hormone. The "male" sex hormone (androgen) is responsible for the red, waxy comb and wattles of the normal laying hen, while the "female" sex hormone (estrogen) controls the typically feminine secondary sex characters such as normal female plumage, absence of spurs, and female sexual behavior.

If, as sometimes happens, a hen develops an ovarian tumor of sufficient size to destroy that part of her ovary which secretes the female hormone, she will gradually assume male characteristics. Her comb and wattles become large and coarse, her new plumage after a molt will be almost exactly like that of a male, and she may even crow. This is the result of the development of the rudimentary right ovary, which contains testicular tissue.

Both egg laying and ovulation are also subject to the external influence of light and darkness. As will be pointed out in discussing the formation of the egg, ovulation normally occurs about thirty minutes after laying. But if laying happens to take place as late as 4:00 P.M., release of the next ovum does not occur until some ten or twelve hours later, unless the hen's normal lighting schedule has been reversed or she is being kept under continuous twenty-four-hour light of constant intensity. Hence no egg will be laid the following day.

If lights are used all night, one might expect the hens to lay both night and day, but this does not happen because there is normally a marked difference in light intensity between the daylight hours and the night hours. If, on the other hand, hens are kept in individual cages in a room from which all natural daylight is excluded, and are subjected to constant twenty-four-hour illumination, they will lay "round the clock"—depositing about half their eggs at night. There is no onset of darkness to delay ovulation and terminate a clutch.

If instead of twenty-four-hour illumination, hens in an artificially lighted room have light from 6 A.M. to 6 P.M. and no light the other twelve hours, they will lay all their eggs in the daytime. But if their lighting schedule is suddenly reversed, so that they get light from 6 P.M. to 6 A.M., and no light during the solar day, they will, in about three days time, shift over so that all their eggs are laid at night.

Time of laying may be influenced also by the feeding schedule. If hens are kept under continuous light, with natural daylight excluded, and are fed only from 8 A.M. to 4 P.M., most of their eggs will be laid during those hours. On the other hand, if feeding is from 8 P.M. to 4 A.M. the hens will adjust to this sort of schedule by laying most of their eggs during the new feeding period.

The Use of Artificial Light

The response of healthy fowls to the influence of light is both prompt and of considerable magnitude, and many poultrymen make use of artificial light to obtain partial control of flock egg production. The nature of the response and the extent to which egg production can be controlled are perhaps most easily explained and understood by considering the effect of light on pullets.

In northern latitudes spring-hatched pullets are subjected to continually increasing natural day length during the first weeks of growth when this sort of change can have its maximum effect on feed intake and consequently on rate of growth. Later in the summer the gradually decreasing length of day operates to prevent precocious sexual maturity and such undesirable results as the onset of laying before body size is sufficient to permit pullets to lay eggs of suitable market size.

December-hatched pullets, on the other hand, if exposed to natural daylight only, will approach laying age at a time when the natural day length is increasing. They will respond to this stimulus by maturing early and beginning to lay in the spring before they have attained normal adult body weight. A high percentage of their eggs will be small and therefore worth less than average market price.

The foregoing comparison suggests immediately that the primary effect of light is on sexual maturity. Unless one keeps this point in mind he can easily be led into faulty conclusions about the use of artificial light and its application to practical egg production control. A related point of extreme importance is that the effect is brought about by changing day length rather than by any specific amount of light. Increasing day length results in earlier maturity. Decreasing day length results in later maturity.

A practical problem is how to control age and weight at sexual maturity in December-hatched pullets, for example, so that their egg-laying performance will be commercially profitable. The key to the solution is found in subjecting them to decreasing day length from the time they are hatched until they are ready to lay—just the opposite of what would happen to them under natural daylight. This could be accomplished by starting the chicks out on a sixteen-hour day, and gradually reducing the day length to about six hours by the time the pullets are five and one-half or six months old, at which time they could be stimulated to come into production by increasing the amount of light to fourteen to sixteen hours. This procedure requires the use of windowless houses from which all natural daylight could be excluded during the latter part of the growing period.

An equally effective procedure is to start the December-hatched chicks out on a twenty-four-hour day and gradually reduce the amount of artificial light, perhaps by weekly decrements of twenty-five minutes, so that by the time the pullets are twenty-four weeks old they will be getting a fourteen-hour day—not much longer than the natural day at that season.   No special construction problems are involved as there will be no need to exclude natural daylight at any time.

Careful studies of this sort conducted by English workers have shown that the delay in sexual maturity amounts to about one and two-thirds days (forty hours) for each one-hour change in day length, and that the maximum delay which can be obtained by this method is about three weeks.   This is sufficient to accomplish the desired objectives with regard to body weight and egg size.   Note, however, that the total change in day length is calculated for the entire period from hatching time to the date of first egg.

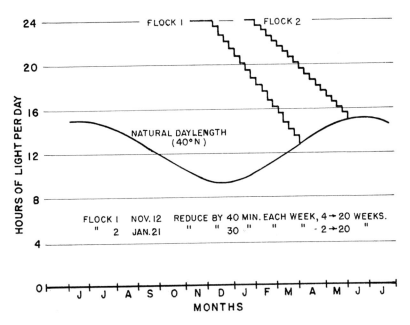

Fig. 2-8.—Examples of light patterns which can be used to delay sexual maturity when pullets are grown at 40° north latitude.   (Courtesy of T. R. Morris.)

The amount of delay which could be accomplished with June-hatched pullets would be small and of little economic importance because a control flock of June-hatched pullets under natural daylight would also be subjected to decreasing day length from hatching time to maturity.   For pullets hatched in other months the effect would be intermediate, but presumably somewhat greater and also more important for pullets hatched between October and January than for those hatched in September or February.

In summary, a schedule of decreasing day length provided by artificial light can be used to delay sexual maturity—specifically to prevent precocious maturity—so that average egg size is much improved in fall and winter-hatched pullets. Total feed intake to 500 days of age is only slightly increased over that of the controls, and there is a compensatory increase in rate of lay during the later months of production which equals and may exceed the early loss in eggs resulting from delay in maturity.

Artificial light can also be used to bring non-laying pullets or hens into production at some desired time, or to postpone the normal drop in rate of laying during the fall months. The necessary stimulus is provided by exposing the fowls to additional light beyond that available during natural daylight hours. The initial response from increased lighting will be obtained in from seven to ten days.

A common procedure is to use artificial light—in the early morning, in the evening, or in combination—to provide a thirteen- or fourteen-hour day. Considerable latitude in total day length is permissible, provided only that it is kept constant or is slowly increasing. One must always remember that a decrease in day length is detrimental. With large flocks a continued decrease in day length or a complete interruption of the lighting schedule can be economically disastrous in terms of egg production. A precise optimum constant day length has never been established and indeed may be non-existent.

It was once thought that the favorable effect of artificial light was gained simply by providing a longer feeding day for the hens, but this has long since been shown not to be true. The stimulus of light by way of the hypothalamus activates the pituitary gland so that secretion of FSH is increased, and ovarian activity follows in due course.

The light stimulus can be provided in various ways, and the time span within the twenty-four hour day is not necessarily critical. All-night light of low intensity, sufficient to permit the hens to find feed and water at any time, is fully as effective as morning or evening light of greater intensity. Flashes of bright light ten seconds long operated once each hour will provide the necessary stimulus, but there is no practical advantage to be gained from using such a procedure.

The light stimulus appears to have a threshold level of intensity beyond which further increases in brightness of the light have no effect. Thus greater egg production cannot be stimulated by using very bright lights. A level of 0.5 to 1 foot candle of light should be provided at the darkest points of exposure of the hen. Although red light is more effective than blue light, white light from an incandescent bulb contains enough red light to provide a satisfactory stimulus. Excessive light is unnecessary and is economically unsound.

Effect of Light on Growth

Rate of growth is also subject to the indirect effect of light. Numerous tests involving various schedules of intermittent lighting, as well as continuous twenty-four-hour light, indicate that the important consideration is feeding time. Exposure to light under conditions of restricted feed intake has no measurable effect on rate of growth. The maximum effect of increased feeding time provided by artificial light will be obtained under continuous twenty-four-hour light during the early weeks of growth. This is an important consideration for commercial broiler growers. For replacement pullets intended for egg laying, the importance of the effect of light on growth rate is secondary to the effects on sexual maturity.

The intensity of light for broilers is also an important factor. In controlled experiments, intensity of 0.5 to 1 foot candle at the feeder was as good or better than higher light intensities. The use of twenty-four-hour light of relatively low intensity is a common practice in commercial broiler production. Low light intensities have also been used to aid in control of feather picking.

Other Endocrine Effects

Several other endocrine effects in the fowl have been well established. The feeding of large doses of either fresh or desiccated thyroid, for example, is followed by rapid molting. It has been shown that the thyroid gland increases in size during that portion of the year when molting normally occurs. Thyroxin, the active principle secreted by the thyroid, also affects the color and form of feathers.

Prolactin, secreted by the anterior lobe of the hypophysis, and so named because it induces milk secretion in mammals, is the controlling factor in broodiness in the fowl. Not only do laying hens, when dosed with prolactin, stop laying and quickly become broody, but male birds given sufficiently high doses likewise become broody, and will brood chicks just like a normal broody hen. The effect disappears quickly when injections of prolactin are stopped, and within a very few days such males are likely to kill the chicks which they previously cared for and defended.

Secretions of the adrenal glands are concerned in metabolism of carbohydrates and of sodium and potassium, and in the regulation of blood pressure. Hormones secreted by the islets of Langerhans, which are scattered through the pancreas, presumably control the level of blood sugar in the fowl as in mammals.

Another example of a complex chain of events set in motion by the initial action of a single hormone, is the chemical or hormone pseudo-caponization of cockerels. This involves the use of synthetic estrogens which are closely related to the female sex hormone.

A 15-milligram pellet of stilbestrol, implanted subcutaneously, will cause a remarkable change in the appearance of a Leghorn cockerel within ten to fifteen days. The comb loses its bright red color, and shrinks in size, until the cockerel resembles a capon in general appearance. There is an immediate increase in feed consumption, accompanied by a greatly increased deposition of fat.

The same changes occur, of course, in any breed of chickens. The Leghorn is mentioned simply because the comb changes are more striking than in breeds with smaller combs.

The pseudo-caponizing effect of estrogens is fairly well understood. The estrogen—in this case stilbestrol—has an inhibiting effect on the pituitary gland, thus shutting off the normal secretion of the gonadotrophic hormones. Lack of these will cause the testes to decrease in size, and will deprive them of the stimulus to secrete the male sex hormone, testosterone. Lack of testosterone will, in turn, result in regression of the secondary sex characters (comb, wattles, ear lobes, mating instinct, and crowing) because of the absence of endocrine encouragement. In time, the "maleness" is so completely submerged by the effect of estrogen, that the pubic bones are spread as in a laying hen, the skin over the abdomen becomes soft and velvety, and the coarse feather follicles characteristic of the adult male are no longer evident.

A secondary effect, not yet fully explained, is interference with calcium metabolism to such an extent that the long bones become brittle and very easily broken. Results similar to those following implantation have been obtained by feeding appropriate amounts of synthetic products such as the dimethyl ether of diethylstilbestrol.

Soon after estrogen treatment is stopped, the pituitary gland recovers its ability to function normally, gonadotrophic hormones are again secreted, the testes increase in size and begin to secrete testosterone, and the secondary sex characters reappear in a short time.

Many other endocrine effects are being studied experimentally and new information is constantly being brought to light. More and more of the hormones are being prepared synthetically, as their chemical nature is determined. Certain protein compounds have been found to have effects which are very similar to those brought about by the natural hormones. Experiments already carried out suggest that it may eventually be possible to control growth, fattening, and reproduction in the fowl to a much greater extent than at present, largely through the administration of synthetic hormones.

Some knowledge and understanding of the principal hormones is important in the practice of selection for physiological characters. Success in selection which is aimed at improving winter egg production when artificial lights are not used depends in part on being able to identify, by their performance, individuals which have a naturally high rate of secretion in respect to the gonadotrophic hormone which stimulates ovarian activity. Non-broody hens, and presumably males, which do not transmit broodiness to their daughters are those which have an inherently low secretion rate for prolactin—the hormone which causes broody behavior. Selection for the ability to fatten easily and quickly may well depend on the extent to which one is able to identify, albeit by indirect means, those individuals which have a higher than average level of estrogen secretion.

REPRODUCTION AND THE FORMATION OF THE EGG

The Reproductive System of the Male

The male fowl possesses two testes which are situated high up in the abdominal cavity, along the back, near the anterior ends of the kidneys. These never descend into an external scrotum, as is the case with other farm animals. In form they are more or less ellipsoid, and in color light yellow, frequently having a reddish cast caused by the numerous much-branched blood vessels on the surface.

In gross structure the testis consists of a large number of very slender, much-convoluted ducts, from the linings of which the sperm are given off. These ducts, called seminiferous tubules. appear in groups separated by delicate membranes which extend inward from a membrane surrounding the organ. They all lead eventually to the ductus deferens, a tube which conducts the sperm outside the body.

Each ductus deferens opens into a small papilla, which together serve as an intromittent organ. These are located on the dorsal wall of the cloaca. The so-called rudimentary copulatory organ of the fowl has no connection with the deferent ducts and is located on the median ventral portion of one of the transverse folds of the cloaca. It is this rudimentary organ, or male process, which is used in the classification of baby chicks according to sex on the basis of cloacal examination.

The Reproductive System of the Female

In early embryonic life there are two gonads in the female, as in the male. Normally, only the left one develops, the right persisting, if at all, only as a functionless rudiment. A few cases have been reported, however, in which both a right and left ovary and oviduct were present and functioning in a mature pullet. More recently it has been shown that an occasional strain may show a rather high incidence of persistent right oviducts.

The functioning ovary is a cluster of many follicles, each of which is independently attached by a very slender stalk. Each sphere is a more or less developed ovum or yolk enclosed in a thin membrane or follicle. The spheres vary in color from pale straw color to deep reddish-yellow or orange, and in size from that of a mature yolk about 40 mm. in diameter down to those so small as not to be visible to the unaided eye.

The Oviduct.—Associated with the ovary is the oviduct. In a laying hen the oviduct appears as a large, much-coiled tube occupying a large part of the left side of the abdominal cavity. It is covered with a network of blood vessels, and is in more or less continuous movement during the time that an egg is being formed.

The oviduct is divided into five rather clearly defined regions. Beginning at the end nearest the ovary, these are: (1) the funnel or

4

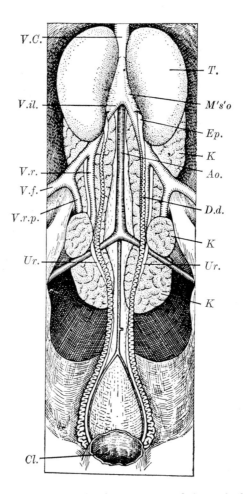

Fig. 2–9.—The reproductive and urinary organs of the male fowl: *T.*, testis; *D.d.*, ductus deferens; *K.*, kidney; *Ur.*, ureter; *Cl.*, cloaca. (Courtesy of L. V. Domm.)

FIG. 2–10.—Ovary from a hen in laying condition, showing ova of various sizes and a ruptured follicle from which an ovum was recently released. (Courtesy of Cornell University.)

infundibulum; (2) the magnum, where the thick white is secreted; (3) the isthmus, which secretes the shell membranes; (4) the uterus or shell gland; and (5) the vagina, which leads into the cloaca.

The Formation of the Egg

The egg of commerce consists of the true egg, or reproductive cell, *i.e.*, the yolk with its germinal disc, and the surrounding envelopes of white, shell membranes and shell. The yolk is formed in the ovary, but the balance of the process occurs in the oviduct.

Formation of the Yolk.—During the early stages of yolk formation, the oöcytes grow very slowly by the gradual accumulation of light yolk. When a diameter of about 6 mm. is reached, certain ova, but only a few at any one time, suddenly begin to grow at an enormously increased rate. They add about 4 mm. to their diameter every twenty-four hours, until full size of about 40 mm. in diameter is reached. An ovum within seven to nine days of laying contains less than 1 per cent of its final complement of yolk, yet those few days suffice to supply the missing 99 parts.

It is during this period of rapid growth that the concentric layers of light and dark yolk are formed. The thickness of each pair of light and dark layers, representing the growth in a twenty-four-hour period, is from 1.5 to 2 mm. The visible white and yellow bands result from periodic deposition of differing amounts of carotinoid pigment. Although yolk deposition continues at a nearly constant rate throughout the twenty-four-hour day, that formed at certain periods is light in color because no dietary pigment is available.

As the yolk enlarges, the germinal disc remains on the surface, and thus leaves behind a trail of white yolk which forms the neck of the flask-shaped mass of white yolk which is a part of every normal egg.

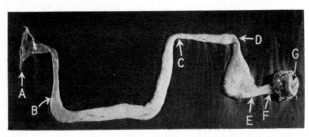

Fig. 2–11.—The oviduct of the hen.   *A–B*, infundibulum; *B–C*, magnum; *C–D*, isthmus; *D–E*, uterus; *E–F*, vagina; *G*, cloaca. (After Scott.)

Ovulation.—When the yolk comes to full size it is released from the ovary by the rupture of the follicle along the stigma. In most instances the ovum probably is discharged into the body cavity and is later engulfed by the funnel of the oviduct through repeated advances and recessions of the edge of the infundibulum over the surface of the ovum. Once completely enclosed, it appears to be forced along by wave-like contractions of the muscles of the oviduct.

Fertilization of the Egg.—Fertilization follows almost immediately after ovulation, the spermatozoa having made their way through the entire length of the oviduct after mating has occurred. Sperm are stored in so-called sperm nests in the infundibulum of the oviduct and apparently are released by the passage of the yolk. They are also stored in glands near the uterovaginal junction. Because of this storage of sperm, hens can remain fertile for seven to ten days after an insemination.

Since the sperm must penetrate the vitelline membrane, which surrounds the yolk, in order to reach the germinal disc, it is of interest to point out that the true vitelline membrane on the freshly ovulated yolk has been found to be only 4 microns thick. After a short time in the oviduct, the membrane becomes swollen and

PLATE I

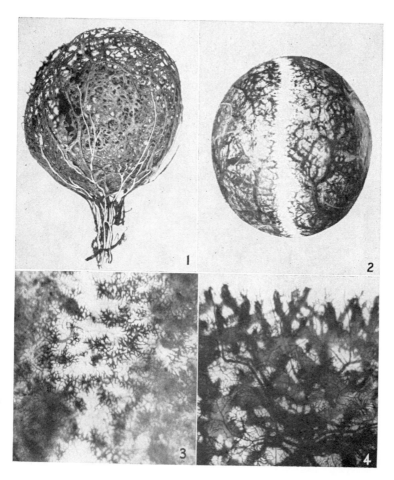

VASCULAR SYSTEM OF THE OVARIAN FOLLICLE
(After Nalbandov and James.)

1. Vinylite resin cast of the vascular system of a mature follicle and its stalk. Arteries white and veins dark.

2. Injected pre-ovulatory follicle. Note that no large blood vessels extend across the stigma.

3. View from inside a follicle showing that vascularization of the stigma consists primarily of a fine capillary network.

4. India ink injection of the vascular system of a pre-ovulatory follicle viewed from the inside. The stigma is at the upper edge of the picture.

thickened, as a result of contact with the secretions of the oviduct. It is also augmented by mucin secretions which thicken and strengthen it as a protection against rupture of the yolk. The complete vitelline membrane from the yolk of a laid egg is about 48 microns thick.

Secretion of the Dense White.—During its passage through the magnum, or albumen-secreting region, the yolk acquires the mass of firm white which makes up about one-half of the total white, by volume. The remainder of the white is not added until after the shell membranes have been formed and the egg has entered the uterus. It has been shown by analyses of egg white at different stages of egg formation that this latter addition is largely water and that no nitrogen is added to the egg in the uterus.

Formation of the Shell Membranes.—The shell membranes are formed in the isthmus. It is an interesting fact that these membranes should be so formed as to enclose the yolk and thick white rather loosely. They do not plump out until the egg receives its final quota of fluid in the uterus.

Formation of the Chalazae.—The two whitish cords, known as chalazae, which extend out from the yolk toward the ends of the egg, though obviously formed from material secreted in the upper part of the oviduct, do not become visible until after the egg has entered the uterus. Their formation appears to be partly the result of a change in the colloidal structure of the layer of white adjacent to the yolk, and partly the result of rotation of the white around the yolk while the egg is in the uterus. Chalaza formation has been artificially induced in eggs removed from the anterior portion of the uterus.

Formation of the Shell.—The shell of the hen's egg consists mostly of calcium carbonate, the reported percentages varying from 93 to 98. This material is deposited in the uterus, and there is considerable shell material deposited on the membranes before the egg has acquired its full quota of white.

The rate of shell deposition is relatively slow during the first three hours. It then increases rapidly until about the fifth hour, after which a constant rate is maintained until the twentieth hour (approximately the time of laying).

While the egg is in the hard-shell stage in the uterus it is possible to locate it by external palpation. This method can be used in keeping egg records except during the breeding season when pedigreeing is being done. At the Utah Station it was found that the whole flock could be handled early each morning and the individual hens which would lay during the day determined with accuracy.

A 5-pound hen laying 300 eggs in a year must deposit in the egg shells about 3.75 pounds of calcium carbonate (1.5 pounds of calcium). Since this is about thirty times the amount of calcium in her entire body, it is obvious that such a hen must be supplied with an abundance of calcium in her feed.

There is considerable evidence to support the view that much of the calcium used in shell formation is first deposited in the long bones and that often no more than 10 to 40 per cent of the calcium in a particular egg comes directly from the feed. For short periods of time all of the calcium may come from the bones, as is normal in wild birds which lay only a few eggs. If, however, laying hens are suddenly deprived of all food calcium their eggs promptly show thin shells, and egg laying stops in ten to fourteen days. It seems entirely possible that some of the complications which often accompany high egg production develop because some hens are unable to replace calcium in their bones as rapidly as it is withdrawn for shell formation.

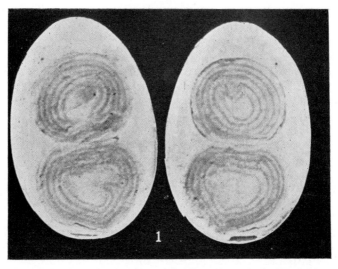

FIG. 2–12.—A double-yolked egg, showing how the yolk is formed in concentric layers. The hen was fed a small amount of a fat-soluble dye (Sudan III) on each of five successive days. (After Gage and Fish.)

Laying of the Egg

Eggs are normally formed small end caudad, that is, with the small end first as they move down the oviduct. This is true of wild birds as well as of the fowl. But curiously enough, if the hen is not disturbed in the act of laying, most eggs are laid large end first. This has puzzled poultry workers for many years. Not until an English investigator made use of radiographic techniques and published his findings in 1951 was the series of events made clear.

As can be seen in Plate II, the fully-formed egg is turned horizontally (not end-over-end) through 180 degrees just prior to laying. In order for this to happen the egg must drop from its normal position high up between the ischia to a point opposite the tips of the pubic bones. This is necessary because the normal egg is too long

Table 2–1.—The Approximate Length of the Various Parts of the Oviduct and the Time Intervals Involved in Egg Formation.

Section of oviduct	Approximate length in centimeters*	Approximate time for the yolk to traverse each section†
Infundibulum (and chalaziferous region) .	11.0	$\frac{1}{4}$ hr.
Magnum	33.6	3 "
Isthmus	10.6	1$\frac{1}{4}$ "
Uterus	10.1⎱	20$\frac{3}{4}$ "
Vagina	6.9⎰	
Interval between laying and next ovulation	....	$\frac{1}{2}$ "

* Illinois data on 70 White Leghorns.
† Adapted from Warren and Scott (1935).

Table 2–2.—Average Time Spent in Different Parts of the Oviduct by Eggs Requiring Various Periods for Their Formation. (After Warren and Scott, 1935.)

Item	Hens with interval lengths of (hours)					
	25	26	27	28	29	30
Time from laying of one egg to entrance of isthmus by next egg	4.3	4.6	4.2	4.7	5.2	5.3
Time spent in uterus . . .	18.0	18.4	19.9	19.8	20.8	21.6
Time from first indication of shell to laying of the egg . . .	13.8	14.7	15.6	16.4	17.0	17.9
Number of eggs observed . .	9	25	20	42	44	21

to turn in a horizontal plane within the pelvic arch. The position of an egg after it has turned and is ready to be laid is shown in Figure 6 of Plate II. Rotation of the egg is accomplished in a matter of one to two minutes. Should the hen be disturbed as she raises herself slightly from the nest when the egg is about to turn, she is very likely to expel it immediately and in that event it will be laid small end first. There is also some variation among hens and no doubt among breeds in the consistency with which they lay eggs large end first. It is not known whether hereditary factors are involved.

No valid reason has been advanced for the fact that eggs are formed small end caudad. As for the reversal prior to laying, it seems reasonable to assume that muscular pressure required for expelling the egg is more effectively applied to the small end.

Time Intervals in Egg Formation.—Careful observations made on anesthetized birds at the Kansas Agricultural Experiment Station, together with autopsy records of hens in laying condition, have made it possible to estimate with considerable accuracy the time required to form the various parts of the egg. These time intervals are summarized in Table 2–1, along with average lengths of the various parts of the oviduct as determined on 70 White Leghorn hens at the Illinois Station.

The time between laying and the next ovulation, as observed at the Kansas Station, ranged from fourteen to seventy-five minutes, and there is also some variation in the rate of passage through the different sections of the oviduct. Hens which have small clutches, with long intervals between eggs, and low intensity, also have long delays in ovulation. Poor production of low-intensity hens is caused not only by the longer period of egg formation but also by a longer delay in ovulation between clutches.

Records on 119 Rhode Island Red pullets for one year at the Massachusetts Station showed an average interval of 26.5 hours between successive eggs in the same clutch. The shortest interval observed for any one hen was twenty-three hours in April, and the longest was 31.7 hours in February. The average interval for all birds was shortest in April (25.7 hours) and longest in February (27.7 hours).

Shape, Size, and Color of Eggs.—The normal or characteristic shape of the egg is determined in the magnum, but the specific shape may be modified by abnormal or unusual conditions in either the isthmus or the uterus.

———————

Legend for Plate II

Radiographic Views of Egg Shell Formation in the Hen.
(After Bradfield and Fozzard in the Journal of Experimental Biology, Vol. 28.)

1. Radiograph of a hen taken six and one-half hours after an egg had been laid. The new yolk has been surrounded by both the white and the shell membranes and has passed into the shell gland (uterus). The first faint outlines of the calcareous shell can barely be detected.

2. The same egg three hours later.

3. The same egg twelve hours after the previous egg had been laid.

4. The same egg still later, twenty-three and one-half hours after the previous egg had been laid. The gradual increase in shell thickness, as shown by x-ray absorption, is clearly evident.

5. A different egg which was observed at frequent intervals during the last few hours before it was due to be laid, so that the rotation could be followed. This radiograph was taken half way through the rotation, and the egg is therefore seen end-on. The picture was slightly blurred by the breathing movements of the hen. Note the lowered position of the egg in the body cavity. The time required for rotation is between one and two minutes.

6. The same egg shown in views 1, 2, 3 and 4, but twenty-five and one-half hours after the previous egg had been laid, and one-half hour before it was itself laid. In the preceding views (1 to 4), the pointed end is caudad, but here the egg has rotated through 180° so as to bring the blunt end caudad.

7. Calcium carbonate suspensions used for comparison.

PLATE II

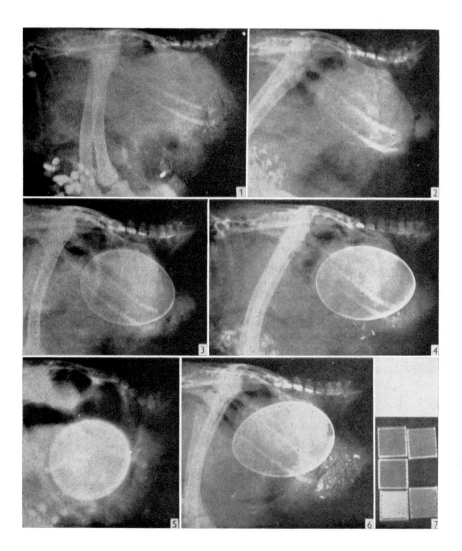

(*Legend on Opposite Page*)

Eggs laid by a hen after the anterior half of her isthmus had been removed were, for the most part, more irregular in shape than eggs laid before the operation. In another hen the isthmus was torn longitudinally and then closed with catgut sutures. After the operation this hen laid eggs with characteristically wrinkled shells, suggesting that the specific shape of the shell membranes, as determined in the isthmus, has a direct influence on shell shape.

Operations on the uterus showed clearly that shape of the egg may also be affected by that portion of the oviduct. Eggs laid by a hen after cotton was placed at the sides of the uterus had a depression reaching more or less around the egg.

That there is great variability in the size of hens' eggs is well known, but the specific causes of this variation are not so well established. It is obvious that the weight of the egg is equal to the sum of the weights of its parts, and that anything affecting the weight of any of the parts may be expected to have some influence on the weight of the entire egg. The small size of the eggs laid by pullets at the beginning of the laying period is due in part to the smaller size of yolk in such eggs, as well as to the lesser amount of albumen. The shell is, of course, formed to fit the egg contents.

The position of an egg in the clutch affects its weight. The second egg of a two-egg clutch is nearly always smaller than the first egg, and in clutches of several eggs, the first egg is usually the heaviest with a progressive decrease in the weight of the egg laid on each successive day. This decrease is almost entirely the result of a decrease in the amount of white, since yolk size appears to be very nearly constant, for any given hen, for all clutch positions.

The color of eggs is in large measure a characteristic of individual hens, all eggs laid by a hen tending to be of the same color except for a gradual change from a darker to a lighter shade during a continuous period of daily laying.

The Completed Egg

The gross parts of an egg are shown diagrammatically in Figure 2–13. Taking these in the order of their formation they are: (1) the germ spot, or blastoderm; (2) the yolk; (3) the white; (4) the shell membranes; and (5) the shell.

The Germ Spot.—The germ spot is closely associated with the yolk. Because its development can be traced back to a point where the cell of which it is a part is yolkless, that is, when no yolk material has been laid down, and also because of its importance as the living part of the egg, it is described separately. Technically it is referred to as the germinal disc in an infertile egg, or prior to fertilization, and as the blastoderm following fertilization, but before development has proceeded very far. It later gives rise to an embryo which ultimately becomes a chick.

The Yolk.—From the standpoint of the packing-house breaking room, the yolk of an egg is a globular mass of more or less highly colored, palatable and very nutritious semi-liquid, for which there is a considerable commercial demand, and without which pastries may not reach their full perfection. In a technical sense the yolk of the kitchen and of commerce, with its germinal disc, or blastoderm, *is the egg*, though it is customary to refer to it as such only when surrounded by its complement of white, shell membrane and shell.

It is enclosed in a transparent membrane known as the vitelline membrane, which is responsible for its maintaining a nearly spherical shape. The material making up the body of the ovum serves as the chick's first and last food during prehatching life, and its first after it escapes the shell.

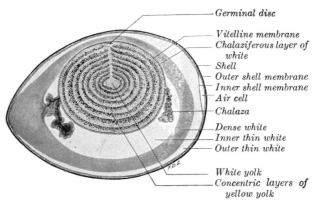

Germinal disc

Vitelline membrane
Chalaziferous layer of
   white
Shell
Outer shell membrane
Inner shell membrane
Air cell
Chalaza

Dense white
Inner thin white
Outer thin white

White yolk
Concentric layers of
   yellow yolk

Fig. 2–13.—Composite diagram showing, in vertical section, the parts of a fresh pullet egg. (Courtesy of F. B. Adamstone.)

The White.—Immediately surrounding the yolk, and adhering closely to the vitelline membrane, is a layer of very dense white called the chalaziferous layer. This is prolonged toward the ends of the egg in two whitish, opalescent, convoluted strands called chalazae, because of a fancied resemblance to hailstones. These prolongations are twisted in opposite directions. The line describing the long axis of the egg passes through them in an egg that has been rotated recently, so that the position of the yolk is central.

Surrounding the chalaziferous white is a spiral layer of faintly pigmented dense albumen referred to as the thick white, which comprises from 40 to 60 per cent by weight of the total white of the egg. The dense white, as a whole, will not flow readily, but holds together in a flattened mass when poured out upon a plate, if the egg is new-laid. This layer of firm white holds an inner layer of liquid white, as can easily be demonstrated by drawing the point of a knife through the firm white of an opened egg. This suggests an explanation for some of the "watery white" eggs of commerce, since rough handling may conceivably bring about a rupture of the layer of dense white, thus causing an apparent liquefaction of the egg. The spiral formation of the white may be noted by carefully dissecting an egg boiled to medium hardness.

Surrounding the thick white in turn is more liquid white (also frequently referred to as "thin," "watery" or "fluid"), which is mucilaginous in character. The difference between the dense and liquid white is easily seen when a new-laid egg is broken into a dish.

Although these four layers of white are readily distinguished in a fresh egg, it is of interest to observe how and when they become differentiated. There is normally no evidence of an inner thin layer until after the forming egg has left the isthmus. The same is true of the chalazae.

Fig. 2–14.—Appearance of a new-laid egg of AA quality. Note how both the yolk and the thick white "stand up."

Through a combination of enzyme action, some dilution of the thick white by the uterine secretion (which approximates normal saline solution in density), and rotation of the egg in the uterus, there is brought about the differentiation of the egg white into the inner or chalaziferous layer; the chalazae; the inner thin white, which is completely enclosed in the dense layer; the thick or dense white, which retains the egg shape when broken out into a saucer; and the outer thin white.

The continued breakdown of the thick white, with corresponding increase in the amount of thin white, is one of the major changes involved in the deterioration of egg quality.

The Shell Membranes.—Surrounding the white of the egg are two white papery membranes referred to as the inner and outer shell membranes. Both are composed of matted organic fibers crossing one another in all directions. The outer membrane is about three times as thick as the inner one, average measurements having been reported as 0.05 and 0.015 mm., respectively.

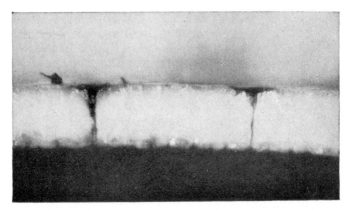

FIG. 2–15.—The edge of a broken shell, showing two pores partially filled with the external cuticle or bloom (enlarged 60 times). (Courtesy of California Agricultural Experiment Station.)

These membranes normally adhere to each other quite closely, except at the large end of the egg where usually they are separated to form the "air cell." The air cell is quite small when the egg is first laid, but progressively increases in size as the egg cools and as water later escapes from the contents by evaporation through the membranes and the shell.

The position of the air cell is quite variable, though usually so situated at the large end that the line describing the long axis of the egg will pass through it at some point. Occasionally, however, it is found at the small end, or at various positions between the ends.

The Shell and Its Cuticle.—The inner shell layer consists of knob-like crystals of calcite. If an egg is removed from the oviduct at the proper stage of development, the shell will be found to consist entirely of this crystalline material.

As shell formation proceeds, there is deposited a chalky layer which comprises about two-thirds of the entire shell. This layer consists of very small calcite crystals of irregular shape, arranged so that their long axes are about perpendicular to the shell surface.

Table 2–3.—Approximate Chemical Composition
of the Egg and Its Parts

	Entire egg	Egg contents	Yolk	White	Shell and membranes
Water	66%	74%	48%	88%	2%
Dry matter . . .	34	26	52	12	98
Protein	12	13	17	11	6
Fat	10	11	33	—	—
Carbohydrates . .	1	1	1	1	—
Ash	11	1	1	—	92

Extending through the egg shell are pores or channels which permit gaseous exchange to take place. In fresh eggs the number of open pores is normally small, but under the influence of high temperature, the number of visible pores is greatly increased. As many as 8000 pores have been observed in a single egg.

When an egg is first laid, it appears moist because it is coated with mucus. This quickly dries, leaving a residue called the cuticle, which partially seals the pores of the shell.

Composition of the Egg

The physical composition of a 2-ounce egg, by weight, is about 10 per cent shell, 30 per cent yolk, and 60 per cent white. The white consists of outer thin white 23 per cent (range from 10 to 60), dense white 57 per cent (range from 30 to 80), inner thin white 17 per cent (range from 1 to 40), and chalaziferous white 3 per cent.

Large eggs contain proportionately more white and less yolk than small eggs. The percentage of shell remains very nearly constant, except that the first eggs laid by pullets carry relatively more shell and less yolk than is characteristic of eggs in general. The last egg of a clutch, at least for clutch sizes of 2 to 7, usually has a thicker shell than the egg which preceded it, presumably because it has spent a somewhat longer time in the uterus.

The approximate chemical composition of the egg and its parts is shown in Table 2–3.

Chapter 3

Principles of Poultry Breeding

PRODUCTIVE poultry breeding has made tremendous progress since the beginning of the present century. Hens with a first-year production of 300 eggs are as common as 200-egg hens were twenty-five years ago. Egg size has been brought under practical genetic control, slow feathering has been eliminated from many flocks, and many other characters have been improved by selection. It is quite evident, however, as was indeed inevitable, that the rate of progress is slowing down, especially with respect to the egg production of superior flocks.

Further improvement will depend on a refinement of selection methods and practices. As we learn more about poultry breeding, it becomes more complex and more difficult. There is no simple, easy, rule-of-thumb method by which a flock average of 300 eggs a year may be attained. Once the basic principles are understood, the most fruitful plan is to apply those principles in a flexible system which permits the breeder to take full advantage both of new information and of families or individuals of exceptional merit whenever they are found. But continued progress will require all the skill of which poultrymen are capable.

HEREDITARY BASIS OF IMPROVEMENT

It is probably correct to say that all characters in the fowl are influenced by both heredity and environment. With some characters the influence of environment is very slight, so slight that there is never any question as to the proper classification of an individual with respect to the character in question. Certain other characters may be so greatly influenced by environment that it is difficult to demonstrate any hereditary influence at all. Those of the first sort—comb type, for example—are said to have a high degree of heritability, because the amount of individual variation which is traceable to environment is extremely small, even non-existent in the case of single comb in the sense that there is never any difficulty about classifying a particular comb as single. Comb size, as influenced by environment, is another matter. Characters at the other extreme are said to have a low degree of heritability because the amount of individual variation traceable to heredity is small, while that traceable to environment is very large.

For single comb, then, it is sufficient to know that it is one form of a character which is highly heritable, that it is recessive to the type of comb called rose, and that selection for the single type is immediately and completely effective.   In other words, if a male and a female possessing single comb are mated together, they will breed true for that character.   All their offspring will have single combs, and they in turn will likewise breed true for that particular character.

Single comb is said to be recessive to rose comb because, if an individual with a single comb is mated to one which is pure for rose comb, the single comb character will not appear in the next generation.   All the offspring will have rose combs, but if any two of these are mated together, the single comb character will reappear in about one-fourth of *their* offspring.   This is an example of the familiar 3:1 Mendelian ratio between simple dominant and recessive characters.   Of those individuals which show the dominant character, about one-third will be true-breeding rose, while two-thirds (one-half of the entire generation) will be like their parents. The true-breeding individuals, either rose or single, are said to be *homozygous*, while the remaining rose-comb individuals are described as *heterozygous*.

Many simple characters in poultry are inherited in the same manner as rose and single comb, while certain others are much more complex.   We shall consider a number of characters for purposes of illustration, proceeding from the simple to the complex and, in a very rough way, from high heritability to low.

Market poultry with yellow skin is prized in some areas, while in others the preference is for white skin.   Genetically, white and yellow skin color constitute a pair of characters just as do rose and single comb, white skin being almost completely dominant to yellow. As every poultryman knows, yellow skin is subject to bleaching until it is practically indistinguishable from skin that is genetically white.   Feeding fowls on a ration which is entirely devoid of the carotenoid pigments will cause the yellow color to disappear after a time.   Females which lay continuously will lose all of their yellow color, even though their ration may be high in xanthophyll for the entire time.   On the other hand, white-skinned fowls will not develop yellow color even when fed rations high in such xanthophyll-containing feeds as yellow corn and green forage.   Here, then, is an example of a character which in a technical sense exhibits high heritability, but only if observed at the right time and under specified conditions.

Plumage colors in poultry are, in general, characterized by a high degree of heritability.   Environmental influences such as inadequate rations may cause some variation, but seldom enough to interfere with accurate classification of individuals with respect to plumage color.   An interesting example, which serves also to illustrate incomplete dominance, is the Blue Andalusian.   These fowls never breed true for color.   The offspring of blue parents occur in the ratio of 1 black to 2 blue to 1 blue-splashed white.   The blacks behave genetically like any other blacks, while the blue-splashed whites are homozygous, and the blues heterozygous, for a gene which dilutes black plumage color. The heterozygous individuals are distinguishable by appearance, and the phenotype ratio is therefore 1:2:1 instead of 3:1. It so happens that the blue heterozygote is the desired type. Breeders may therefore maintain stocks of black and blue-splashed white fowls in order to obtain 100 per cent blue offspring when these two kinds are crossed.

The common 3:1 ratio may be modified in other ways as, for example, by any one of several lethal or semi-lethal genes which interfere with or prevent normal hatching. The short-legged mutation known as creeper is caused by a gene which in homozygous condition completely prevents hatching and in heterozygous condition reduces it slightly. Here again the observed creeper condition in mature fowls is the heterozygous form. When creepers are mated together, the resulting offspring consist of creepers and normals in the ratio of approximately 2:1. Some of the heterozygous creepers die just before hatching, while all of the homozygotes die earlier, and the common 3:1 ratio is therefore changed not to 1:2:1 but to 0:2:1. The creeper condition is regarded by most poultrymen as undesirable. It can be eliminated by the simple procedure of discarding creepers and breeding only from normal fowls. Recessive lethal genes, on the other hand, pose more of a problem because individuals carrying such genes in heterozygous condition cannot be distinguished from normals by appearance. They can be detected only by suitable breeding tests to be explained later.

SEX DETERMINATION AND SEX LINKAGE

To return to plumage color for another example, all fowls so far as is known, carry either the gene for silver or the gene for gold. The gene for silver gives the plumage a silver (white) background on which various black patterns are superimposed, while the gene for gold causes a gold (red, brown or buff) background for such patterns. The presence of either gene may be masked by solid black or by the presence of genes which inhibit color. In the inheritance of characters of the sort previously chosen as examples, it makes no difference in the progeny whether it is through the sire or the dam that the dominant gene of a given pair is introduced. But in the case of genes for silver and gold, and indeed for several other gene pairs in the fowl, it makes considerable difference. This is because the genes for silver and gold are carried on the sex chromosomes, of which the male fowl always has two and the female only one.

Every fertilized egg receives a sex chromosome from the male parent, but whether or not the egg contains a sex chromosome from the female which laid the egg is purely a matter of chance. Approximately half of them do, while the other half do not. If the egg carries a sex chromosome it will, when fertilized, give rise to a male chick. If the egg does not contain a sex chromosome it will, after fertilization contain only one, and will therefore produce a female chick. By this simple device the sexes are maintained in approximately equal numbers.

Because females produce eggs both with and without a sex chromosome and thereby determine, albeit entirely by chance, which are to become males and which are to develop into females, the females are said to be *heterogametic*. Other chromosomes, often called *autosomes*, invariably occur in pairs so that an individual not only has the same number of chromosomes in all its body cells as every other individual of the same species, but has a pair of genes for every character in question, one from its sire and one from its dam. If the genes are alike, the individual is *homozygous* for that gene and will breed true in respect to it. If the genes are unlike, the individual may transmit either to any individual offspring and is therefore *heterozygous* with respect to the character. It is only in the case of the sex chromosomes, and then only in the female, that an individual may receive but a single gene for a particular character. Genes of this sort, that is, all genes which are carried on the sex chromosomes, are called *sex-linked* genes, and the characters which they determine are called sex-linked characters. Barring as found in Barred Plymouth Rocks is another example.

Fig. 3–1.—The Blue Andalusian is a heterozygous form which never breeds true for color. (Courtesy of Poultry Tribune.)

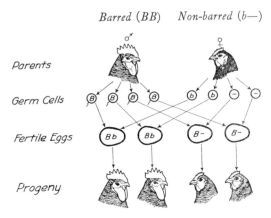

Barred (BB)   Non-barred (b—)

Parents

Germ Cells

Fertile Eggs

Progeny

Fig. 3–2.—Showing the transmission of a dominant sex-linked character, barring (dominant to non-barring) when introduced by a male pure for the character. (Compare with Figure 3–3.)

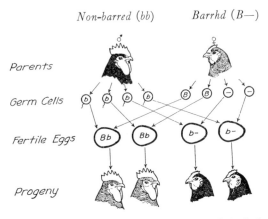

Non-barred (bb)   Barrhd (B—)

Parents

Germ Cells

Fertile Eggs

Progeny

Fig. 3–3.—Showing the transmission of a dominant sex-linked character, barring (dominant to non-barring) when introduced by a female showing the character. (Compare with Figure 3–2.)

Making Use of Sex Linkage

The manner in which sex-linked characters are transmitted makes it possible to use some of these characters for rapid and accurate sex identification of day-old chicks. The only requirement is that the character be one that can be seen at hatching time. Any silver female, when mated with a gold male, produces chicks in which the males are genetically silver and the females gold. Unless they are obscured by some form of dark down color, it is therefore a simple matter to separate the silver (male) chicks from the gold females. If the cross is made the other way around, silver male and gold female, all the chicks will be silver and the recessive gold will not appear, provided the male parent is homozygous for the gene for silver.

Exactly the same procedure can be followed with respect to the genes for barring and non-barring. If barred females are bred to non-barred colored (usually black or red) males, the resulting male chicks will be barred, as evidenced by a characteristic white head spot appearing on the black down, while the females will be solid black in head color. If a pure-bred (homozygous) barred male is used with non-barred females, all of the chicks will be barred.

Another sex-linked gene affects rate of feathering in chicks, and it can be used in the same manner. Leghorns and some other breeds

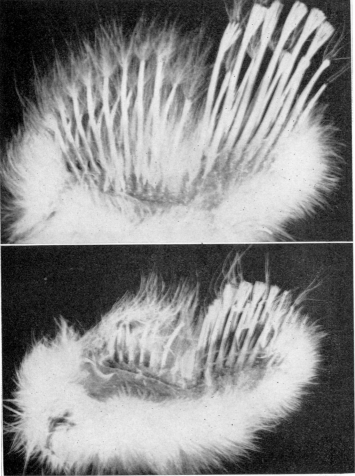

FIG. 3–4.—Slow feathering is dominant to rapid feathering and sex-linked. The difference is apparent in newly hatched chicks. In the rapid-feathering chick (*above*) the primaries and secondaries are longer than the coverts. In the slow-feathering chick (*below*) the primaries and coverts are about equal in length.

are characteristically rapid feathering, whereas most of the American and other heavy breeds are slow feathering. Slow feathering is dominant to rapid, and if the cross is to be used for sex-identification it is therefore necessary to mate rapid-feathering males with slow-feathering females. At hatching time the rapid-feathering female chicks from such a cross show well-developed primaries and secondaries which not only extend well beyond the down, but which are also longer than the associated wing coverts. In the slow-feathering male chicks, by contrast, the primaries are much shorter, are of about the same length as the coverts, and the secondaries are either absent or very poorly developed. Later on, at about ten days of age, the rapid-feathering chicks show well-developed tail feathers, wing feathers extending to the tail, and a small tuft of feathers on each shoulder. The slow-feathering chicks show no tails and much shorter wings. These differences are shown in the accompanying pictures (Figs. 3–4, 3–5).

It must be remembered that feathering is influenced by other genes as well, and that even more serious to broiler growers in particular is the type of slow feathering which is autosomal rather

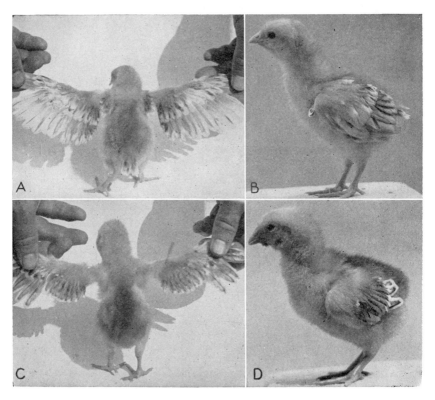

Fig. 3–5.—Showing the difference between rapid feathering (*above*) and slow feathering (*below*) at ten days of age.

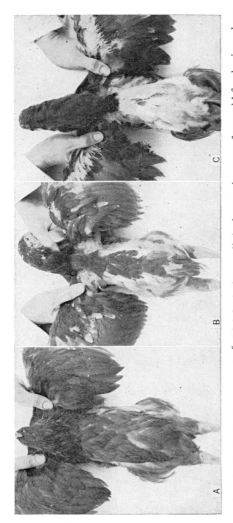

Fig. 3-6.—In breeds or strains which lack the sex-linked recessive gene for rapid feathering, there is often great variation in rate of back feathering caused by autosomal genes. (Courtesy of Massachusetts Agricultural Experiment Station.)

than sex-linked. It has been shown that family selection for good back feathering at eight weeks of age is rather quickly effective. The characteristic differences in back feathering are shown in Figure 3–6. Various other modifying genes affect both rate and condition of feathering, but they are less important than the ones which have just been discussed.

QUANTITATIVE CHARACTERS

All the characters thus far considered belong in what may be described as an "either or" category. There is no gradation by almost imperceptible degrees from rose comb on the one hand through some intermediate form to single comb at the other extreme. But with most of the economically important characters, variation is of the continuous type found in all quantitative characters. Egg size, for example, varies all the way from something under 45 grams to as much as 75 grams. It would not be difficult to find eggs among those produced by almost any large flock which would represent every weight, by one-gram intervals, from 45 to 75 grams. If enough eggs were weighed, it would undoubtedly be possible to find also individual eggs weighing 45.1, 45.2, 45.3 grams each, and so on by one-tenth-gram intervals up to 74.7, 74.8 and 74.9 grams. How then is one to describe and classify eggs according to weight for the purpose of determining how egg weight is inherited? Classifications must obviously be made in some arbitrary manner. And after the upper and lower limits have been chosen for small, medium and large eggs, how is one to determine what genes are involved, and how many pairs of such genes are there? Clearly, this is not so simple a problem as the inheritance of rose and single comb.

For our purpose it is not so important to determine exactly how many pairs of genes are involved, as to recognize that variation in egg size is the result of the influence of more than one pair of genes, that the exact number cannot easily be determined, and that selection for egg size is therefore a somewhat different problem from selection for comb type or plumage color.

A great many things have been learned about egg size, and some of this knowledge can be useful to poultry breeders. We know that egg size is correlated with body size, especially among the smaller breeds of chickens. Selection for large egg size within a breed or variety tends to increase body size at the same time, though not all large fowls lay large eggs.

Since the quantity of feed nutrients which must be digested, metabolized and deposited in 300 small eggs is less than for the same number of large eggs, it is easier to develop families and strains of high-producing fowls if no attention is paid to egg size. Conversely, selection for large egg size places a handicap on the rate of improvement which can be made in egg production, but market demands make it almost mandatory on poultry breeders to strive for egg production performance which not only includes a reasonable minimum average egg weight of between 24 and 25 ounces to the dozen, but which involves a minimum number of small eggs from each pullet.

It has been repeatedly demonstrated that selection for increased egg size is rather quickly effective, so that the present market standard of a 2-ounce minimum for individual eggs can be attained within a period of two to four years of family selection. This is perhaps comparable to the problem of increasing average flock egg production to about 160 eggs a year. Whether it would be any easier to increase average egg weight to $2\frac{1}{2}$ ounces than to increase average egg production to 240 has apparently never been determined. For practical purposes, however, we can say that egg size, within the limits of present market desirability, has a fairly high degree of heritability.

Body size is another quantitative character in which many poultrymen have a direct interest. For our purpose it is important to distinguish between adult weight, and various intermediate weights which may vary widely because of differences in rate of growth to the age at which weight is measured. By no stretch of the imagination could we expect a chick hatched from an egg laid by a bantam hen and fertilized by a bantam male to grow to the size of an adult Plymouth Rock, but the percentage rate of growth of bantams and Plymouth Rocks for a short time after hatching might not be so very different. Rate of growth as reflected by average weight at, let us say twelve weeks of age, is greatly influenced by environment, including the kind and amount of feed consumed. Final adult weight on the other hand, is largely determined by genetic influences, though the time required to reach the maximum may show wide variation, depending on the effects of environment.

Crosses between large and small breeds of chickens, such as Leghorn and Brahma or Hamburg and Cornish, always produce offspring which at maturity are intermediate in size, usually averaging somewhat above the midpoint between the parental stocks. On the other hand, crosses between breeds which are of about the same size often produce offspring which outstrip their parents in rate of growth to ten or telve weeks of age. This characteristic is important to producers of commercial broilers.

There can be no doubt that both adult weight and rate of early growth are highly variable within breeds as well as among breeds, or that they are influenced directly and indirectly by a great many different genes. And yet each is readily influenced by selection. Even mass selection with no reference to family performance will bring about a significant change. This can only mean that both of these quantitative characters have rather high heritability.

EGG PRODUCTION

Breeding laying hens for the production of market eggs is one of the most complex challenges for the application of the principles of genetics. Nearly all the economically important traits that must be developed in a laying hen are quantitative characters that cannot be ascribed to any specific number of genes and that vary in their relative susceptibility to change by selection. The effects of environment on the expression of genetically inherent ability to lay are very large. Annual production of a hen can be greatly affected by diet, housing, lighting, disease, and several other factors. Progress in breeding programs is very often difficult to separate from the effects of improved environment.

The traits considered of economic importance which were measured in Random Sample Egg Laying Tests as reported in the 1966 USDA combined summary of the tests conducted in 1964–65, included: rearing mortality, laying mortality, age at 50 per cent production, hen-housed production, hen-day production, feed per 24-ounce dozen of eggs, egg weight, the percentage of large and extra large eggs, body weight, albumen quality, blood spots, meat spots, and shell thickness. The development of laying hens equally desirable in all traits presents a prodigious task that cannot always be readily solved.

Provided that egg quality characters are adequately considered, the trait most desired by poultrymen is high annual egg production Egg production is measured in two ways, a hen-housed average obtained by dividing the total number of eggs laid during the year by the number of pullets housed at the beginning of the year, or a hen-day average which is simply an expression of the number of eggs laid in relation to the days a hen could lay. Hen-housed averages are greatly affected by laying house mortality, so that a flock may have a high hen-day production average but a low hen-housed production because of high mortality.

Analysis of Laying Performance

No one knows the number of genes that determine whether a hen has the potential to become a good layer or a poor layer. The basic requirement for high production is that a hen lay an egg as often as possible.

The annual production of a flock high-producing laying hens is usually characterized by a peak in rate of production in the second to third month of lay and a steady gradual reduction in the flock rate during the remainder of the laying year.

A comprehensive analysis of the pattern of egg production in a large number of commercial strains was reported by Marble, using data from the New York Random Sample egg-laying tests. He concluded that there is a close relationship between rate of lay at peak production and the level of production that a flock can maintain for the remainder of the year. In Figure 3–7, the egg production curves of several strains of laying hens are grouped according to annual egg production. Those with the highest annual production also peaked at the highest rate. Following peak production, the decline in rate of lay was similar in all three groups. If a flock does not reach a high peak production early in the laying year, the eggs lost during this period are rarely, if ever, regained later in the laying year.

High peak production of a flock means that individual hens that make up the flock must be laying at a high rate. In a flock that peaks at 85 per cent production on a hen-day basis, the average hen in the flock must lay an egg, on the average, more than eight out of every ten days. Hens laying at such a rate are said to have high intensity of lay.

Intensity of lay is largely determined by size of the clutch, the number of eggs laid by a hen on consecutive days. Clutch size is

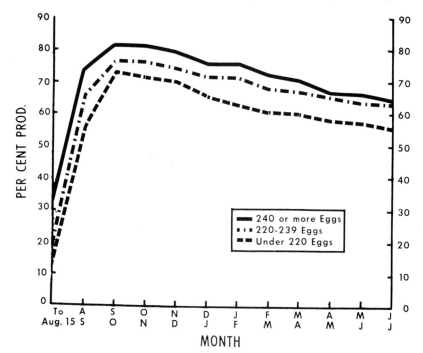

Fig. 3–7.—Production curves for flocks with different average annual egg production. Flocks must have a high peak intensity of lay to produce large numbers of eggs during a laying year. (After Marble.)

usually considered to be a separate hereditary characteristic that helps to determine the annual egg record. The influence of clutch size on egg production is illustrated in Figure 3–8. If a hen lays in clutches consisting of a single egg, the most she can lay in a thirty-day month is 15 eggs; if she lays 2 eggs per clutch, her maximum is 20 eggs. If she lays 3 eggs per clutch, she can make 23 eggs. Further increases in clutch size to 4 and 5 eggs add only about one additional egg to the maximum thirty-day total. The clutch size of an individual hen is likely to be fairly constant, once established, and will be consistent as long as she is laying.

Intensity of lay can be measured over shorter periods of time than a full laying year. The number of eggs in a ten-day, thirty-day or one hundred-day period might be used as a measure of the capability of a hen to lay at a high intensity. Many variations are possible depending on the preference of the breeder and the form in which his records are kept.

The shape of the production curves shown in Figure 3–7 represents the changes in production of entire flocks of chickens. This is the summation of the production records of all the hens that make up these flocks. The decline in production that occurs as the production year advances is not due just to a decrease in rate of lay. That is, hens laying 5 and 6 eggs per clutch do not begin laying clutches of 2 and 3 eggs that result in a lowered intensity of lay. This decline in flock production is usually due to some hens not laying for varying lengths of time, or to hens that may cease laying completely. Hens that pause in production may return to production as others pause. These production stoppages can be caused by environmental factors that become more important as the laying year progresses. Disease, unfavorable weather, broodiness, may be factors that affect the production of individual hens during a laying year. The net result is an overall reduction in the rate of lay of an entire flock. Hens that cease production early in the laying year often are said to have poor persistency.

CLUTCH SIZE	1	2	3	4	5	6	7	8	9	10	11	12	13	14	15	16	17	18	19	20	21	22	23	24	25	26	27	28	29	30	TOTAL
1	x		x		x		x		x		x		x		x		x		x		x		x		x		x		x		15
2	x	x		x	x		x	x		x	x		x	x		x	x		x	x		x	x		x	x		x	x		20
3	x	x	x		x	x	x		x	x	x		x	x	x		x	x	x		x	x	x		x	x	x		x	x	23
4	x	x	x	x		x	x	x	x		x	x	x	x		x	x	x	x		x	x	x	x		x	x	x	x		24
5	x	x	x	x	x		x	x	x	x	x		x	x	x	x	x		x	x	x	x	x		x	x	x	x	x		25
6	x	x	x	x	x	x		x	x	x	x	x	x		x	x	x	x	x	x		x	x	x	x	x	x		x	x	26
7	x	x	x	x	x	x	x		x	x	x	x	x	x	x		x	x	x	x	x	x	x		x	x	x	x	x	x	27
8	x	x	x	x	x	x	x	x		x	x	x	x	x	x	x	x		x	x	x	x	x	x	x	x		x	x	x	27
9	x	x	x	x	x	x	x	x	x		x	x	x	x	x	x	x	x	x		x	x	x	x	x	x	x	x	x		27
10	x	x	x	x	x	x	x	x	x	x		x	x	x	x	x	x	x	x	x	x		x	x	x	x	x	x	x	x	28

FIG. 3–8.—Effect of clutch size (number of eggs laid without a skip) on the total number of eggs laid in a thirty-day period. An average clutch size of three or more is essential to making a high annual egg record.

Although production pauses and persistency of lay have been considered as separate genetic characters, there is relatively little evidence to suggest that selection for good persistency or short production pauses separately from rate of lay or total annual production will bring about marked improvements in the laying ability of hens.

Broodiness.—Some hens will stop production and attempt to incubate their eggs. This type of behavior, necessary for reproduction in wild birds, is hereditary, and hens that become broody will usually lay fewer eggs in the course of a year. Brooding behavior is under endocrine control and can be induced by injections of the hormone, prolactin, which is normally produced by the anterior pituitary gland.

Selection against broodiness is quite effective, and rapid progress to reduce this character to a low level can be made if all broody females and their close relatives are discarded. Broodiness has been nearly eliminated in modern egg-laying strains. Heavy breeds are more susceptible than White Leghorns, and some broodiness may be encountered in broiler breeding stock.

Age at First Egg.—When egg production is measured to a given age, the age at sexual maturity is an important factor in determining the number of eggs laid. The age at first egg is one measure of sexual maturity, and for a flock this is often measured as days of age to 50 per cent production. Sexual maturity can be greatly advanced or delayed by the lighting program followed during rearing. The

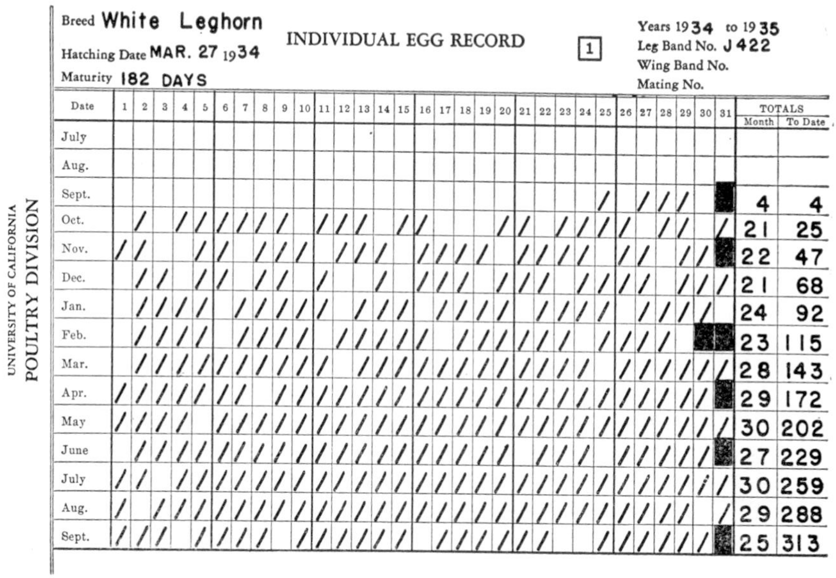

Breed **White Leghorn** — INDIVIDUAL EGG RECORD — Years 19**34** to 19**35**
Hatching Date **MAR. 27** 19**34** — Leg Band No. **J 422** — Wing Band No. — Mating No.
Maturity **182 DAYS** — [1]

UNIVERSITY OF CALIFORNIA — POULTRY DIVISION

Date	Month	To Date
July		
Aug.		
Sept.	4	4
Oct.	21	25
Nov.	22	47
Dec.	21	68
Jan.	24	92
Feb.	23	115
Mar.	28	143
Apr.	29	172
May	30	202
June	27	229
July	30	259
Aug.	29	288
Sept.	25	313

FIG. 3-9.—The record of a "300-egg" hen. (Courtesy of California Agricultural Experiment Station.)

influence of light is probably the most important environmental factor affecting this character in laying hens, but other factors such as feeding programs and disease can delay age at first egg.

Age at maturity is hereditary and when environmental variations are controlled, it is fairly easy to establish desired maturity in a flock. The optimum age when laying commences must be somewhat of a compromise between considerations of the costs of feed and housing for a longer rearing period, and those of optimum egg size. Egg size in pullets coming into lay is largely a function of age. If a hen comes into production late, she will lay fewer small eggs. The age to 50 per cent production in the 1963–64 Central New York Random Sample Egg Laying Test ranged from 167 to 189 days for the 33 strains tested.

HATCHABILITY

The final character chosen for discussion in this chapter is hatchability. By definition, it is usually taken to mean the percentage of fertile eggs which hatch under artificial incubation. It is influenced by many things such as age of breeding stock; rate of egg production of the breeders and the rations they have been fed; season of year; size of eggs; character of egg shells; length of holding time after laying, and conditions under which eggs for hatching are held; temperature, humidity and other conditions in the incubator; as well as by genetic influences working through the hens that laid the eggs or the males that fertilized them.

The emphasis here is on the environmental rather than the genetic influences. It is true that there are some 16 lethal genes which either reduce or prevent hatching. It is also true that the indirect effect of certain other genes which influence egg size and shell quality may reduce the percentage of eggs which hatch. But by and large, the problem of improving hatchability is a problem of improving the environment. Hatchability for a given flock in any given season may be improved by eliminating individual hens which show poor hatchability early in the season, but it is futile to select as future breeders hens which give high hatchability, and sons of such hens, with the expectation that average hatchability of a flock will thereby be greatly improved by reason of inheritance. Some writers have referred to specific genes for hatchability, but all available evidence supports the view that heritability of this character is very low. Except for selection against the lethals, and against such indirect effects as large and small egg size and poor shell texture, genetics has little place in the improvement of hatchability. The problem of rations which are nutritionally adequate, and the management methods which help to insure a high percentage hatch will be discussed in later chapters.

SYSTEMS OF BREEDING

Only a small fraction of all the chickens on farms and ranches ever become a part of any planned system of breeding. Most of them, however, are influenced in some degree by the systems in use by breeders, and in particular by the selection and improvement procedures carried out by commercial hatcheries. Seldom is any one system used exclusively by a breeder, and it is probable that the most successful breeders make use of all the accepted systems from time to time and in combination.

Inbreeding

A simple and easily understood definition of inbreeding is that it involves the mating together of closely related individuals. The closest inbreeding which the poultryman can use is continued brother × sister mating for several successive generations. A lesser degree of inbreeding results from the mating of father × daughter, mother × son, half-brother and sister, or cousins.

Some degree of inbreeding is essential to the development of uniform stocks. Close inbreeding makes for greater uniformity but, since undesirable genes as well as desirable genes are concentrated in the inbred line, the overall effect is frequently disappointing. Close inbreeding by itself is, therefore, not often profitable.

It must be clearly understood that maintaining a closed breeding flock, even if the total number of females in any one year is no more than 100, is not necessarily inbreeding in the accepted sense. So long as the breeders are chosen more or less at random, and several males are used each year, there is very little risk of any sort of trouble which can be ascribed solely and specifically to inbreeding. On the contrary, the success of many breeders can be attributed in part to the fact that they have chosen to follow the closed flock plan.

Outbreeding

Outbreeding is essentially the mating together of individuals which are less closely related than the average of the flock with which the breeder is working. The poultryman often speaks of it as introducing new blood. With flocks in which several desirable characteristics are well established, it should be done very cautiously, if at all.

There are numerous instances in which a strain has been ruined by the unwise introduction of new stock in such a manner as to involve the whole flock. Test matings, involving a small fraction of the flock, should always be made before risking the entire breeding program, assuming that one has highly productive stock with which to start.

Outbreeding often increases the average performance of the individuals in the next generation—average egg production, for example —so that the breeder may think he is making real progress. The trouble is that the breeding value of his best birds is lowered by making them more heterozygous than they were before, thus lessening the chances of being able to carry on their good qualities to the next generation. If the stock is not to be used for future breeding, there is no objection to such a change in genetic make-up.

Crossbreeding

For the same reason that outbreeding frequently improves the average performance of the first generation, crossbreeding of totally unrelated breeds sometimes produces rather startling results. The new combination of genes often results in a high degree of heterosis or hybrid vigor. This usually is apparent in rapid growth, uniformity, and sometimes in increased egg production. Whatever is gained in these lines with respect to individual performance is offset

6

by lowered breeding value. Hence crossbreeding is most useful when applied to the production of stock which is to be grown for meat purposes, or kept no more than a year or two for egg laying, and then sold without any attempt to use it for breeding.

Crossing of Inbred Lines

Many breeders have been interested in the crossing of highly inbred lines belonging to the same or different breeds, on the supposition that such a procedure might duplicate for poultry some of the known advantages of hybrid corn. The chickens so produced are commonly referred to as hybrids, and the system of breeding used is often called hybridization.

When highly inbred lines from two different breeds are crossed, the resulting chicks have a much higher degree of heterozygosity than do chicks from a mating between random samples of the same two breeds. This increases the predictability of results, whether good or bad, so that one can make additional matings between the same two inbred lines with the expectation of getting substantially the same results.

Production and maintenance of the inbred lines is costly, and many of them have to be discarded after trial because they do not combine well with other lines.

The egg production of such hybrid chickens as have been commercially available has been good enough to make certain that still more of them will be produced.

Strain Crossing

As already mentioned, close inbreeding gradually makes a population more homozygous for both desirable and undesirable genes. Very frequently the concentration of unfavorable genes puts an end to the inbreeding program, at least in some of the lines. In fact, there is some reason to believe that continued brother × sister matings for several generations are possible only because of natural and controlled selection against this very homozygosity, so that the eighth or ninth generation is not so closely inbred as the calculated coefficient of inbreeding would indicate. It may even be that a certain amount of heterozygosity is a basic essential of being alive. Many geneticists are of the opinion that the best performance comes not from individuals which are homozygous for a large number of desirable genes, but rather from individuals which are somewhat if not highly heterozygous.

Within breeds there are strains that may be quite unrelated to each other, having been developed as closed flocks for many years or having had little recent common ancestry. Some of these strains, when crossed, give offspring that perform considerably better than the parent strains. When the use of a particular strain in a cross nearly always gives a good result, this strain is said to have general combining ability.   In other cases, strains are useful only when crossed with another specific strain.   These strains have specific combining ability.   Some strains combine well only when used as the male parent, and others must be the female parent to do well. To discover useful strain crosses, many strains must be tested for their combining ability.   When two strains are discovered that give outstanding offspring when crossed, these strains can be maintained as parent stock for the production of the commercial strain cross chicks.

More than two strains may be useful in a cross so that the final chick produced for sale could be a three- or four-way cross.

Strain crossing has been particularly useful in the breeding of laying hens.   Nearly 50 per cent of all the entries in the Random Sample Egg Production Tests in the United States in 1964 were classified as strain crosses.

Improving Strain Crosses

When strains are found that combine well in a strain or breed cross, the breeder is faced with several possibilities.   He can maintain the parent strains as a random breeding population in an effort to retain the good combining ability of the strains.   Alternatively, he can select to improve each strain in the hope that the strain cross will also be improved.   In a third breeding system, individuals would be selected for mating within each strain on the basis of their ability to combine well in the strain cross.   In this system, the individual strains are maintained but selection within the strain depends on the performance of the strain cross.   This breeding plan, aimed at improving the specific combining ability of strains, has been termed reciprocal recurrent selection.

Making a Breeding System Work

No matter what system is used, the breeding value of a given individual must be judged either from its own performance or from the performance of its relatives.   This means that the breeder must use great care to avoid confusing the effects of environment with those of heredity.   Variations caused by environment can be very large in such characters as egg production, and they can be very important economically, but they do not change the hereditary makeup of the individuals so affected.   They are therefore not transmitted to the next generation.   They can be reproduced only by repeating the environmental conditions which produced them originally.

Improvements brought about by heredity, on the other hand, tend to be permanent, and the cost of making them may be returned many times over in future generations.   This means that different characters in any selection program should be given emphasis in proportion to both their heritability and their economic value.

It is important to remember that while the gene is the actual unit of inheritance, the individual fowl is the smallest unit that can be saved or rejected for breeding purposes. This is bound to temper one's judgment as to the value of inbreeding, for example, except for specific purposes. Inbreeding is, in fact, a much stronger force for lowering annual egg production than selection is for increasing it. The effect of close inbreeding in a small flock could not be overcome by any amount of selection pressure in the direction of increased egg production.

Successful breeding systems of the future will no doubt be applied principally to large flocks which consist of many fairly large families of full or half sisters. They will be designed to take full advantage of all known methods of improvement, including some complex selection indexes. They will also include careful consideration of such things as the optimum proportion of pullets to older hens and of cockerels to older males in the breeding flock, because these things are important in determining both the intensity of selection for desired characters and the interval between generations. Selection methods are discussed in more detail in the next chapter.

Chapter 4

Selection and Improvement

SELECTION, as used in connection with breeding, refers to the choosing of parents for the next generation. Its skilled performance is the foundation of constructive breeding practice. One should remember that selection will be operating no matter what system of breeding is used, even though in the simplest case it may be reduced to mere chance. Furthermore, selection cannot change or alter any genetic process any more than will trap-nesting or pedigree breeding. All that it can do, if successful, is change the gene frequency by preventing the poorer individuals from being hatched, and thus carry the breeder more rapidly in the direction of his ultimate goal.

SELECTION METHODS

Selection of individual males and females for breeding may be based on:
1. The past—in which the pedigree of the individual is examined for several preceding generations.
2. The present—in which the appearance or performance of the individual and its sibs (sisters and brothers) is used in making final judgment.
3. The future—in which the breeding worth of the individual is judged by the appearance or performance of its descendants, usually only its sons and daughters.

Two or more of these bases may sometimes be used in combination, especially the second and third. The constructive breeder attempts by selection to segregate individuals which are pure for certain desirable genes and, through intelligent mating, to assemble in new individuals still more desirable combinations of genes.

Pedigree Selection

A good individual with a good ancestry is to be preferred to an equally good individual with a poor ancestry, but it should be emphasized that a good ancestry only improves the chances for desirable breeding performance; it is no guarantee of such performance. Since genes and chromosomes occur in pairs, and are halved for any individual in each generation, it is immediately apparent that a particular remote ancestor can have very little influence on the genetic makeup of an individual which is being considered in selection. It can be shown by suitable calculation that an ancestor which appears but once in the tenth preceding generation will have contributed less than one-tenth of one per cent to the total genetic makeup of the individual. A similar ancestor in the fifth generation will have contributed, on the average, only a little more than 3 per cent.

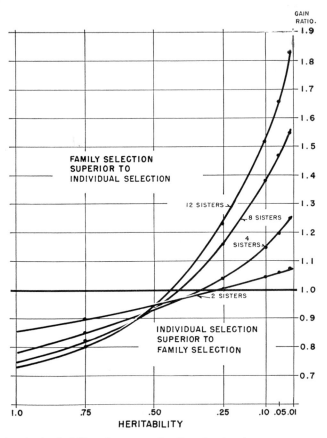

Fig. 4–1.—As heritability decreases, family selection becomes more and more important, especially when large families of full sisters are available. The curves show the ratio of expected gains from family selection alone over individual selection alone. (Adapted from Lerner.) Note: single comb has an heritability of 1.0; the production index about .05.

Pedigree selection is of value in a broad sense in that one would certainly choose a breeding cockerel whose dam had laid 250 eggs in preference to one whose dam's record was only 150. But one should also remember that two cockerels from the 250-egg hen may give widely differing performance as measured by the egg production of their daughters. Furthermore, a difference between 250 eggs and 150 eggs in a dam's record may be important in selection, whereas a difference between 275 and 250, or even between 300 and 250 may not.

Individual or Mass Selection

Mass selection is predicated on the assumption that the appearance or performance of an individual can be taken as an indication of its breeding worth. For some characters this assumption is correct, and selection is then very simple. All one need do is identify the desired individuals with respect to some reliable measure of the character in question. For many characters, however, and especially for those of economic importance which are influenced by many different genes, the assumption is so far from the truth as to be completely misleading. This arises not only because the presence of many genes makes their enumeration and recognition difficult, but because the effect of environment on the expression of the genetic character may be and frequently is very great.

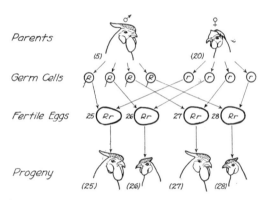

FIG. 4–2.—Showing the test for purity of a simple character. The male indicated here is pure for rose comb. (Compare with Figure 4–3.)

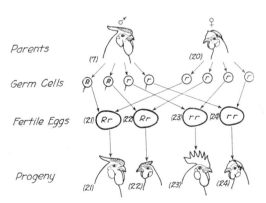

FIG. 4–3.—Showing the test for purity of a simple character. The male indicated here is not pure for rose comb. (Compare with Figure 4–2.)

Mass selection, based on phenotypic performance, may be effective through the low to medium range of a given quantitative character and quite ineffective in the upper range. Egg production is a good example. There can be no doubt about the effectiveness of individual or mass selection in improving average egg production up to 160, 180, or perhaps 200 eggs per pullet per year—the exact limit depending both on the sort of stock with which one is working and the environment under which it is kept. But continued dependence on mass selection can only lead to disappointment when it ceases to bring any further progress.

A great deal of improvement in poultry flocks has been the result of widely applied mass selection practices, particularly in the elimination of such undesirable individuals as slow growers, poor layers, and those which detract from a reasonably uniform appearance of flocks. Many flocks can still be improved by this method of selection, but as performance moves up the scale it is necessary to use more refined selection methods or accept something less than maximum performance as the end and aim of a breeding program.

Fig. 4–4.—Single cages make it easy to obtain individual records of egg production with nearly 100 per cent accuracy. Furthermore, one person can keep track of about four times as many hens in cages as when they are floor housed and trap-nested. (Courtesy of Heisdorf and Nelson, Inc. Kirkland, Washington.)

Family Selection

Modern breeding methods involve a great deal more than a detailed record of the performance of individuals. They consider rather the extent to which individuals reflect the performance of a family. The distinction is important. Sons of a 240-egg hen which was one of eight sisters laying between 230 and 260 eggs each are much more likely to transmit desirable genes for egg production to their daughters than are the sons of a 280-egg hen whose sisters finished the year with records of 190 to 230 eggs. But there is still no assurance that the particular son of the 240-egg hen chosen to head a new breeding pen will be able to equal the breeding performance of his sire. Hopes may be built upon ancestry, individuality, and sibs, but the only sure basis for forming a judgment concerning the ability of an individual to transmit genes for desired characters to most or all of its progeny is breeding it. This part of family selection is usually referred to as the progeny test.

By progeny testing is meant a careful analysis of the results secured from various matings in order that future matings may be made with greater assurance of success. Any mating that has given unusually good results should be repeated or, in terms of today's

Fig. 4–5.—On breeding farms where many small matings are necessary, trap-nesting is conveniently done from a central corridor. (Courtesy of Kimber Farms, Inc., Fremont, California.)

procedure on many breeding farms, continued. The progeny test is also used for the purpose of distinguishing between individuals which are homozygous and those which are heterozygous for some simple character such as rose comb or white skin color. Only one single-comb chick is needed from a mating of two individuals with rose comb to show that *both* parents are heterozygous for rose comb. Similarly, if any of the offspring of two white-skin parents have yellow skin, both parents must be heterozygous for skin color. When it is desired to check a given male to find out whether he is homozygous for rose comb, the simplest procedure is to mate him with a few single-comb hens. If even one chick hatched has a single comb, the male is heterozygous. If, on the other hand, there are no single combs among as many as twelve or fifteen chicks, one can be practically certain that the male is homozygous.

More often, however, a breeder is concerned with the progeny test as a measure of breeding worth in respect to some quantitative character such as annual egg production, egg weight, mature body weight of females, or survival through a full year of egg production. This calls for records which are sufficiently complete to provide the necessary measures. Just what they are will depend on the particular characters under observation, but certain details are necessary in any case. Some of these are indicated in the following section.

Blood Group Systems

In many animal species there are several distinct blood groups, but they are seldom directly comparable to the A–B–O groups in humans. The number of blood group systems so far identified in the chicken is seven, and each group is controlled by a group of genes forming an allelic series. The significance of this for the poultryman lies in the finding that chickens which are heterozygous for certain blood group genes, having received unlike genes from their two parents, possess somewhat better survival characteristics than do homozygous individuals of otherwise similar breeding. Since high survival tends to be associated with such desirable economic traits as high hatchability, high egg production and rapid growth rate, some commercial breeders are using comprehensive blood typing procedures, followed by performance testing of various crosses, to help fix desirable characteristics in the strains with which they are working.

BREEDING AND PERFORMANCE RECORDS

From the preceding discussion of the bases of selection, it should be clear that complete breeding and performance records are essential items in the progressive production-breeder's equipment.

Steps in Keeping a Complete Record

The steps in keeping a complete record are: (1) marking prospective breeders; (2) recording egg production; (3) recording the matings made; (4) identifying the eggs to be hatched; (5) pedigree hatching; (6) recording fertility and hatchability; (7) marking and recording the chicks; (8) recording livability, rate of growth, rate of feathering, and the like; and (9) making family summaries.

Record systems may be simple or complex, depending on the number of characters under observation, but an elaborate set of records is of little real value unless the data are carefully analyzed. A few simple records well kept and carefully studied will be much more helpful than a complete set which involves so much work that there is no time for its analysis.

Record forms may be purchased, but since no one system of records can be best for all purposes, the breeder will usually do better by developing such forms as best suit his own particular needs.

Making Use of Records

The records to be kept and the use to be made of them will naturally vary with the objectives which the individual breeder has in mind. The following suggestions will serve as a guide in using family, individual, and progeny test records when the breeding objective is high production of market eggs.

Minimum standards for birds to be saved as breeders should be set for each factor considered, or all birds may be given a grade of A, B, or C on each separate factor and on overall breeding value. The standards may be raised from time to time as the flock improves. Those indicated here are for purposes of illustration only.

Factors Known Prior to the Hatching Season.—Certain factors can be measured early in the life of the individual, while others must wait for performance of its progeny. Some of those in the first class are:

(a) Family size (5 or more full sisters).

(b) Family egg production (hen-housed average of 240 eggs or better—also known as the production index)

(c) Family egg quality (size—2 ounces within sixty days from first egg; color, shape, and interior quality standards as desired).

(d) Family survival to specified age (95 per cent to six months of age; 85 per cent in laying house, before any culling).

(e) Family record of physical characters (body weight, rate of feathering, etc.).

(f) Hen's individual record of egg production.

Age at first egg—175 days or less.

Non-pause—no pause of seven days or more.

Non-broodiness—no broody periods.

Intensity—clutch size of 3 or more eggs, or 50 eggs in sixty consecutive days.

Persistency—late molt, and still laying at three hundred and fifteen days from date of first egg.

Factors Based on Hatching Season and Progeny Test.— Although peliminary selection of breeders must nearly always be made before any record of progeny performance is available, a final check on the value of a breeding bird can be made only after its offspring have had an opportunity to perform in the laying house. Some of the additional factors which can then be applied are:

(g) Hen's own record of fertility (90 per cent or better).
(h) Hen's own record of hatchability (85 per cent or better).
(i) Number of daughters raised.
(j) Rate of growth of chicks.
(k) Rate of feathering of chicks.
(l) Daughters' average egg production.
(m) Daughters' average egg quality.
(n) Daughters' record of survival.

SELECTION IN PRACTICE

The foregoing discussion may suggest to some persons that breeding for egg production can easily be reduced to a matter of keeping individual egg records, assembling them into family averages, choosing the better families for breeding, and by so doing to keep on improving flock average egg production year after year. Unfortunately, it is not that simple. Perhaps the chief reason why it cannot be that simple is that no poultry breeder can afford to be satisfied with improving a single trait such as number of eggs. His stock must be of acceptable body size and general appearance; it must live well; the chicks must grow rapidly and feather properly; and the eggs laid by surviving pullets must be of suitable size, shape, color, shell texture and interior quality.

Suppose, for illustration, that a poultryman is satisfied to use in his breeding program any sires which, on the basis of family performance, are above the average of his entire flock. Only about half of all the sires can be above average in any measure of family egg production, for the other half must be below. Similarly, only about half can be above average in respect to family egg size. But the chance for a given sire to be above average in both respects becomes $\frac{1}{2} \times \frac{1}{2}$, or $\frac{1}{4}$. That is, only one in four can be expected to excel in both characteristics. If, now, we add a requirement that a sire excel also in respect to suitable measures of body size, interior egg quality and shell color, we reduce the mathematical chance of finding such a sire to 1 in 32. A small breeder may not even have a total of 32 tested sires in any one season.

There are other important characters for which selection should be practiced. For instance, no sire should be used which did not come from a family of some reasonable minimum size, and he in turn must have a reasonable number of daughters as a basis for evaluating his own breeding worth. And all will agree that choosing males which merely exceed the *average* in respect to the desired qualities does not constitute very rigid selection. If we say that the males chosen must be in the upper 25 per cent of the flock in respect to five different character measurements, then instead of finding 1 in 32, we can expect by chance to find only 1 in 1024 (namely, $\frac{1}{4} \times \frac{1}{4} \times \frac{1}{4} \times \frac{1}{4} \times \frac{1}{4}$). And if we set the requirement at the upper 20 per cent level, we still further reduce the changes to 1 in 3125. At 10 per cent it becomes 1 in 100,000. This is just another way of saying that poultry breeding is difficult and complex, and that progress toward the upper physiological limit in terms of production performance is bound to be slow.

The preceding discussion should make it clear that if high average egg production is the chief aim of a breeding program, each additional character for which selection is made, if at the same time and to the same extent, automatically reduces the intensity of selection which can be applied to the main objective. In the example just used, if 10 per cent of the available males must be saved for breeding purposes, and if family average egg production is the only character considered, the top 10 per cent of the males can be chosen. But if two characters are considered, assuming no correlation between them, only about 1/10 of the males which qualify in the first character will also be in the top 10 per cent with respect to the second. Therefore the remaining 9/10 of the males which must be saved to provide the minimum total number will fall below the desirable standard in one or both measures.

If we select for as many as five characters simultaneously, provided they are not correlated and assuming that we want the best 10 per cent of all males as before, the intensity of selection for any one character is reduced a great deal further, actually to the equivalent of $\sqrt[5]{1/10}$. Hence it is very important when making selections not to give undue weight to those characters which are of minor significance. If a breeder feels that he must select for a certain shade of plumage color, in addition to perhaps five economically important characteristics, he must accept the obvious corollary that progress toward his main objective of high average egg production will be slowed just that much more.

Fortunately, there are some short cuts. A breeder may find it wise to concentrate on one or two characters at a time. He can use production to January 1 as his measure of egg-laying ability instead of insisting on full yearly records; he can use the median instead of the mean for measuring such family traits as age at first egg; he can breed from pullets instead of from older hens in order to get ten generations in ten years instead of only five. All of these will help because they save time, in terms of breeding progress, and because they enable a poultryman with a specified number of breeding pens to increase the selection pressure which he applies to his stock. But even when all these things are taken into account, poultry breeding today is big business. It calls for extensive facilities in the way of physical equipment, large numbers of fowls, and a great deal of labor both in the keeping of detailed records and in their analysis. Some breeding operations involve more than 500 small pens for flock matings headed by individual males. The larger breeding farms make extensive use of punch cards and tabulating equipment in handling thousands upon thousands of individual records.

All of this has come about, not merely as expansion and growth, but in an attempt to discover and apply more refined and precise methods of selection to the business of increasing egg production. As pointed out earlier, poultry breeders have come a long way by the use of a common sense approach to the problem, so that a prospective purchaser of chicks or breeding stock today can obtain at nominal cost the kind of chickens which not so many years ago were known on but few farms in the country. But because better and better performance is demanded, breeders will continue to use all means at their disposal to reach still higher goals.

For many years, while egg production has been increasing from low to mediocre to good, the amount of variation traceable to heredity has been large enough to make selection—even mass selection—highly effective. Concurrently much has been learned about how to improve egg production performance by providing better environment. The stimulus of artificial light, the favorable effect of the best possible rations, the increase in fall egg production resulting from consistently early hatching, the construction of houses of a size and type which will conserve the heat energy produced by the hens themselves and so provide more comfortable winter quarters, have combined to increase the opportunities for improving egg production through the influence of environment. An inevitable result has been that as mass selection approached the limit of effectiveness, the amount of individual variation traceable to environment increased. The indications are that in many of today's better bred flocks the heritability of egg production, that is, the amount of variation directly traceable to heredity, is no more than 30 per cent, and that the heritability of the production index, because it includes the effect of mortality, probably does not exceed 5 per cent.

This low degree of heritability does not mean, however, that poultrymen should discard all selection and breeding efforts to concentrate on methods by which egg production can be further improved through environment. It does mean that the individual has become of little importance in selection except as it helps to make up a family average, or as it is representative of a family with high average performance. It means also that further progress will be slow, even with increased selection pressure. And it means that as this continued progress is made, the heritability figure will decline still further as the barrier to increased egg production through genetic means is raised higher and higher. The detailed theory behind this reasoning is too intricate to be included here, but to the student of poultry genetics it is a fascinating subject.

ESTIMATING EGG PRODUCTION FROM EXTERNAL APPEARANCE

Routine culling of laying flocks is seldom practiced on commercial egg farms, simply because it is no longer economically important.

When average flock egg production was no more than 200 eggs per hen, with one-third or more of the individuals laying fewer than 175 eggs, a substantial saving in feed cost could be made by getting rid of the low producers as they reached the end of their laying year. But with today's better bred stock capable of laying 240 to 250 eggs a year, and with very few individuals turning out to be really poor layers, there is little to be gained by routine culling. With cage-managed flocks, culling would be a very simple procedure, but most operators have found that as a practical matter the removal of the few hens that are obviously out of condition is all that is necessary. The entire flock is retained for a laying period of twelve to fifteen months and then replaced.

There are, however, thousands of flock owners who are not in the commercial class, who do no breeding, but who are still very much interested in methods of separating high-producing hens from their low-producing flock mates. Furthermore, a detailed study of production characteristics of laying hens is one of the better ways of gaining an understanding of biological processes in poultry. The essential facts about methods of estimating egg production from external examination and appearance of hens are given in the following pages.

The Relation of Selection and Culling

In actual practice the selection and culling of poultry should begin when the chicks are taken from the incubator and should continue as long as they live and make up a part of the flock.

Although frequently used as synonyms, the terms "selection" and "culling" are strictly opposite in their implication. Selection aims at progress. It is positive and constructive. It deals with the very cream of the flock, including at the most the top 25 per cent, and more commonly only the top 10 or 15 per cent.

Culling, on the other hand, is negative, has no necessary relation to breeding, deals with the least productive fraction of the flock, and is aimed at the prevention of retrogression rather than at progress.

It is unfortunate that the term "cull" should have come to mean one thing to the poultry producer and quite another thing to the buyer of market poultry. In marketing practice a "cull" is an inferior product from a meat standpoint, whereas to the producer a cull hen is simply a non-layer or one that has made a low record. As the term is short and descriptive, it seems likely to persist in both usages, but the distinction between them should be clearly understood.

Physical Characters Related to Laying

As applied to the laying flock, the judging of fowls for egg production really consists of two distinctly different phases which in practice are nearly always considered simultaneously. These are (1) the separation of the laying from the non-laying hens with the object of disposing of the ones that have stopped for the season, and (2) sorting hens on the basis of their ability to lay eggs throughout the year.

It is significant that the second phase has to do largely with estimating past production, and that most of our knowledge in respect to the judging of laying ability is closely tied up with the fact that high egg production leaves its mark in the way of discernible physical characteristics. To the extent that a good hen in any one year tends to repeat the performance, the selection of high layers on the basis of past production has a commercial value that is not necessarily related to the breeding problem, though it is commonly used as a part of a general improvement program.

A   *B*

Fig. 4–6.—*A*, The head of a high producer, 281 eggs in one year; and *B*, of a low producer, 106 eggs in one year. Note the contrast in appearance of the eye, and in fleshing of the face. (Courtesy of Kansas Agricultural Experiment Station.)

Head Type.—The appearance of the head is variable because of differences in size, shape and expression. Some of these differences are undoubtedly related to laying performance, and several different attempts have been made to arrive at more or less exact correlations in order that head types may be accurately classified and used as a basis for the estimation of laying ability. While this objective has not been, and perhaps never will be, wholly realized, it is entirely possible to group head types according to the degree of refinement, and to show some relation between this and the egg records. Hens with coarse, phlegmatic, masculine, or "beefy" heads are not likely to lay very many eggs. Those with clear-cut rugged, alert heads that are at the same time fine in quality, are likely to be among the best layers in the flock.

Body Type.—Type or shape of body is essentially a breed characteristic and, therefore, is directly the result of, and is influenced by selection. It is obvious that in order to lay for a long time and at a high rate a hen must have the capacity and ability to utilize large amounts of feed rapidly and efficiently. This means, among other things, that there must be ample room in the body cavity for the functioning of the vital organs. Further than this, there does not seem to be any reasonable basis for assuming a causal relationship between body type and egg production.

Body Changes.—When laying, a hen has a large, moist vent, showing a dilated, pliable condition in contrast to the puckered hardness of the vent of a non-laying hen. The abdominal region is enlarged in the layer, as compared with the non-layer. The pelvic bones move apart and become comparatively elastic and pliable.

In an individual that is not laying, these bones almost come together just below the vent. The same individual when in full laying may show a distance of three or even four fingers' between

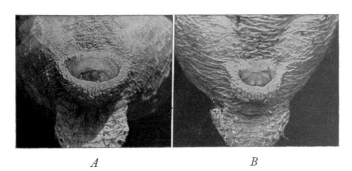

A   B

FIG. 4–7.—*A*, The vent of a laying hen, and *B*, of a non-laying hen. (Courtesy of Kansas Agricultural Experiment Station.)

them. The distance from the pelvic bone to the point of the keel (breast bone) is increased at the same time. These changes provide room for the passage of the egg, the enormous increase in the size of the ovary, with its several rapidly growing ova, and for the distention of the alimentary tract to accommodate large amounts of feed.

The rate of egg production is indicated in a measure by the relative softness and pliability of the skin and the thinness and elasticity of the pelvic bones. The subcutaneous fat of the abdomen is used up by laying, so that the abdominal skin of the heavy producer becomes velvety and the whole abdomen soft and flexible. The pelvic bones feel thin, tapering and elastic. In the non-layer they are likely to feel thick, blunt and stiff, while the whole abdomen is surrounded under the skin with a layer of hard fat if the bird is on full feed.

Among the most valuable indications of the heavy layer are the refinement of the head and the closeness and dryness of feathering. The wattles and earlobes fit close to the beak and are not loose and flabby. The face is clean cut and rather thin. Puffiness in the face indicates meat rather than eggs. The eye is full, round and prominent as viewed across the tip of the beak. The high layer is trimmer in feathering than the poor layer, but after prolonged heavy production the oil does not keep the plumage so sleek and glossy. It becomes worn and frayed.

There is a close correlation between the relative size of the comb and wattles and ovarian activity. If they are comparatively large, full, smooth, hard and waxy, the hen is probably laying heavily; if the comb is limp the bird may be laying slowly; but if it is dried, shrunken and cold, she is not laying at all. When the comb is expanding in advance of another period of production it often feels warm to the touch.

Pigmentation.—In those varieties showing yellow pigment in the subcutaneous fat, shanks (and earlobes in Mediterranean and Continental breeds), the pigment tends to disappear as laying progresses. The presence or absence of this pigment in the fowl or its eggs is directly correlated with the presence or absence in the feed of a carotenoid pigment called xanthophyll. For this reason a hen fed on a ration devoid of such feeds as yellow corn and green forage, which carry it in considerable amounts, might have the appearance of laying so far as pigment is concerned, though she had never produced an egg. The character of the feed the hen has been receiving should, therefore, always be considered in relation to her condition with reference to pigment.

When hens have feeds carrying an abundance of pigment, and the skin, shanks and beak are not normally pale as in the English breeds, the beginning of laying diverts all the pigment received in the feed to the ovary, where it finds its way into the developing yolks. The pigment of other parts gradually disappears as a result of the natural physiological change in the structure of the skin. It is not replaced as long as the individual continues to lay.

The vent loses its pigment very quickly so that a white or pink vent in a yellow-skinned variety usually indicates that the bird is laying, while a yellow vent indicates that she is not laying.

The eyering formed by the inner edges of the eyelids loses its pigment a trifle more slowly than the vent. The earlobes of the Mediterranean breeds bleach out somewhat more slowly than the eyering, so that in these breeds a white earlobe on a vigorous bird usually means a longer period of continuous laying than does a bleached vent or eyelid.

The color disappears from the beak next, beginning at the base and remaining longest at the tip. The lower part loses color more rapidly than the upper. With the average yellow-skinned bird a bleached beak means that laying has been in progress for from four to six weeks.

The shanks are the last to lose their color. Bleached shanks, therefore, indicate a much longer period of production than does the bleaching of the other parts. The pigment disappears from the front of the shank first and finally from the back. A bleached shank usually indicates continued egg production for at least fifteen to twenty weeks.

When laying stops, the pigment reappears in the several regions in the same order in which it disappeared. The relative rapidity of loss and regain in the various parts is probably correlated with the thickness of the skin, the pigment change being slowest where the epidermal covering is thickest. The fact that a given hen stopped laying two or three weeks back sometimes may be determined by the fact that the tip of the beak is colorless while the base is yellow.

Molting.—The shedding and renewal of feathers normally occurs once a year, though it may occur in certain individuals twice in one year and, more rarely, only once in a period of two years. In the wild fowl it would have no relation whatever to egg production. Under the influence of domestication, however, the laying period has been gradually lengthened until it often overlaps the natural molting season.

Under the influence of the genes for high production, and particularly of those related to persistency and the length of the laying period, the natural tendency is for a good hen to continue to lay as late in the fall as she possibly can. The result is that she either molts late, *i.e.*, after her long laying period is over, or molts and lays at the same time. The low-producing hen, on the other hand, stops laying in July or August well in advance of the time that

FIG. 4–8.—A wing showing four new primary feathers partly grown. Note the axial feather. (Courtesy of Kansas Agricultural Experiment Station.)

growth of a new feather coat must begin in order to put the hen in condition to resist the cold weather of winter.

Observation of the conditions that most commonly occur in laying flocks has led many persons into two faulty conclusions with regard to molt. One is that the onset of molt is a cause of the cessation of laying, and the other is that hens never lay and molt at the same time. The facts seem to be, rather, that a hen molts late because she lays late, and that hens bred for continous production at a high rate not only may, but often do, lay and molt at the same time. This latter condition probably does not occur except when a hen is increasing, or at least maintaining, her body weight.

The order in which the different sections of the fowl lose their feathers is fairly definite. The usual order is head, neck, body (including breast, back, and abdomen), wing and tail. Not only this, but there is a high degree of regularity about the order of molt within the several sections. The wing primaries, for example, begin to drop before the secondaries. The first primary to be shed is the inside one, next to the axial feather, and the remainder are shed in succession until the last one to be dropped is the outermost primary near the tip of the wing.

The order of molt of the secondary feathers is not so regular as that of the primaries, but the most common order, when the secondaries are numbered from the axial feather toward the body, has been reported as 11, 12, 13, 14, 10, 2, 3, 4, 5, 6, 7, 8, 9, 1. The axial feather is dropped at the same time as the secondary next to it.

In addition to being a late molter, the high-producing hen is also likely to be a rapid molter. Extensive observations have shown that there is no difference in the rate at which high-producing and low-producing hens grow new feathers, but that there is a decided difference in the rate at which the old feathers are shed. In no instance did an individual primary feather become completely grown in less than six weeks, and some feathers required seven weeks to complete their growth. The feathers made about 20 per cent of their growth in each of the first three weeks, and from 12 to 15 per cent during each of the second three weeks.

The rate of laying is not materially affected by the molt, in the case of hens that lay and molt at the same time, but the rate of molt is slowed up by production. The net result is that the advantage gained by the late molter, as measured by length of the period of non-production, is due, not to differences in the number of feathers dropped or to the rate of growth of an individual feather, but to the fact that two jobs are performed at one and the same time.

It should be remembered also that time and rate of molt are influenced to a considerable extent by weight and physical condition of the hens, and by environmental conditions including feeding and management.

Temperament.—A good layer is more active, more alert, and yet at the same time more easily handled than a poor layer. She is among the first off the perch in the morning and among the last on it at night. When not on the nest she is busy and business-like, scratching or ranging in an eager search for feed. The great layer is a bird of a seldom satisfied appetite.

Applying the Theory in Practice

From what has preceded, it should be fairly obvious that any method which will identify the hens that (1) begin to lay at an early age, (2) lay at a high rate without pauses of any sort, and (3) continue to lay late into the fall at the end of their laying year, will automatically select the most productive hens in the flock. One method of accomplishing this objective is to use trap-nests all through

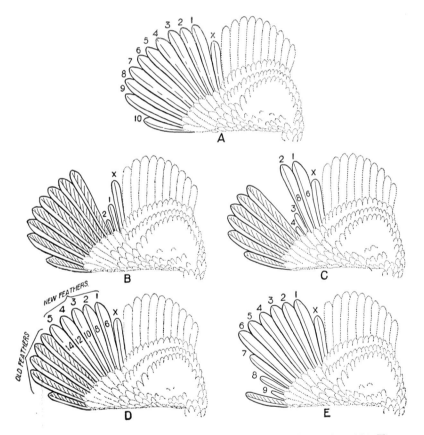

FIG. 4–9.—*A*, a normal wing showing the primary feathers, *1* to *10*. They are separated from the secondaries (shown in dotted outline) by the short axial feather, *x*. *B*, the beginning of a wing molt. *1* and *2* are new feathers growing in. *C*, an eight-week molt. Elapsed time in weeks is indicated on each feather. *D*, an unusual instance in which only five primaries were molted. *E*, a wing as it appears near the completion of a normal molt. (Courtesy of Kansas Agricultural Experiment Station.)

the year. It is only by this means that we have been able to find out the things that are known about selecting hens for egg production.

In practice, however, it is usually not feasible to run trap-nests throughout the year, and the flock owner is compelled to depend upon judgments that, in turn, are based upon his observation of the external physical characteristics that have just been discussed. If he is interested merely in getting rid of the poorer individuals in order that they may be replaced with pullets, a single sorting of the flock in the month of September may be all that is required. If, on the other hand, he is interested in making as accurate a selection as possible in order to save the best of the flock for breeding purposes, he will find it necessary to do much more than this. Several observations, distributed throughout the year, will enable him to sort the flock into various production groups with a fairly high degree of accuracy.

A Banding Scheme May be Used.—If the pullets are not given numbered bands, colored celluloid bands may be used as markers. Blue, red and white bands may be placed on the left leg to indicate successive differences in time of starting to lay. Green bands may be used to mark those individuals that show a winter pause and molt. A black band may be put on every hen that goes broody, and the blue, red and white bands may be used again in reverse order, on the right leg, to indicate successive differences in time of stopping to lay in the fall. With this scheme, the entire flock will be handled some six or seven times during the year, and a very reliable index of the laying ability of each individual will be secured. It will lack only the quantitative character of a trap-nest record.

A Substitute for the Trap-Nest.—In discussing the formation of the egg it was pointed out that if hens are examined early in the morning, those which are going to lay on that day can be detected by feeling the egg in the uterus. If one cares to go through this procedure on three successive days each month, keeping a record of each individual hen handled, he will have, at the end of the year, a highly accurate record of the relative laying ability of the hens that make up the flock and also a basis upon which to estimate the actual number of eggs laid by each hen. The correlation between the number of eggs laid in a period of thirty-six days made up of the first three in each of twelve months, and the total number of eggs laid during the year, is very high. The actual correlation coefficients obtained in analyzing one series of records were:

White Leghorns	+0.897	±0.007
White Wyandottes	+0.939	±0.007
Rhode Island Reds	+0.874	±0.011
Barred Plymouth Rocks	+0.858	±0.017

Disturbing Factors.—No matter what method is used in attempting to apply the theory of production judging to practical use, it should be remembered that even under the most favorable conditions some mistakes will be made. The inevitable biological error is considerable and, though there is much of practical value in the whole plan of selecting laying hens on the basis of external physical characters, it is futile to attempt to accomplish worthwhile results by the use of some one or two characteristics alone.

THE NATIONAL POULTRY IMPROVEMENT PLAN

The National Poultry Improvement Plan became operative July 1, 1935. It is administered in each State by an Official State Agency cooperating with the U. S. Department of Agriculture. Authority for an official state agency to administer the plan within the state is a memorandum of agreement between it and the U. S. Department of Agriculture. The Department of Agriculture is responsible for coordinating the program among the cooperating states.

The objectives of the plan are to improve the production and market qualities of chickens and to reduce losses from hatchery-disseminated diseases. The National Turkey Improvement Plan is operated on a very similar basis.

Table 4–1.—Hatchery Participation in the National Poultry Improvement Plan, 1964–65. Number and Egg Capacity by Regions, with Data for Selected States. As Reported by the U. S. Department of Agriculture.

| | | Egg Capacity | |
| | | Total | Average |
Region or State	Number	(Million eggs)	(Thousand eggs)
North Atlantic	196	34.8	178
Massachusetts	46	2.9	623
Connecticut	26	7.2	278
Pennsylvania	53	11.7	221
East North Central	313	41.1	131
Indiana	102	15.4	150
Illinois	93	12.0	129
West North Central	331	42.8	129
Minnesota	95	9.3	97
Missouri	56	12.8	228
South Atlantic	316	119.0	337
North Carolina	78	23.8	305
Georgia	115	43.1	375
South Central	174	65.6	377
Mississippi	35	19.6	561
Arkansas	36	21.8	605
Western	88	13.3	151
Washington	21	3.5	168
California	12	3.7	305
United States	1,418	316.6	258

Table 4–2.—Flock Participation in the National Poultry Improvement Plan, 1964–65. Number and Size of Flocks by Regions, with Data for Selected States. As Reported by the U. S. Department of Agriculture.

Region or State	Number of flocks	Total Birds (Millions)	Av. number per flock
North Atlantic	1,089	3.8	3,515
Maine	175	0.7	4,045
Massachusetts	113	0.5	4,400
Pennsylvania	431	1.1	2,660
East North Central	3,321	2.6	785
Indiana	1,163	1.1	964
Illinois	1,178	0.6	536
West North Central	4,017	2.7	663
Iowa	686	0.6	855
Missouri	1,620	0.7	422
South Atlantic	3,407	14.3	4,195
North Carolina	1,582	5.7	3,583
Georgia	978	6.1	6,249
South Central	2,097	8.3	3,959
Alabama	437	2.7	6,070
Mississippi	328	2.1	6,502
Western	481	1.2	2,586
Oregon	173	0.3	1,454
California	42	0.4	10,074
United States	14,412	32.9	2,286

The provisions of the plans are changed from time to time to conform with the development of the industry and with new information as it becomes available. These changes are based upon recommendations made at the biennial National Plans Conferences by official delegates representing participating flockowners, breeders, and hatcherymen from all cooperating states.

Complete details regarding the plans are available in Miscellaneous Publication No. 739, issued by the U. S. Department of Agriculture. The latest revision is dated April, 1963.

From 1959–60 to 1964–65 the number of flocks participating in the National Poultry Improvement Plan decreased by 60 per cent, from 36,838 to 14,412, but because of an increase in average size of individual flocks from 980 to 2,286, the decrease in total number of birds in participating flocks was only 8 per cent.

Of the 33 million birds tested for pullorum disease and fowl typhoid in 1964–65, only 1,461—a mere .004 per cent—proved to be reactors.

Chapter 5

Incubation

With the rapid growth of the hatchery business, fewer and fewer chicks have been hatched on the farms where they are grown until about 96 per cent of all chicks raised, either as farm chickens or as commercial broilers, are now bought as baby chicks. The breeding flocks which supply the hatching eggs are nevertheless widely distributed on farms, and it is therefore important for any student of poultry production and management to know something of the factors which influence hatchability, especially those which operate before the eggs are placed in incubators.

SELECTING EGGS FOR HATCHING

There are certain characteristics of individual eggs which are known to interfere with hatchability. Selection against these conditions will be effective in terms of the immediate hatching percentage, without regard to any considerations of heredity.

Workers at the Beltsville Agricultural Research Center selected from 47,950 eggs, by candling, those which had any one, but only one, of eight different defects. These eggs were incubated weekly over a period of one year, and the hatching results compared with those for control eggs which showed none of the defects and were therefore considered normal. Eggs showing two or more defects were excluded from the study.

The percentage hatch of fertile eggs was 80 for small eggs (45 grams or less), 72 for eggs containing large blood spots, 71 for extra large eggs (65 grams or more), 68 for eggs with air cells located in positions other than the blunt end, 53 for slightly cracked eggs, 49 for misshapen eggs, 47 for eggs with rough or thin shells, and 32 for eggs with loose air cells. These figures are to be compared with a percentage hatch of 87 for the control eggs, which ranged in size from 50 to 59 grams and had none of the specified defects.

Hereditary differences in egg shell quality are responsible for wide variation in the loss of weight by evaporation of moisture from eggs during incubation. This is important from the standpoint of both hatchability and the keeping quality of eggs for market purposes.

There is some evidence to support the opinion that dark brown and medium brown eggs hatch better than light brown eggs from the same flocks, but this may be due in part to the tendency for eggs

HIGH WEIGHT LOSS

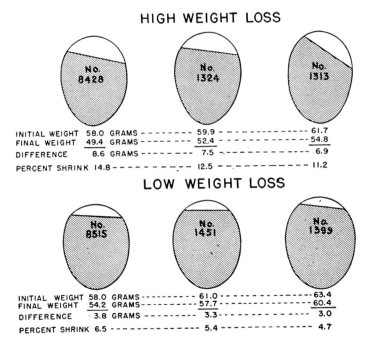

INITIAL WEIGHT	58.0 GRAMS	59.9	61.7
FINAL WEIGHT	49.4 GRAMS	52.4	54.8
DIFFERENCE	8.6 GRAMS	7.5	6.9
PERCENT SHRINK	14.8	12.5	11.2

LOW WEIGHT LOSS

INITIAL WEIGHT	58.0 GRAMS	61.0	63.4
FINAL WEIGHT	54.2 GRAMS	57.7	60.4
DIFFERENCE	3.8 GRAMS	3.3	3.0
PERCENT SHRINK	6.5	5.4	4.7

Fig. 5–1.—There is a wide variation among hens in weight loss of their eggs during incubation, because of hereditary differences in egg shell quality. (After Quinn, Gordon, and Godfrey.)

of light color (among brown eggs) to have rough, thin or porous shells.

Breeders who want to hatch as many eggs as possible from hens with known records, rather than from pullets, are usually faced with the problem of large eggs and their known lower hatchability when incubated along with medium or small eggs. If enough large eggs are being used to make it worth while, they can be set twelve hours ahead of the pullet eggs. It is still better, from the standpoint of hatchability, to set them in separate machines so that they can be given slightly lower relative humidity during the incubation period. This will insure maximum hatchability of the large eggs and will bring all chicks out at about the same time.

Predetermining Fertility and Sex

The manifest advantage of being able to ascertain, by external examination, which eggs are fertile before setting them, and which are males or females, is so great that it has led to much speculation. The claim has been made that an egg with high specific gravity is fertile, and that one with relatively low specific gravity is likely to be infertile. The truth is that differences in specific gravity may be observed in both fertile and infertile eggs.

Egg shape is likewise of no value as an indicator of the sex of the future chick. Both long narrow eggs, sometimes credited with hatching only males, and short round eggs, supposed to produce mostly females, will produce about equal numbers of both sexes.

The position of the air cell in the egg, for which a similar claim has sometimes been made, is equally unreliable as a means of determining which eggs are destined to produce chicks of the desired sex.

CARE OF HATCHING EGGS

At the time of laying, the fertile egg is usually in a fairly advanced stage of development from an early embryological standpoint, having been incubated within the body of the hen for approximately twenty hours. It would seem that the ideal method of caring for hatching eggs would be to allow development to proceed without being checked, by setting the eggs at once. Poultrymen, however, usually are under the necessity of holding them for a longer or shorter period. During this period development is suspended, or at least is very slow, and the very practical question of how to handle eggs with the least possible damage to their vitality and hatching power presents itself.

Length of Holding Period

It is the modern view that holding eggs for hatching is a necessary evil, to be practiced as little as possible, even under the best conditions. Although there are a few records of chicks having hatched from eggs held as long as thirty-five days, all available data are in agreement in showing that hatchability decreases as the time of holding is increased. Commercial hatchery practice is to set twice a week, and many operators will not accept eggs more than one week old. Individual breeders may find it advisable to hold eggs for incubation as long as ten days if correct holding conditions are provided.

Curiously enough, the time required for incubation seems to be directly related to the age of the eggs set. Observations at the Missouri Station were that eggs which were from fourteen to twenty-one days old required from fourteen to eighteen hours longer for incubation than did eggs which were less than eight days old when set. Other studies have shown similar results.

Holding Temperature

It is the general belief that the sooner the embryonic development under way at the time of laying is checked, the better are the chances of holding eggs successfully for hatching. This belief has led to the widespread adoption of the practice of gathering eggs frequently during the incubating season, and putting them in a cool place immediately.

Repeated tests have shown that eggs held at 50° to 55° F. hatch better then those held at 30° to 40° or at 60° to 75° F. The upper and lower limits are not specific because the time of holding is also involved, but holding for prolonged periods at either the high or the low temperatures causes many of the embryos to die during the first few days of incubation.

When it is necessary or desirable to hold hatching eggs for more than seven days, the percentage hatch can be significantly increased by warming the eggs at 100° F. for one to five hours early in the holding period. Similar improvement has resulted from holding over night at room temperatures of about 70° F. The reason why such treatment is effective is not known.

Position

If eggs for incubation are to be held not more than a week, their position is not of great importance. They may be held in ordinary egg cases, preferably being packed large end up, or they may be laid in trays in the natural horizontal position.

Turning

As already pointed out, the yolk, with the germ spot uppermost, tends to float near the shell. It is prevented from coming in actual contact with the shell membrane by the dense layer of white which surrounds it. When left in the same position for a considerable time a constant though gentle tendency upward parts the dense white and allows the germinal disc to come in contact with the shell membrane. With evaporation constantly taking place, the tiny embryo may adhere to the membrane and be destroyed. When the eggs are not allowed to remain in the same position, but are turned fairly frequently, a new point of contact is given, and more white brought between the germ and the shell membrane. Turning is of no practical importance if eggs are to be held no longer than one week. If they are to be held for a longer period, there is a distinct advantage in turning them daily.

DEVELOPMENT OF THE CHICK

It is a matter of common observation that the reproductive cycle of birds differs from that of domestic mammals in at least two particulars. First, the fertilized ovum never forms an organic connection with the mother, and second, embryonic development, for the most part, takes place outside the body of the mother.

The normal incubation period of chicken eggs is twenty-one days, though there is some variation in each direction. The eggs of Leghorns and other light breeds commonly hatch a few hours earlier than those of the heavier breeds. For a general statement it is well to remember that for each species of birds the incubation period is of definite duration; that under conditions of artificial incubation it can be lengthened somewhat with ease, but that it can be shortened only with extreme difficulty.

In general, the smaller the bird, the smaller is the egg, the higher is the body temperature and the shorter is the incubation period, though there are numerous exceptions.

It should also be remembered that in its embryonic development the bird is much more rapid than the mammal, and that this is very likely an adaptation to life within the egg.

Structural Development

Structural development begins shortly after fertilization by division of the single female germ cell on the surface of the yolk into two daughter cells. These cells in turn divide, and a continuous proliferation of cells is inaugurated which (except for the period after laying until the egg is set), continues actively, not only during incubation but throughout subsequent growth until maturity.

The first division or cleavage of the germ cell occurs about the time the egg enters the isthmus, and the second follows in about twenty minutes. The third division, to form the 8-cell stage, also takes place in the isthmus, and by the time the egg is well within the uterus it has advanced to the 16-cell stage. Within the next four hours it advances by continued cell division to approximately the 256-cell stage.

As a result of this process of cell division while the egg is still in the oviduct, a disc-shaped layer of cells is formed. It is first a single layer of cells, but later on is several layers thick. This layer of cells, in intimate contact with the underlying yolk, constitutes the undifferentiated blastoderm as shown in magnified form in Figure 5–2.

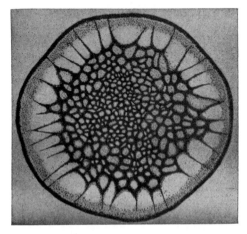

Fig. 5–2.—Appearance of the blastoderm (magnified) of a hen's egg after eight hours in the oviduct. It shows 346 cells, 34 marginal and 312 central. (After Patterson.)

Eventually the cells in the center of the blastoderm become detached from the surface of the yolk to form a cavity called the blastocoele. Because these cells are no longer attached to the yolk, this central area is transparent—the *area pellucida*, while the outer portion which remains in contact with the yolk is opaque—the *area opaca*. It is in the center of the area pellucida that the development of the embryo proper takes place.

Before laying, or very soon thereafter, the blastoderm becomes differentiated into two layers of cells by a process referred to as gastrulation (gut formation). This involves the rapid proliferation of cells along one portion of the margin of the blastoderm, to form a second layer of cells. This second layer of cells, by its inward growth eventually divides the cavity (blastocoele) into two. The lower cavity is the gut or gastrocoele. It is in this manner that the blastoderm becomes differentiated into two of the three germ layers—the ectoderm above, and the layer of entoderm below growing into the blastocoele (*see* Figs. 5-3 and 5-4).

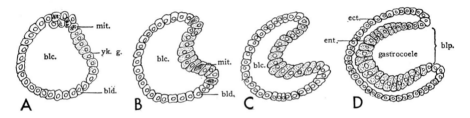

GASTRULATION IN FORM WITH ISOLECITHAL EGG HAVING ALMOST NO YOLK—AMPHIOXUS.

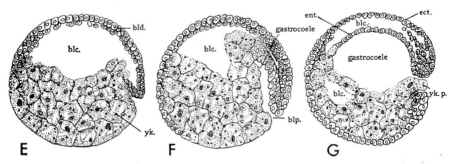

GASTRULATION IN FORM WITH TELOLECITHAL EGG CONTAINING MODERATE
AMOUNT OF YOLK—AMPHIBIA.

Fig. 5-3.—Schematic diagrams to show the effect of yolk on gastrulation. (From Patten, *Early Embryology of the Chick*, 4th edition. By permission of The Blakiston Division, McGraw-Hill Book Co., Inc.) In the case of the chick, the still greater amount of yolk effectively prevents the formation of an open blastopore.

Abbreviations: (blc.) blastocoele; (bld.) blastoderm; (blp.) blastopore; (ect.) ectoderm; (ent.) entoderm; (mit.) cell undergoing mitosis; (yk.) yolk; (yk. g.) yolk granules; (yk. p.) yolk plug.

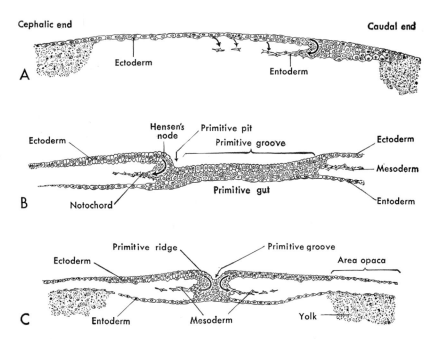

Fig. 5–4.—Schematic diagrams indicating the cell movements involved in the gastrulation of chick embryos. (From Patten, *Early Embryology of the Chick*, 4th edition. By permission of The Blakiston Division, McGraw-Hill Book Co., Inc.) (A) Longitudinal section of the blastoderm from a pre-primitive streak chick during entoderm formation. (B) Longitudinal plan of embryo of approximately seventeen hours of incubation to show the relations of the various parts. (C) Cross section of an embryo in the primitive streak stage to show the turning in of cells at the primitive groove to enter the mesodermal layers.

Shortly after incubation begins, the third germ layer, or mesoderm, originates or becomes differentiated by growing into the blastocoele between the ectoderm and the entoderm in much the same way that the entoderm earlier pushed into the blastocoele. Thus the blastoderm at this stage consists of three distinct layers of cells resting on the surface of the yolk, *i.e.*, ectoderm, mesoderm and entoderm. These three layers constitute the materials out of which the various organs and systems of the body are to be developed.

From the ectoderm, the skin, feathers, beak, claws, nervous system, lens and retina of the eye and the linings of the mouth and vent are developed. The bones, muscles, blood, reproductive and excretory organs develop from the mesoderm, while the entoderm produces the linings of the digestive tract and the respiratory and secretory organs.

Gastrulation is usually, though by no means always, complete by the time the egg is laid. It seems to have been shown conclusively that the period of the gastrulation process is an exceedingly critical one, while the early postgastrula stage, during which most eggs are laid, is comparatively non-critical.

The stage of embryonic development in fresh-laid fertile eggs tends to be characteristic of individual hens, and appears to be correlated with hatching power.   At the Massachusetts Station, pre-gastrula and early gastrula were the most common stages of development in eggs from low-hatching hens.   Early gastrula stages were characteristic of hens with medium hatching power, and well-advanced gastrula was most commonly found in eggs from hens which gave a high percentage hatch.

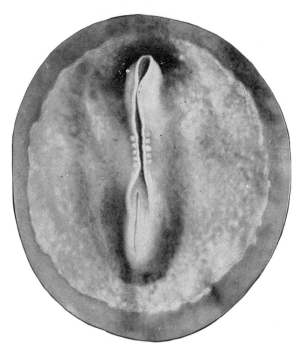

Fig. 5–5.—Chick embryo of twenty-five to twenty-six hours photographed by reflected light to show its external configuration. (From Patten, *Early Embryology of the Chick*, 4th edition.   By permission of The Blakiston Division, McGraw-Hill Book Co., Inc.)

Too much development at the time of laying may be as detrimental as too little.   Observations made by workers in the U. S. Department of Agriculture indicate that maximum hatchability occurs when the interval between successive eggs is twenty-seven hours, and that there is a marked decrease when the interval is in excess of twenty-eight hours.

One of the first marked changes in structure after the egg has begun to incubate is the appearance of the primitive streak.   Simultaneously with the differentiation of the mesoderm, the primitive streak arises as two thickenings in the ectoderm, starting near the point of origin of the entoderm. The primitive streak eventually disappears completely, but it serves to mark out the future longitudinal axis of the body of the embryo and its posterior extremity. Although the embryonic axis is fairly uniform, it is not absolutely fixed. It usually lies approximately at right angles to the long axis of the egg, being directed away from the observer when the small end of the egg is to the right.

The growth and development of the embryo from the cells in the area pellucida soon shows a more rapid growth of cells in certain regions than in others. This uneven growth gives rise to a series of

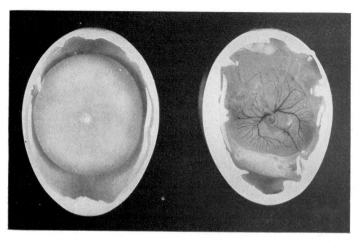

Fig. 5–6.—An infertile (*left*) and a fertile egg after being held for seventy-two hours at a temperature of 102° F. (Courtesy of Illinois Agricultural Experiment Station.)

folds in which the various germ layers are involved. It is these folds which mark off the embryo proper from the rest of the blastoderm. The first of these, the head fold, lifts the anterior end of the embryo above the remainder of the blastoderm. Later the tail fold undercuts the posterior extremity of the embryo to elevate it. Both of these join with the lateral folds which mark out the sides of the embryo. Eventually this undercutting or folding lifts the embryo well above the yolk, leaving only a narrow stalk to serve as a connection between them.

During the first twenty-four hours the head of the embryo becomes clearly defined and in it may be observed the beginnings of the central nervous system as well as the foregut, the forerunner of the alimentary tract. Blood islands appear in the area opaca outside the body of the embryo. The blastoderm enlarges considerably, embarking on the process of growth in which it ultimately surrounds the yolk.

8

The second day sees the embryo beginning to turn on its left side, the formation of the heart which may be observed to beat at about the thirtieth hour, the primary divisions of the brain, the beginning of the formation of the eyes, the ear pits and the formation of the tail bud.

The Extra-Embryonic Membranes

There are four extra-embryonic membranes which are essential to the normal growth of the embryo. They are the amnion, chorion, yolk sac and allantois.

The amnion and the chorion originate together from a fold of the extra-embryonic tissue which first appears in the head region, but which eventually encircles the entire embryo. This fold, consisting of ectoderm and a layer of mesoderm, grows upward and over the embryo to fuse eventually at the top. The outer portion, with ectoderm above and mesoderm beneath, is the chorion, while the inner part of the fold with the position of the germ layers reversed is the amnion.

The amnion is a transparent membranous sac filled with a colorless fluid which serves as a protection from mechanical shock and allows the embryo to move about rather freely as it develops.

A third extra-embryonic membrane, the yolk sac, consists of a layer of entoderm and mesoderm growing over the surface of the yolk, with the entoderm next to the yolk. The walls of the yolk sac become lined with a special glandular and absorbing epithelium which digests and absorbs the yolk material. Yolk material does not pass through the yolk stalk to the embryo even though a narrow opening or lumen in the stalk is still in evidence at the end of the incubation period.

At approximately ninety-six hours of incubation there is an out-growth of the entoderm from the hind gut which pushes a layer of mesoderm ahead of it into the extra-embryonic cavity, to form the allantois. This fourth extra-embryonic membrane continues to enlarge until it eventually fills the entire extra-embryonic cavity and thus occupies the space between the amnion and the chorion. It is a highly vascular sac which fuses with the chorion, thus bringing its capillaries in direct contact with the shell membrane.

The allantois has four functions. It serves as an embryonic respiratory organ; it receives the excretions of the embryonic kidneys; it absorbs albumen which serves as nutriment for the embryo; and it absorbs calcium from the shell for the structural needs of the embryo.

The growth of the amnion constricts the opening from the intestine to the yolk sac, thereby forming what is called the yolk stalk. It also brings the yolk stalk into close contact with the allantoic stalk. These with their blood vessels are included in an extension of the embryonic body wall to form the umbilical cord.

Up to the sixth or seventh day there is nothing about the chick embryo which would help one to distinguish it from the embryo of other familiar animals. On the sixth day the main divisions of the legs and wings can be observed. The body, which has been very small in proportion to the head, begins to develop more rapidly. What appears to be voluntary movement may be noticed if the egg is opened.

During the eighth day the feather germs appear in definite tracts and on the ninth the contour of the embryo becomes quite birdlike.

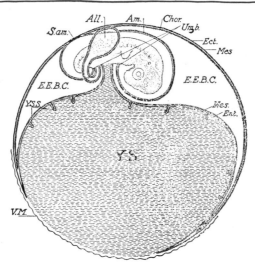

Fig. 5–7.—Diagram of the chick and its embryonic membranes during the fourth day of incubation. The abbreviations used in this and also in Figure 5–8 are as follows: *Alb.* albumen; *Alb.S.*, albumen sac; *All.*, allantois; *All.C.*, cavity of allantois; *All.I.*, inner wall of allantois; *All.S.*, stalk of allantois; *Am.*, amnion; *Am.C.*, amniotic cavity; *Chor.*, chorion; *C.T.R.*, connective tissue ring; *Ect.*, ectoderm; *E.E.B.C.*, extra-embryonic body cavity; *Ent.*, entoderm., *Mes.*, mesoderm; *S.-Am.*, sero-amniotic connection; *S.Y.S.U.*, sac of yolk sac umbilicus; *Umb.*, umbilicus; *V.M.*, vitelline membrane; *Y.S.*, yolk sac; *Y.S.S.*, yolk sac septa. (After Lillie.)

There is a chalky deposit about the mouth opening which is the beginning of the horny beak. By this time the allantois nearly surrounds the embryo, amnion and yolk. By the thirteenth day the down is distributed over the body and its color may be seen through the thin walls of the sacs which still enclose the individual down feathers. On this day the scales and nails appear on the legs and feet. By the sixteenth day they are quite firm and horny, as is also the beak.

By the fourteenth day the embryo has accommodated itself to the form of the egg, so as to lie parallel to the long axis. By the sixteenth the albumen is nearly gone and the yolk becomes increasingly the main source of nutriment.

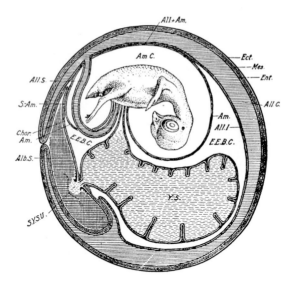

FIG. 5–8.—Diagram of the chick and its membranes during the twelfth day of incubation. For the designation of parts see legend of Figure 5–7. (After Lillie.)

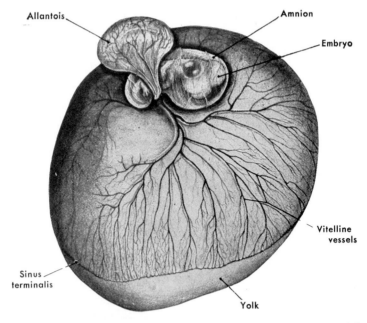

FIG. 5–9.—Chick of about five and one-half days incubation taken out of the shell with the yolk intact. (Modified from Kerr.) The chorion and the white of the egg have been removed to expose the embryo lying within the amnion, and the allantois has been displaced upward in order to show the allantoic stalk. (From Patten, *Early Embryology of the Chick*, 4th edition. By permission of The Blakiston Division, McGraw-Hill Book Co., Inc.)

On the seventeenth day the amniotic fluid begins to decrease On the nineteenth the yolk sac begins to enter the body through the umbilicus, apparently forced by the muscular tension of the amnion. The beak usually pierces the air cell and the lungs begin to function, though it is not until the shell is pipped, generally on the twentieth day, that full pulmonary respiration becomes a fact, and the allantoic circulation and respiration cease.

When fully formed, the chick is normally placed with the forepart of the body toward the large end of the egg, its head bent forward beneath the right wing and the legs brought up toward the head. The end of the upper mandible of the beak is equipped with a horny cap which bears a sharp point. By means of this, while slowly revolving in the shell, a circular path is chipped around the large end of the egg, the shell membranes being cut at the same time. When the shell is nearly cut around a final convulsion finishes the break, and the chick can emerge.

Physiological Development

The physiological changes that occur during the development of the embryo are as full of interest to the inquiring student as are the structural changes that have just been described.

The metabolism of the developing embryo is a matter of special importance and some of the facts concerning it should be understood by the student of poultry husbandry.

With the exception of oxygen, the materials out of which the embryo is formed are all found in the various parts of the egg. They are protein, carbohydrates, fats and minerals. Of the minerals, calcium is to be noted especially because it is found largely in the shell rather than in the egg contents.

Though protein, carbohydrates and fat are all used as sources of energy, each of these serves in turn as the most important source of energy during three successive stages of development. Up to and including the fourth day it appears reasonable to believe that the carbohydrate in the egg contents is the main source. After the fourth day, and before the ninth, the production of urea is very intense, which suggests that protein is being rapidly broken down, and is therefore available as a source of energy. During the latter part of incubation fat is quite evidently the source.

It should not be inferred that any one of the three materials is the sole source of energy at a particular time. Analyses of the allantoic and amniotic fluids during development show that uric acid accumulates in the allantoic cavity beginning at some time during the fifth day of incubation, or not long after the embryonic kidney has entered into communication with the allantois. Uric acid continues to accumulate up to the time of hatching, the period of its most intense production being from the seventh to the eleventh days. This, of course, means a continued oxidation of protein. Similarly, carbohydrate is utilized, insofar as it is available, through–

out the period of incubation, although it is of special importance at the beginning. Fat, on the other hand, is not used directly until rather late in the incubation period, though the possibility of a transference of fat into carbohydrate during the early stages of development has been suggested.

Of the mineral elements involved in the metabolism of the embryo, calcium is by far the most important, if for no other reason than that for about one hundred years it was a subject of keen controversy, particularly with respect to whether calcium is actually transferred from the shell to the embryo. Concerning the essential facts there is now no important difference of opinion. They may be stated briefly as follows:

The calcium content of the inside of the egg, including the embryo, rises markedly during incubation, the rise beginning about the twelfth day.

The calcium content of the embryo increases in a parallel fashion, i.e., at the same rate and during the same time, but remains always quantitatively below that of the whole egg.

The calcium content of the yolk rises slightly during the incubation period.

The calcium content of the shell membranes increases from the beginning of incubation, and rises very sharply from about the seventh day to the time of hatching.

Infertile eggs, when incubated along with fertile ones, never contain any more calcium than do unincubated eggs.

These results can be explained only on the basis of a distinct transfer of calcium from the shell to the embryo. It is further evident that the transfer is due to the presence of the embryo, for infertile eggs are not affected. Of particular interest is the fact that the embryo seems to draw on the shell exclusively for its supply of calcium without making use of what is in the yolk until after hatching.

Critical Periods

Embryo mortality is not uniformly distributed over the twenty-one days of incubation. Instead, there are definite peaks in the mortality curve. About half of the total mortality normally occurs during the last three or four days, with the nineteenth day representing the maximum. Another significant peak, though it is quantitatively less important, is during the second, third, and fourth days. A third, though usually lower, peak occurs between the tenth and fourteenth days.

This general pattern of embryo mortality is seen under all normal incubation conditions, whether total hatchability is high or low. Some causes of death are, however, more important at one peak than at another. Low-hatching hens tend to have an exaggerated early embryo mortality, indicating the difficulty of certain physiological adjustments in the early development of the embryo. Nutritional deficiencies in the ration of breeding hens will cause peaks in mortality that depend on the degree of deficiency encountered. Similarly, the late peak of mortality is likely to be increased materially, in relation to the other two, if incubating conditions are faulty. Unsuitable holding conditions for eggs prior to incubation may show up at either the early or the late peak periods.

OPTIMUM CONDITIONS FOR INCUBATION

Many of the investigations that have had as their object the study of optimum conditions for the developing egg rather than embryological development itself have been based for the most part on a comparison of the conditions of eggs and their surroundings under natural incubation, and in commercial incubators.

There is some danger, however, in assuming that the hen and her nest furnish optimum conditions. The attitude that Nature may not be improved upon in some particulars, or stating it differently, may not be assisted to better serve man's needs, is a mistaken one. If it were not, there would be no hens laying 300 eggs in a year. In nature no such number of eggs is needed to secure the survival and increase the numbers of the race. The same may be said of the hatchability of eggs. Nature's needs and man's wants do not necessarily coincide.

Position of Eggs

It is generally understood among poultrymen that the position of the egg during the period of incubation has a profound influence upon its development. It is a matter of common knowledge that the head of the chick normally develops at the large end of the egg. Usually, both in the nest and in the incubator, the large end of the egg is higher than the small end. This is due to the shape of the egg, and to the lessening of the specific gravity of the large end as incubation proceeds, because of the increasing size of the air cell.

When eggs are incubated large-end-up, about 2 per cent of the embryos develop with their heads in the small end of the egg. In eggs incubated in a horizontal position the percentage is about 3.5, but in eggs incubated small-end-up it is about 60. When expressed as a percentage of the dead-in-shell eggs, the corresponding figures are 7, 23, and 67.

By reversing the position of eggs which were incubated either large-end-up or small-end-up for different lengths of time, it was found that the malposition head-in-small-end-of-egg is usually determined during the second week of incubation.

Changing Position.—The hen turns the eggs she is incubating in two ways. The first is by peculiar lateral movements of the body with which she settles on the nest after feeding and which she continues from time to time throughout the day, and probably throughout the night. The purpose of these lateral movements is presumably to seek a more comfortable position. The practical results are to bring the body in closer contact with the eggs and so closer to the developing germ, and also, to turn the eggs. The second is by reaching under her body and moving the eggs with her beak. Observations of hens in glass nests have shown that the eggs were turned at least every hour both day and night, and in one instance as many as ten times in two hours.

Such observations as have been reported, show that in artificial incubation, fairly frequent turnings increase the hatching power of eggs. The usual commercial practice is to turn eggs three or four times daily, but there is ample experimental evidence to indicate that increased turning, up to eight times daily, will increase the percentage of eggs which hatch. Additional turnings cannot be justified in practice, though eggs may be turned as often as ninety-six times daily, i.e., once every fifteen minutes, without detrimental results, provided they are turned back and forth about their long axes. If turned in only one direction, there is high embryonic mortality caused by ruptured blood-vessels and broken yolk sacs.

Temperature

In reviewing the papers concerned with incubation temperatures, one cannot but be impressed with the fact that both the interest and the point of view of the avian embryologist differ greatly from that of the student of incubation problems. Embryologists have confined their careful work mostly to the early stages, lost in an admiration-compelling endeavor to understand the mysteries of that development. Needham, in his comprehensive review of "The Metabolism of the Developing Egg," speaking from the viewpoint of the biochemist interested in the bewildering series of chemical changes taking place within the limits defined by the shell of the egg, was led to make the remark that "the data of classical embryology are not very useful for our purpose because the majority of embryologists have been histologists, and for them the major interest has been in the first few hours of development. The primitive streak, the neural groove; these were the kind of phenomena they preferred to study— after the tenth day the embryo ceased to interest them, it became anatomical."

Some of the more recent experimental studies have been aimed at the effect of incubation temperatures on hatching results, and these are much more helpful to both the practical poultryman and the student of incubation.

Temperatures of Eggs under Natural Incubation.—The temperature at which eggs are naturally incubated depends primarily upon the temperature of the hen. This is quite variable, both among hens on the same day and for the same hen from day to day, though the variation appears to be much less among broody hens than among non-broodies.

There is a popular supposition that the temperature of a broody hen is relatively high, and that one of the characteristics of broodiness is the so-called "broody fever." The facts are that the temperatures reported for broody hens average about 2° F. below those for non-broody hens, being comparable to the temperatures of non-broody hens at times of minimum activity.

Observations made at the Montana Station showed that the temperature at the top of eggs containing live embryos remained fairly constant, averaging 102.3° F. The temperature at the bottom of the egg, however, increased several degrees as incubation progressed. During the first few days it was from 15° to 18° lower than the temperature at the top of the egg, but during the last few days it was only 10° or 12° lower. These readings were made with eggs in a horizontal position.

Temperatures of Eggs during Artificial Incubation.—Just how to apply these findings to the problem of artificial incubation is none too clear when the several different types of incubators are taken into account. Presumably there is an optimum temperature condition for each type of incubator, and occasionally for an individual machine. Not only this, but optimum temperature must always be a relative matter in that it is partially dependent upon humidity and air movement, as well as upon the exact location of the thermometer.

With the advent of mammoth incubators of the forced-draft type it soon became apparent that actual optimum incubating temperatures were lower than had commonly been supposed. Instead of 102° to 103° F., as measured by a thermometer with its bulb at the same level as the top of the eggs, either under the hen or in a still-air machine, the actual egg temperature was about 100° F. or a little less.

Extensive tests at the National Agricultural Research Center, Beltsville, Maryland, have shown an optimum incubation temperature of 100° F. when the relative humidity was kept at 60 per cent, the concentration of oxygen at 21 per cent, the carbon dioxide below 0.5 per cent, and the air movement past the eggs approximately 12 cm. (5 inches) per minute. In these tests the percentage hatch decreased at temperatures above and below 100° F., until at 96° and at 103.5° F. nearly all the embryos died.

Effects of High Temperature.—The permissible temperature range above normal is much more limited than the range below. This is not altogether surprising perhaps, since in natural incubation the opportunities for overheating appear to be very much less than for underheating.

Three principal effects of high temperatures are (1) marked speeding up in the rate of development, with an accompanying increase in carbon dioxide output; (2) the production of abnormal embryos in the early stages; and (3) the lowering of the per cent of fertile eggs which hatch.

The speeding up of development as the result of abnormally high temperatures with an accompanying increase in CO_2 output has been observed by a number of workers. During the greater part of the incubation period the developing chick reacts to increases in temperature as a cold-blooded animal, by increasing the discharge of CO_2. From about the nineteenth day until hatching it is neutral in this respect, and raising the external temperature does not seem to affect the CO_2 production. The day after hatching the chick responds to rises in external temperature as a warm-blooded animal, by decreasing the output of CO_2.

The effect of temperature on the length of the incubation period is shown in Figure 5–10.

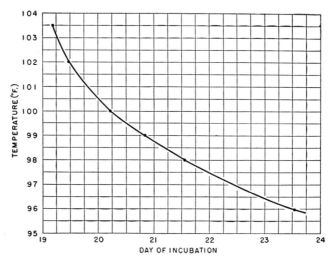

Fig. 5–10.—Effect of temperature on total incubation time. As the incubation temperature is decreased from 103.5° to 96° F., the number of days from the beginning of incubation to hatching increases from slightly more than nineteen to twenty-three and one half. (Courtesy of U. S. Department of Agriculture.)

High lethal internal egg temperatures have been determined as ranging from 106° to 110° F. during the first five days of incubation, and from 114° to 118° thereafter.

An accompaniment of high, though not necessarily lethal temperatures, is the production of abnormalities of various sorts, including crooked toes, crooked necks, and sprawling legs which prevent the chick from standing on its feet.

Effects of Low Temperatures.—Harvey, in 1651, observed that as the three-day embryo was cooled, the heart beat slower and slower until it ceased. The pulsations would resume when the temperature was raised. This is perhaps the first direct observation of the effect of abnormally low incubating temperature upon the embryo. Since then a large number of investigators have studied its effects.

In general, these effects may be placed in three classes which are undoubtedly closely related. These are: (1) the slowing down of the developmental processes accompanied by a diminution of the CO_2 output; (2) the production of abnormal embryos in early stages; and (3) the reduction of the per cent of fertile eggs which hatch.

Fig. 5–11.—A row of incubators in the Townsend Hatchery, Millsboro, Delaware. (USDA Photo.)

Certain contingencies may arise which necessitate holding eggs at subnormal temperatures for a few hours while incubation is in progress, and it is well to know something about how much cooling eggs will stand.

Workers studying this problem at the Storrs Station in 1916–1917 found that after the first twenty-four hours of incubation chick embryos from certain hens would stand from four to five hours' exposure at a temperature of 50° F. From this point on, the time limit increased up to fifteen hours for eggs which had been incubated for ten to twelve days, but after the seventeenth day continued exposure to a temperature of 50° F. for more than six hours usually caused the death of the embryos so treated.

FIG. 5-12.—Cut-away view of a room-type mammoth incubator showing fans for air circulation and setting trays in racks for easy tilting. (Courtesy of Buckeye Incubator Company.)

Recent studies at the Maryland Station have shown that at internal egg temperatures of 29° to 30° F. it was necessary to use an exposure time of 95 minutes in order to kill half the embryos during the first week of incubation, and from seventy to eighty minutes at later stages. This does not mean, however, that half the eggs so treated will hatch.

At the California Station it was found that twelve hours of current interruption in electric incubators, under room temperatures approximating 70° F., produced an average decrease of 3.4 per cent in the number of chicks hatched.

Cooling Eggs.—The once nearly universal custom of cooling eggs during the incubation period probably arose from a desire to imitate

Fig. 5–13.—A modern hatcher with hatching trays contained in a movable dolly. (Courtesy of Robbins Incubator Company.)

Nature.   When a hen leaves her nest to feed, the eggs become more or less cool.   Because this happens in Nature, it has been assumed that better hatches will result if the eggs are cooled when artificially incubated.   There appears to be little evidence that this supposition is well founded.

With the increased popularity of the forced-draft type of incubator, in which no cooling is practiced, it came to be more generally recognized that cooling is unnecessary.   The result is that whereas in times past nearly all eggs were cooled regularly, now very few are so treated, regardless of the type of incubator used.

Respiration

In animal organisms, respiration refers to the interchange of gases between the organism and the surrounding medium.   With land-dwelling animals the surrounding medium is the air, and the gases exchanged are chiefly oxygen (O_2), carbon dioxide (CO_2) and water vapor (H_2O).

Several investigators have studied the effects upon the developing embryo of sealing the pores of egg shells and thus stopping the gas exchange.   Various materials, including varnish, shellac and water-glass were used.   The net results of these studies, insofar as they

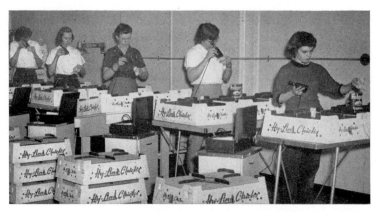

Fig. 5–14.—Instrument sexing of chicks at Hy-Line production plant, Johnston, Iowa. A trained operator can handle 500 to 600 chicks an hour. (Courtesy of Hatchery and Feed.)

have a bearing on incubation problems, seem to be (1) that the air cell normally performs an important function in embryonic respiration and (2) that the developing embryo is somewhat adaptable and may survive and even develop without the aid of the air cell, absorbing oxygen and discharging carbon dioxide through the shell at other places than the large end.

Oxygen Requirements.—Air contains about 21 per cent of oxygen and it is therefore impossible in incubation to have an excess above this amount unless it is artificially supplied. Without adequate ventilation it is very easy to have a deficiency, because the carbon dioxide produced is at the expense of oxygen.

From tests at the National Agricultural Research Center it is apparent that it is very important for normal embryonic development that the oxygen concentration not be allowed to decrease below the amount in normal air. An excess of oxygen is not nearly so detrimental as a deficiency. A deficiency of 5 per cent of oxygen reduced the hatch about one-third, or from 81 to 55 per cent, but it took an excess of 25 per cent to reduce the hatch that much.

Carbon Dioxide Toleration.—That the amount of carbon dioxide in the air immediately surrounding incubating eggs might have some effect upon their development, was recognized by the early students of incubation problems.

Lamson and Edmond, at the Storrs Station, spent some five years studying this problem, and as the result of a great many individual trials and determinations they showed "that if the carbon dioxide in the air of the incubator goes above 150 parts in 10,000 there will be a high mortality of the chick embryos and that this dying will be greatly increased when the carbon dioxide rises above 200 parts" (or 2 per cent).

More recent tests have shown that when the percentage of oxygen is held constant at 21, along with constant temperature, humidity

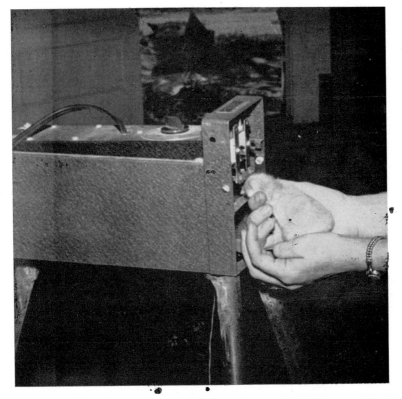

FIG. 5–15.—An electric debeaker in use. Many thousands of chicks are debeaked when only one day old. (Courtesy of Hatchery and Feed.)

and air movement, the decrease in percentage hatch is proportional to the increase in CO_2. All results are in agreement in suggesting a maximum CO_2 content of 0.5 per cent if optimum hatching results are to be secured.

Relative Humidity

The capacity of air to absorb and hold moisture increases rapidly as its temperature rises, and the drier the air in an incubator, the more moisture it will take up from the eggs. Control of relative humidity is therefore important in artificial incubation.

There is a relationship between relative humidity and temperature, at least in forced-draft incubators. With three machines operating at the same dry bulb temperature (99° F.) there was a spread of forty-eight hours in time of hatching when they were operated at wet bulb temperatures of 75°, 85° and 90° F., respectively. These correspond to relative humidities of 33 per cent, 56 per cent and 70 per cent. When the temperature in the low humidity machine was adjusted to 100° F., and that in the high

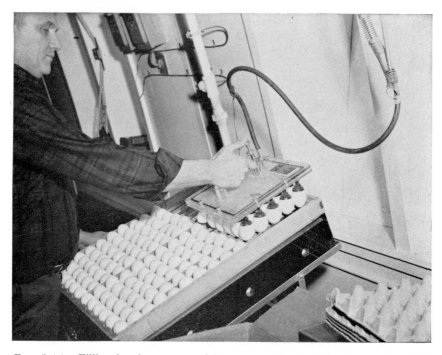

FIG. 5–16.—Filling hatchery trays with a pneumatic egg lift saves considerable labor at Babcock Poultry Farm, Inc., Ithaca, N. Y.

humidity machine to 98° F., all three machines hatched together in the normal period of twenty-one days. The inference seems clear that, at least in the forced-draft type of incubator, as the humidity is increased, the temperature requirement is decreased.

Barott, at the Beltsville Research Center, found that with the temperature held constant at 100° F., the oxygen content kept at 21 per cent, the CO_2 content kept below 0.5 per cent, and the rate of air movement at 12 cm. per minute, the best hatches were obtained at a relative humidity of 61 per cent. The true optimum might easily be slightly above or below this figure, and a variation of five, or even ten points either way would not be seriously detrimental to hatching results.

That high humidity may be important in other ways than its effect on the hatching percentage is well illustrated by experiments conducted at the Kansas Station which showed that the maintenance of a wet bulb reading of 95° F. in a forced-draft incubator at hatching time practically eliminated the spread of pullorum disease from infected to non-infected chicks hatching in the same machine.

The mortality to two weeks of age among chicks hatched from eggs laid by non-reactor hens, and hatched in the same machine with eggs from reactor hens, was 29 per cent, 15 per cent and 6 per cent when the wet bulb readings at hatching time were 75°, 85° and 95° F., respectively. At the same time the mortality among healthy control chicks was 5 per cent.

Testing.—It was formerly customary to test eggs by candling one or more times during the incubation period in order to remove any that were not developing normally. If fertility was poor, the eggs from two trays might be combined in one. Under present-day conditions very little such testing is done, partly because of the labor involved and partly because improved methods of feeding and management have so increased the normal percentage hatch that there will be very few eggs to remove.

Two classes of eggs can be removed on the basis of an early test— "infertiles" and "dead germs." In a technical sense the term infertile refers to an egg that has never been fertilized, but practically it includes those that have started to develop but that have died at such an early age that they cannot readily be distinguished by candling. A dead germ is a fertile egg in which the embryo has died after developing to a point such that it is easily identified by candling.

The so-called infertile egg appears to be clear save for a floating shadow, which is easily distinguished as the yolk.

The live germ is spider-like in appearance during the first few days, the body of the embryo representing the body of the spider and the radiating blood vessels its legs. The live germ floats about freely in the contents of the egg when the egg is rotated before the candling lamp.

The dead germ may be recognized by the absence of the blood vessels, by its adhering to the shell, or by the quite typical pink ring surrounding it which is called a blood ring.

A second test may be made after fourteen to sixteen days of incubation. If the first has been accurately done there will be only dead germs to test out. The live embryo at this time appears nearly to fill the egg. In the one or two light spaces which are usually present, blood vessels will be noticed and the embryo chick will frequently be seen to move when the egg is rotated.

The dead germs may vary in appearance from typical blood rings to embryo chicks of nearly normal size. The latter will usually be readily recognized by the absence of blood vessels, a general indefiniteness of outline, and a quite different color from that of eggs containing live embryos.

If suitable equipment is used, infertile eggs may be detected with a high degree of accuracy after fifteen to eighteen hours of incubation. A 75-watt blue bulb is used. In each fertile egg there can be seen on the surface of the yolk a small spot about the size of a dime. This is the tiny embryo. No such spot can be seen in an infertile egg.

Even fifteen hours of incubation will cause a marked deterioration in the market quality of infertile eggs. Eggs of AA quality, after fifteen hours at incubation temperature, may grade no better than B quality.

SUMMARY OF FACTORS INFLUENCING HATCHABILITY

Through research and observation by many investigators there has been accumulated a large amount of information concerning various factors which influence the hatchability of eggs. The following summary gives some idea of the variety of conditions which must be taken into account in explaining high or low hatching results.

High summer temperatures are detrimental to hatchability and thereby increase the cost of producing chicks.

Severe cold spells during the winter are detrimental to the hatchability of eggs laid immediately following such cold spells.

Eggs laid by pullets usually hatch better than eggs laid by hens kept under the same sort of conditions.

High egg production is not in itself detrimental to hatchability. Eggs from hens with medium high records usually hatch better than eggs from hens with low records.

Large eggs do not hatch as well as medium to small eggs. The frequency of certain malpositions is higher among embryos developing in the large eggs.

Eggs with tremulous air cells do not hatch as well as normal eggs.

Hens laying at a high rate will, in general, give better hatching results than hens laying at a low rate under the same conditions of feeding and management.

Inbreeding commonly results in decreased hatchability.

Crossing low-hatching strains of two different breeds or varieties will almost invariably improve the hatching results.

The hatchability of eggs held for no longer than one week is not improved by turning prior to incubation.

When eggs are held longer than one week, there is a marked decrease in hatchability which is directly proportional to the holding time.

The time required for incubation is related to the age of the eggs set, the older eggs requiring several hours longer to hatch than eggs held for only a few days.

Chilling eggs at temperatures as low as 38° F. has no apparent harmful effect on hatching results until the period of chilling exceeds forty-eight hours.

The optimum constant holding temperature seems to be in the range of 50° to 55° F.

On the basis of data now available, the optimum conditions for incubation appear to be (1) a temperature of 100° F. (or perhaps $99\frac{3}{4}$), (2) a relative humidity of 60 per cent, (3) oxygen content of the incubator air 21 per cent, (4) carbon dioxide content 0.5 per cent or below, (5) eggs to be held with the large end slightly raised, i.e., at an angle of 30° above the horizontal, and (6) all eggs to be gently turned eight or more times during each twenty-four hours.

HATCHERY OPERATION

The hatching of chicks as a business has long been an important part of the poultry industry in the United States, but the type of operation being carried on today is very different from that of even ten years ago. Some of the changes are indicated by the following tabulation as reported by the U. S. Department of Agriculture.

Year	Number of hatcheries	Total egg capacity	Average egg capacity
1934	11,405	276,287,000	24,000
1943	10,112	504,640,000	50,000
1953	8,233	616,976,000	80,000
1959	4,939	575,601,000	116,000
1965	2,365	471,318,000	199,000

Many small community hatcheries have gone out of business, and the larger operators have tended to concentrate on producing either broiler-type or egg-type chicks. In addition to this type of specialization, many hatcheries are under franchise to produce only chicks that come from eggs produced on farms owned and operated by a single breeder organization.

Hatchery operation is a year-round business. Prior to the growth of the broiler industry, hatching was primarily a springtime activity. In 1939, 65 per cent of all commercial chicks were hatched in the three months of March, April, and May. Commercial chick production figures for 1959 and 1965, shown in Table 5–1, illustrate the

Table 5–1.—Commercial Chick Production, by Months, for Selected Years, as Reported by the U.S. Department of Agriculture

	1959		1965	
	Broiler-type	Egg-type	Broiler-type	Egg-type
	Millions			
January	154	36	191	31
February	150	62	188	37
March	183	118	217	60
April	180	130	223	74
May	175	86	238	68
June	169	27	226	47
July	166	14	223	32
August	150	13	207	29
September	122	14	186	28
October	122	14	193	27
November	130	13	196	26
December	142	14	209	27
Total	1,843	541	2,500	492

recent trends toward year-round hatching. In 1959, 62 per cent of the egg-type chicks were hatched in March, April, and May, whereas only 29 per cent of the broiler chicks produced were hatched in those three months. The hatching of egg-type chicks in these months of 1965 accounted for only 42 per cent of those hatched for that year. The rearing of replacement pullets for laying flocks has steadily become a year-round operation. This is a remarkable illustration of how changes in methods of housing, rearing and lighting have resulted in less seasonal influence on egg production.

These changes have altered the former position of the hatchery-man, who was in effect a manufacturer who bought his raw materials from and sold his finished product to the same class of people. He is still rendering an essential service, but often as a part of a large integrated organization instead of as an independent operator. His supply flocks are much larger, and fewer in number than before, just as his customers may be fewer and individual chick orders very much larger than in the early days of the hatchery business.

Chapter 6

Brooding and Rearing

BROODING and rearing deal with the growth of the chick after hatching, and more specifically with those factors affecting growth that are more or less completely under the control of the poultryman. The growth attained by an individual will depend upon its inherited ability to grow, its food supply, and such environmental factors as temperature, air supply and protection from parasites and diseases. Reference has already been made to the marked influence of heredity. Nutrient requirements and their importance are given special consideration in a later chapter.

Aside from their nutritional needs, there is little basic information concerning the requirements of chicks during the brooding period. Yet in many ways this is the most critical and difficult period in the management of domestic birds. No poultry business can long succeed without a practical and efficient chick-rearing department. Chickens must be well grown before they can yield a monetary return to their owner, regardless of the nature of the particular poultry product he is selling.

Successful brooding is still largely an art, though information is gradually being accumulated which may eventually put artificial brooding on a scientific basis.

Commercial installations of large capacity have been developed through the application of principles which have proved successful in smaller units. It is not uncommon to find 5000 or 6000 chicks being brooded together as a unit, or to find houses and equipment so arranged that one caretaker is responsible for as many as 25,000 or 30,000 chicks.

BROODING REQUIREMENTS

The requirements of brooding appear to be essentially those of housing, with the addition of temperature regulation. A complete brooder is simply a special form of house designed for the purpose of keeping chicks comfortable. To be commercially practical, brooding equipment must also be reasonably low in cost.

Temperature

There is no general agreement among poultrymen as to what constitutes exactly the proper hover temperature for chicks just out of the incubator or at succeeding ages. There is no cumulative

experimental evidence determining definitely what these temperatures should be.

Ideal temperature conditions probably exist when there is a range
in temperature always available to the chicks, from a maximum of
not less than 100° F. to a minimum of 60° or 70° F. When they
have opportunity for a choice, chicks soon learn to find the temperature that is most comfortable to them. Trouble comes not so
much from temporary exposure to low or to variable temperatures,
as from continuous exposure to temperatures that are too high or
too low, with no opportunity for the chicks to move at will to more
comfortable temperatures.

Careful tests have shown that, with the temperature taken $2\frac{1}{2}$
inches above the litter, baby chicks are apparently comfortable at all

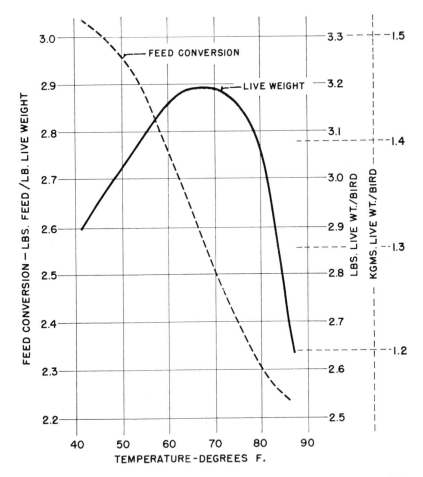

Fig. 6–1.—9-week average live weight and feed conversion data for Athens
randombred broilers grown at various environmental temperatures. (After Ota
and McNally.)

temperatures in the range from 80° to 110° F. Not until the air temperature is some five degrees above or below this range is there definite indication of discomfort and of a tendency to avoid such areas. On the other hand, extensive tests at the Beltsville Agricultural Research Center involving 72 experiments with 30 chicks each, showed a maximum growth response during the first nine days after hatching when the average temperature was 91° F., dropping from 94° on the first day to 88° on the ninth. In a later series of 53 similar experiments, best results were obtained when the temperature was reduced uniformly from 94° on the first day to 80° on the eighteenth. Variation in controlled relative humidity from 35 per cent to 75 per cent made no appreciable difference in growth to eighteen days of age.

In recent tests by Ota and McNally at Beltsville, broiler-type chickens were grown to nine weeks of age in calorimeters which permitted accurate control of temperature, air movement and relative humidity. After initial brooding temperatures of 85° to 94° F., various lots were subjected to continuous temperatures of 41°, 50°, 59°, 68°, 77° and 86° F. (5°, 10°, 15°, 20°, 25° and 30° C.). Because the calorimeters were not very large, it was necessary to reduce the number of chickens from 100 at the start to 15 in each lot at the end of a nine-week test. Air flow in the calorimeters was 10 to 11 cubic feet per minute for 100 day-old chicks, and was gradually increased to as high as 25 cubic feet per minute for 15 broilers at eight or nine weeks. Relative humidity was maintained at near 75 per cent.

Fig. 6–2.—Gas-heated brooders are widely used in broiler production. (Courtesy of A. R. Wood Manufacturing Company.)

The final live weight and feed conversion data, as related to the different environmental temperatures, are of particular interest. The results are shown in Figure 6–1. Environmental temperatures can be either too high or too low, when maintained at a constant level. The best growth occurred at a constant temperature of 68° F. Efficiency of feed conversion increased steadily throughout the experimental temperature range of 41° to 86°.

These results should not be taken to mean that temperatures in commercial broiler houses can safely be reduced to 68° during the early brooding period. Higher brooding temperatures are necessary, especially in winter, to offst the effect of cold wall surfaces and possible drafts, and to make certain that there is always opportunity for chicks to move to a warm area if they wish.

Effects of Chilling.—A little chick, compelled to remain in the cold after he begins to feel chilly, soon becomes helpless. This is apparently caused by paralysis of the breathing apparatus. The lungs are located on either side of the median line of the back at the circumference of the body cavity. Lobes of the lungs extend between the ribs and are protected from the outside temperature only by a thin membrane, the skin, and a coat of down. It is not surprising that when the chick is chilled the lungs are quickly affected.

In natural brooding, the back and lungs are the best protected portions of the body. When a chick becomes uncomfortably cold under conditions of artificial brooding, and is unable to locate heat enough to warm him quickly, he seems to obey that instinct which tells him to get his back up against the mother hen. The result is that he tries to crawl under the other chicks. This, taken up by more and more chicks, results in bunching and crowding with the accompanying evils of smothered chicks and a diminution of thrift on the part of the entire flock.

Diarrhea can be produced experimentally in baby chicks by exposing them to moderate changes in temperature. A sudden increase in temperature is just as detrimental as a decrease. Chicks kept under observation for a period of ten weeks showed that though the exposure to a change in temperature was not always fatal, there was a serious disturbance in metabolism which resulted in abnormal development.

The low lethal internal body temperature has been studied by several workers, and ranges from 62° F. on the day of hatch to about 67° at two weeks of age, with a gradual increase to about 73° at maturity. Maryland workers found that 2-day-old chicks could stand 35 minutes exposure at −10° F., and that at twenty days of age they could stand 75 minutes before half of them succumbed.

Effects of Overheating.—Overheating occurs comparatively seldom, because chicks instinctively move away from the source of heat when too warm. If confined under a hover when the temperature runs up, they die rather quickly.

The high lethal body temperature for the chick is the same as that for older fowls, 117° F. This body temperature is reached in about ten minutes when chicks are exposed to an air temperature of 160° F. At room temperatures of 100° F., death losses among day-old chicks in sealed summer-size fibre-board chick boxes were found by Wilson at the California Station to range from 20 to 50 per cent. New Hampshire chicks were more susceptible to overheating than were White Leghorns.

Ventilation.—Adequate ventilation is as important for growing chickens as for laying hens, and brooders should be so arranged that there will be a constantly changing supply of fresh air. The main problem is moisture removal. Broiler fecal material contains about 80 per cent of moisture, and considerable air movement is necessary to keep the brooding area dry. Early studies at the California Station showed that as much as four cubic feet of air per 100 chicks per minute, when chicks were three weeks old, would not keep the hover area under electric brooders entirely dry.

In commercial broiler houses containing several thousand birds approaching market weight, ventilation rates may need to be as high as one cubic foot per broiler per minute and fan capacities should exceed this by a considerable margin. Workers at the Arkansas Station make the following recommendations for ventilation rates to control moisture when inside conditions are maintained at 75° F. and 85 per cent relative humidity. Their tests were conducted in a well-insulated house 24 × 124 feet in size containing 3,200 broilers.

Average weight per broiler (pounds)	Outside temperature (Degrees F.)			
	0	32	40	50
	Rate in c.f.m. per broiler			
0.5	.05	.06	.07	.16
1.0	.09	.11	.13	.31
2.0	.18	.23	.27	.62
3.0	.28	.34	.40	.93
4.0	.37	.45	.53	1.25

As ventilation is increased to remove the greater amounts of moisture produced by broilers as they grow in size, more cold air is drawn in from outside, and some supplementary heat should be provided to heat this extra volume of cold air. Experience of broiler growers in many parts of the country supports the theoretical calculation that an indoor temperature of 70° to 75° F. should be maintained, even when the broilers are near market weight.

Workers at the University of Idaho have used the following heat and moisture output data as a basis for determining ventilation

Fig. 6–3.—A hot water brooding system in California.   During the first ten to fourteen days chicks are kept close to the hover area by a corrugated paper guard. Some poultrymen use aluminum guards.   (Courtesy of Pacific Poultryman.)

Fig. 6-4.—A convenient arrangement for keeping chicks or poults close to the hover for the first few days. (Courtesy of Big Dutchman, Inc.)

Fig. 6-5.—Fins help to radiate heat from hot water pipes in this installation. (Courtesy of Poultry Tribune.)

Fig. 6-6.—This central hot air heating system can be adjusted by raising or lowering the hovers. (Courtesy of Broiler Business.)

FIG. 6–7.—White Leghorn pullets in brooder house at Creighton Brothers, Warsaw, Indiana. (J. C. Allen and Son Photo.)

requirements. For cold winter weather and high precipitation conditions in the northwest they recommend insulated houses with an "R" value of 10 in the walls and 14 or 15 in the ceilings See Chapter 7 for a discussion of R value.

Heat and Moisture Output of Broilers of Indicated Weights

Age	Average weight (pounds)	Heat output in B.t.u. per 1,000 broilers per hour	Water output in pounds per 1,000 broilers per day
1 day	0.10	1,200	15
1 week	0.17	2,100	60
2 weeks	0.35	4,200	110
3 weeks	0.70	7,950	150
4 weeks	1.20	13,200	200
5 weeks	1.65	18,000	240
6 weeks	2.20	24,000	280
7 weeks	2.80	30,100	310
8 weeks	3.40	36,100	350

Hover and Floor Space

Well-fed chicks grow rapidly, often doubling their weight as many as five successive times in the first six weeks. As they grow, their need for supplementary heat becomes less, with the result that floor space in the brooder house is more likely to become critical than heated hover space. Furthermore, the optimum floor area for greatest biological efficiency may not coincide with the optimum for greatest economic efficiency. It is considered sound practice to provide 7 square inches of brooder space under the hovers for each chick started, and ½ square foot of total brooder house floor area. For chicks reared in confinement, this will be adequate for the first four to six weeks, but only about half enough for the succeeding four to six weeks.

A decision must also be made as to how many chicks to place under a single hover or heating unit, even with several units in one large house. Large flocks mean some saving in labor and equipment, but for rapid growth and low mortality it is wise to think in terms of 300 to 400 chicks when brooding replacement stock and perhaps 500 to 600 for broilers.

Brooding Equipment

Portable brooders are made in a number of different styles and sizes, but in commercial use the gas-heated types have largely replaced the once-popular coal stoves. Oil-heated brooders are also used in some areas. Commercial broiler growers often use hot water or hot air types with a central heating system. Several of the more common types of equipment in use today are shown in the accompanying illustrations.

Other Equipment

Feeding equipment which is suited to a six-week-old flock will not do for day-old chicks, and special means must be used to make sure that chicks learn to eat when they are first placed in the brooder. Inverted chick-box lids, filler flats, or narrow, shallow troughs may be used until the chicks are able to eat from larger feeding equipment. Today's commercial broiler chicks have an inherited capacity for growth that is fantastic by comparison with that of their counterparts of thirty years ago, but they still have to learn to eat and drink, and this calls for the simple but important application of good husbandry on the part of a caretaker.

As soon as the chicks have learned to eat from regular feeders, they should have about 100 linear inches of feeding space per 100 chicks. By the time they are three weeks old they will need nearly 200 linear inches, and after six weeks 300 linear inches per 100 chicks. Warm weather conditions may require even more space.

Two 1-gallon water fountains will accommodate 100 chicks at the start, but capacity will have to be increased as the chicks grow. If trough-type watering equipment is used, each 100 chicks will need about 20 linear inches at the start and 40 to 50 inches later.

Management Problems

Many different materials can be used as litter—sawdust, shavings, ground corn cobs, sugar cane fiber, cottonseed hulls, to name a few. A 2-inch layer is satisfactory at the start. More may be added, if desired, as the chicks grow.

In cold weather, a guard of corrugated paper, metal or wall board should be placed around or along the hover, two to three feet from its edge to prevent floor drafts and to keep chicks from straying too far from the source of heat till they learn to find it easily. In warm weather wire may be used. The guard can be removed at the end of the first week.

Many operators like to use dim all-night lights, about 15 watts to each 200 square feet of floor area. In windowless houses some flock owners prefer to use red bulbs and grow their chicks in semi-darkness. This keeps the chicks quiet, prevents cannibalism, and may have a slight effect on feed efficiency because of lessened activity.

Another practical system for windowless broiler houses is to start with 24-hour light at a fairly high level, perhaps with a 40-watt bulb for each 25 square feet. The amount of light is then reduced each week, first by turning out part of the bulbs, and later by substituting 25-watt bulbs for the 40-watt size, and finally dropping as low as one $7\frac{1}{2}$-watt bulb for each 75 square feet. This avoids any necessity for completely lightproofing the house. It may be advisable to raise lighting levels for the last twenty-four to thirty-six hours prior to marketing, as broilers raised under low-light conditions are not easily driven into catching crates.

FIG. 6–8.—Some farm flocks of pullets are still grown on range. Large commercial flocks are commonly grown in confinement. (J. C. Allen and Son Photo.)

FIG. 6–9.—An all-purpose type of range shelter for farm flocks of pullets. The sides can be enclosed with solid panels. (Courtesy of Illinois Agricultural Experiment Station.)

Fɪɢ. 6–10.—Many thousands of replacement pullets are grown on wire floors. Building paper covers the hover area during the first few days. (J. C. Allen and Son Photo.)

If pullet chicks are being grown as replacements and are to be floor-housed as adults, low roosts should be installed when the chicks are about four weeks of age. A sloping platform with small roosts is usually best. If the frame is covered with hardware cloth it provides natural and easy access to the roosts. Necessary roosting space is four to five inches per chick. If the layers are to be placed in cages, roosts during the growing period are optional. Many thousands of replacement pullets are grown on wire floors not only for convenience, but also because there is no later problem of adjustment to the wire floors of laying cages.

Except for small flocks, not many replacement pullets are grown on range, but when they are so grown, roosting sheds or range shelters of some sort are necessary. These are simply light frame sheds provided with a tight roof and wire sides. They commonly have wire floors. The only interior equipment needed is roosts, because feed is supplied in large outdoor hoppers.

CAPON PRODUCTION

The purpose of caponizing is to improve the quality of poultry meat. Farmers regularly castrate calves, pigs and lambs, but usually consider caponizing a much more difficult operation because it involves opening of the abdominal cavity. Actually, the operation is very simple and the method can be learned quickly by almost anyone.

A small flock of capons could be raised to advantage on many farms, either for family use or for sale to local customers. Larger flocks often compete seriously with laying hens and pullets for house room, which is one important reason why they are not often found on general farms. Unless they can be kept for two to four months beyond the time at which the cockerels would normally be sold as roasters, it is not worth while to take the trouble to caponize.

Selection of Cockerels to Caponize

The size and condition of the young cockerels to be caponized is more important than their age or variety. Leghorn cockerels make excellent small capons, and Plymouth Rocks, Orpingtons, Rhode Island Reds, and various crossbreds are all suitable for large capons. It is very important that the operation be performed before the cockerels become too large. This means choosing heavy breed cockerels weighing 1 to $1\frac{1}{2}$ pounds, or Leghorns weighing $\frac{3}{4}$ to 1 pound. In fact, with suitable equipment, it is entirely possible to caponize cockerels when they are no more than two or three weeks old. The most common error is to attempt the operation on larger cockerels, with consequent high mortality and more slips, or incompletely castrated individuals. Only rapidly growing, vigorous cockerels should be chosen.

Preparation for the Operation

It is always desirable to withhold feed for eighteen hours and water for the last twelve hours prior to the operation, in order that the intestines may become empty and thus permit better vision into the body cavity. There is also much less danger of puncturing the intestines during the operation.

Performing the Operation

A first requirement for successful caponizing is good light. Bright daylight, preferably not in direct sunshine, is ideal. Artificial light may be used, if necessary.

Some means of restraining the birds in a convenient position must be provided. The usual procedure is to fasten the wings and legs by straps or cords so that sufficient tension can be applied to hold the bird well stretched out. If both testicles are to be removed through one incision, the bird should be placed on its left side.

The instruments needed are a sharp knife or scalpel, a small probe which has a tearing hook on one end, a spreader for holding

10

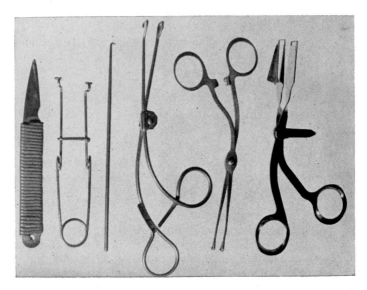

FIG. 6–11.—Instruments used for caponizing. Left to right: knife, spreader, tearing hook and probe, forceps for removal of the gonads, small forceps for operating on two-week old cockerels, and an All-In-One instrument. (Courtesy of Kansas Agricultural Experiment Station.)

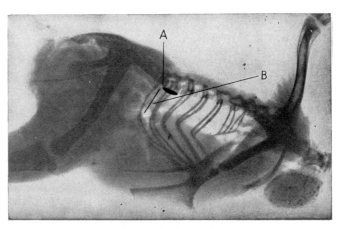

FIG. 6–12.—Radiograph of a living cockerel. The right testicle has been sketched in at *A*. The line of incision is indicated at *B*.

the ribs apart after the incision has been made, and a remover for taking out the testicles. Several different types of removers are available, but a forceps type is preferred by most operators.

Making the Incision

It is usually necessary to pluck a few feathers from the area through which the incision is to be made. A little cold water may be used to moisten the surrounding feathers so that they will lie down out of the way. Next, find the last two ribs with the fingers of the left hand; slide the skin upward and backward toward the thigh, making sure that the underlying thigh muscles are out of the way; force the knife through the skin and flesh between the last two ribs; lengthen the incision to about 1 inch, keeping it centered between the ribs and not too near the back; and insert the spreader so as to hold the ribs about $\frac{1}{2}$ inch apart. If the knife has not severed the peritoneal membranes, they should be torn with the hook so as to expose the testicles to the view of the operator.

Removing the Testicles

The lower, or left testicle should be removed first. It is not visible, as a rule, and must be lifted into view by the forceps before it can be grasped. The entire organ and the connecting portion of the spermatic duct must be taken out in order to prevent the bird from becoming a "slip." Care must be taken, however, not to rupture any of the primary blood vessels, or internal hemorrhage will result in death before the bird is removed from the operating table.

The remover is carefully worked over the testicle and so manipulated as to enclose the entire organ. It is then drawn out with a slight twisting motion. The same procedure is followed with the upper testicle. As soon as the spreader is removed, and the tension on the bird released, the skin and thigh muscles slip back over the incision, affording natural protection.

Because of the relatively high body temperature of chickens, it is possible to perform this sort of operation with little danger of infection. Ordinary cleanliness is all that is required.

Care After the Operation

No special care of young capons is necessary, other than to give them a clean pen and range area where they do not have to compete with other chickens. Any good growing ration will be satisfactory.

Wind puffs often develop because air escapes from within the abdominal cavity before the incision between the ribs is healed, and becomes trapped beneath the skin. It is sometimes necessary to puncture these puffs four or five times on alternate days following the operation.

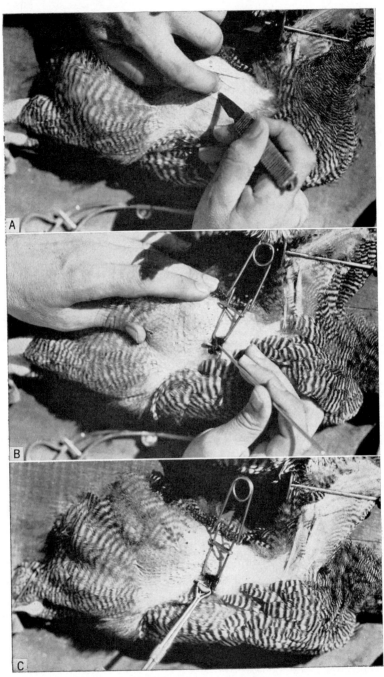

Fig. 6-13.—Performing the operation of caponizing. *A*, The skin and thigh muscle being drawn back preparatory to making the incision; *B*, tearing the peritoneal membranes after inserting a spreader to hold the ribs apart; *C*, removing the testicle. (Courtesy of Kansas Agricultural Experiment Station.)

Slips result when some portion of the testicle is left in the body cavity. Occasionally a testicle is dropped inside the body after having been torn loose. If it is not removed, the bird will become a slip and will have all the external appearance of a normal cockerel. This is because the testicle, or in other cases a very small portion of it, becomes attached to the inner abdominal wall and continues to secrete the male sex hormone in sufficient quantity to cause enlargement of the comb and wattles and later toughening of the flesh.

Marketing Capons

Persons who have once enjoyed roast capon of top quality are likely to be repeat customers year after year, and there is undoubtedly a potential market for capons which has never been explored. Common practice, however, has been to produce capons largely for local consumption. A few persons have developed a nice business in the sale of started capons, operated on at three weeks of age and sold at five or six weeks to customers who grow them to market age.

Chapter 7

Houses and Equipment

Housing of poultry for egg or meat production is important as a means of keeping many environmental conditions under the control of the operator. It also helps to insure maximum use of feed energy for productive purposes rather than in overcoming the effects of unfavorable weather.

With the right kind of stock, and a suitable food supply, production of eggs is likely to be in direct proportion to the comfort of the hens. The natural laying and breeding season is in the spring, and conditions then are those which provide comfort plus the stimulus of a gradually increasing length of day. A successful hen house will furnish its occupants with permanent protection from extremes of temperature and other unfavorable weather conditions. It will also enable the operator to provide the stimulus of artificial light when needed. In addition, it will be so arranged as to permit the necessary work of caring for the flock to be done with a minimum expenditure of time and effort.

THE HOUSING PROBLEM

Beginning about 1900 and continuing for more than twenty-five years, there was a period of much practical experimenting with different styles and types of poultry houses. The open scratching shed, the roosting closet, the "fresh-air" house, the muslin front, the straw loft, the half-monitor, and the warm tight house each had its staunch supporters. Gradually the cumulative results began to point to a few common recommendations on which nearly all could agree. But it was not until the poultry physiologist and the engineer began to give serious thought to the basic biological and weather problems involved that there was any accurate and dependable information on which to base recommendations for poultry house design and construction.

In mild climates the housing of poultry is very simple, but when winter temperatures average below 10° F., with average relative humidity above 80 per cent, and with sunshine amounting to less than five hours a day, the proper housing of highly productive flocks becomes a difficult problem. To understand the complicated nature of the problem, and the means by which it can be solved, it is necessary to look at poultry housing from three viewpoints: (1) As a problem in biology, (2) As a problem in engineering, and (3) As a problem in economics, as each is related to the matter of "weather" control in the hen house.   This means that we need to know the ideal conditions of temperature, humidity, and air change for maximum egg production performance, the engineering design which will make it possible to control these conditions for a flock of given size, and the range or tolerance above and below the optimum which may be permitted for each factor without seriously interfering with production, so that we may decide what variations are permissible while still keeping construction costs within reasonable limits.

Aside from such matters as light, floor space, litter materials, and the kind and amount of essential equipment, housing requirements

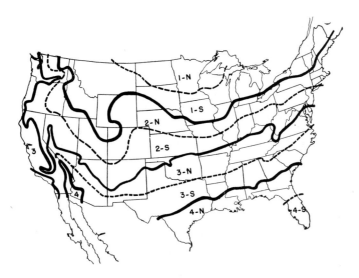

Fig. 7–1.—Temperature zones as related to poultry house construction.   Average January temperature in Zone 1 below 20° F.; in Zone 2 20°–35°; in Zone 3 35°–50°; in Zone 4 above 50° F.   Based on data from the U. S. Department of Agriculture.

for hens can be stated only in terms of temperature, relative humidity, and the number of air changes to maintain the necessary minimum amount of oxygen and the maximum permissible amount of carbon dioxide.   This is easy to say but difficult to determine.   It may be even more difficult to maintain any specified set of conditions.

TEMPERATURE

Chickens, like all other warm-blooded animals, produce heat, moisture and carbon dioxide as by-products of their biological activity. The entire process operates to maintain body temperature at about 106.5° F. (range from 104 to 109).   Since this is nearly always above the air temperature in the poultry house by from 10 to as much as 100 degrees, the hen is constantly losing heat to her surroundings. This heat must as constantly be replaced or body temperature will fall and the hen cannot long survive.

These facts might suggest that it would be desirable and perhaps practical to maintain laying house temperatures as high as 75° F. in order to minimize heat loss to the air. But carefully controlled tests at the Beltsville Research Center indicate that a constant temperature of 55° F. is better than temperatures much above or below, at least for Rhode Island Reds. Hens kept at 55° F. laid

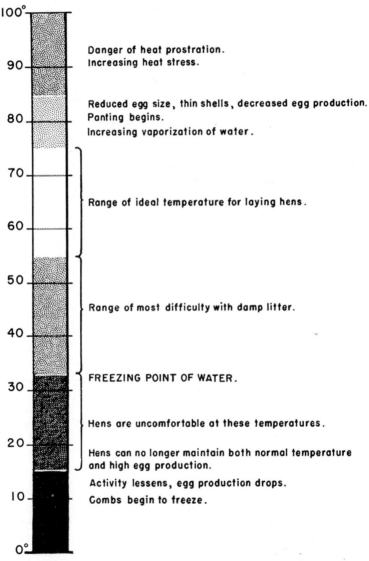

FIG. 7–2.—Showing how temperature affects the laying hen.

at a rate of 75 per cent and consumed 3.5 pounds of feed for each pound of eggs. Those maintained at 85° F. laid at a rate of only 50 per cent and ate 4 pounds of feed for each pound of eggs, while those kept at 23° F., the lowest temperature tested, laid at a rate of only 26 per cent and consumed 12.3 pounds of feed for each pound of eggs. Temperatures no more than 10° above or below 55° F. had only a slight effect on performance.

Heat Production vs. Heat Loss

If the rate of heat loss is increased for any reason, as during a period of cold weather, heat production must be increased by a corresponding amount. Similarly, if heat production is increased, as by increased activity with no change in the surrounding air temperature, there must be a prompt increase in heat loss in order to prevent the body temperature from rising. Many different

Heat loss *increased* by:	Heat production *increased* by:
Low air temperature	Physical activity
Increased air movement	Increased feed consumption
Low wall or floor temperature	Unbalanced rations
High humidity on cold days	"Chemical regulation" of body temperature when environmental temperature falls below the critical point
Loss of feathers (molting)	
"Physical regulation" of body temperature	

HEAT LOSS *In Balance With* HEAT PRODUCTION

Heat loss *decreased* by:	Heat production *decreased* by:
High air temperature	Decreased activity
Decreased air movement	Decreased feed intake
High wall or floor temperature	(No way of decreasing heat production when profitable egg yields are required. Feed a well-balanced ration to keep heat production at a minimum for the expected production and activity.)
Heavy feather coat	
Insulation of hen houses, with consequent increase in air and wall temperatures	

FIG. 7–3.—Factors influencing heat loss and heat production in the fowl.

factors affect the rate of heat loss and the rate of heat production. The more important ones are shown in Figure 7–3.

Heat loss will be greater in winter than in summer because of the greater difference in temperature between the hen and her surroundings. If hens are exposed to wind, the increased volume of air moving past them, picking up heat as it goes, results in an increased rate of heat loss. Low wall or floor temperatures can result in greatly increased heat loss so that hens may be uncomfortable in a building which has cold walls, even though the air temperature, as indicated by a thermometer, is not unreasonably low. High humidity makes air a better conductor, and moist air on a cold day will therefore absorb more heat from the hens than will dry air.

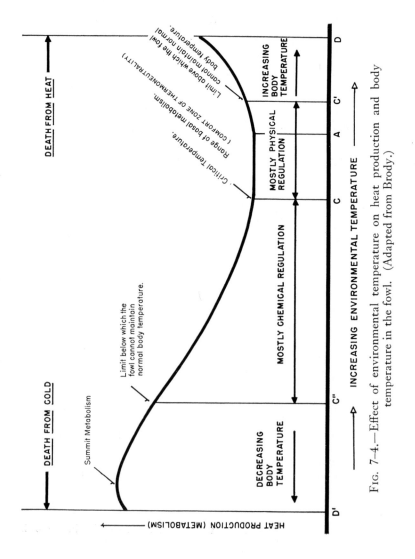

FIG. 7–4.—Effect of environmental temperature on heat production and body temperature in the fowl. (Adapted from Brody.)

An increase in heat loss from any of the foregoing causes calls for increased heat production simply to maintain a balance and to keep the body temperature near normal. But heat production may vary independently of the demand caused by varying heat loss. Physical activity will increase heat production because energy is incompletely used in doing work and the wasted energy appears as heat. Increased feed consumption will increase heat production because the feed energy is not completely used, and heat is released in the process. The feeding of unbalanced rations, which leave excess nutrients to be oxidized and eliminated, will increase the total heat production. At environmental temperatures below the point at which physical regulation of body temperature is no longer effective, the so-called chemical regulation of heat production comes into play, causing an increase in heat production in order to maintain the normal body temperature as long as possible (see Fig. 7–4).

Conversely, heat loss from the body will be decreased by higher environmental temperatures, by decreased air movement, and by high wall and floor temperatures. As explained later, high humidity on hot days interferes with necessary heat loss.

Heat production will be lowered by decreased activity and by decreased feed intake, but since profitable egg yields are dependent on maximum feed consumption, there is no way to make practical use of this relationship except to feed rations that are reasonably well balanced, thereby keeping heat production at a minimum for the expected production and activity. The minimum heat production for hens at rest occurs at about 70° F.

MOISTURE

Of more practical concern to many poultrymen is the moisture given off by hens incidental to their use of feed. It often creates a real problem during cold weather. Unless it is removed by adequate ventilation or by the use of artificial heat, both the litter and the walls of the hen house may become soaking wet with condensed water vapor.

A complete water balance equation would have to take into account the fountain water consumed, free and hygroscopic water in the feed, the metabolic water released in connection with the digestion and metabolism of feed, as well as water removed in the eggs produced. In practice, however, the important components are the amount of water voided in the droppings and released to the air, the water vaporized by the hens, and the amount of water brought into the poultry house by incoming air on damp days. These will be considered in some detail.

Water Voided in Droppings

Poultry feces, as voided, contain a high percentage of water. Reported figures range from 70 to 80 per cent, depending on whether they are based on hourly or twenty-four-hour samples, and on the kind of feed consumed. Not all this moisture is lost to the air. Manure separated from poultry house litter under air dry conditions contains about 16 per cent moisture, equivalent to about 4 per cent of the original weight. But the moisture content of manure allowed to accumulate beneath cages or roosts seldom drops below 70 per cent. Under average winter conditions, with the lower moisture content resulting from today's concentrated high-energy rations, it is doubtful whether more than 20 per cent of the original weight of voided manure is released to the poultry house air as moisture. The use of artificial heat might raise this figure.

The weight of manure voided will be from 20 to 30 per cent greater than the weight of feed consumed. Under some conditions it may

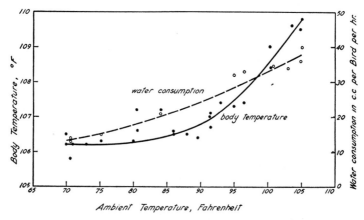

Fig. 7–5.—Effect of ambient temperature on body temperature and water consumption of White Leghorn pullets. (After Wilson.)

be less than this, and if bulky, low-energy feeds are fed, it will be very much greater—as much as 75 per cent greater than the weight of feed consumed. The total feed intake of a flock of 100 4½-pound hens laying 75 to 80 eggs a day, and fed a typical high-energy ration, will be about 23 to 25 pounds. The corresponding amount of manure voided will therefore be from 28 to 32 pounds. If 20 per cent of this is to become free water in the hen house, there will be about 6 pounds of water a day from each 100 hens to create dampness in the house unless it is removed by adequate ventilation.

This is one reason why more and more poultrymen are using mechanical cleaning systems for frequent removal of manure from poultry houses. Even twice-a-week removal will greatly reduce the moisture problem. Such a schedule will also help to keep flies at a minimum during warm weather. Some installations provide for daily removal of manure.

It should be clear that the moisture problem results from the presence of the hens and from their consumption of feed and water.

In tests at the New Hampshire station it was found that litter samples taken from empty houses in January and February contained about 15 per cent of moisture, while those from pens filled with laying hens averaged about 35 per cent for insulated houses and ranged up to more than 60 per cent in uninsulated houses.

For broilers, the moisture content of fecal material is about 80 per cent or slightly higher. When broilers approach market weight, the weight of fecal material excreted daily will be about half the sum of water and feed consumed.

Vaporized Water and Heat Loss

In addition to the water excreted in the droppings, there is a considerable amount of water which leaves the body by vaporization from the lungs. Since fowls have no sweat glands, there is very little opportunity for heat loss by evaporation from the skin. The amount vaporized from the lungs and air sacs varies widely with environmental temperature and humidity. It may also be influenced indirectly by the kind of feed. Substitution of corn for all of the oats and half of the wheat middlings in a standard low-energy ration reduced litter moisture significantly in tests at the Storrs Station.

Vaporization of water removes heat,* and variation in the quantity vaporized (indicated in the fowl by the rate of panting) is therefore an important means of varying the necessary heat loss from the body. At high air temperatures—approaching the normal body temperature—it is the only means by which the fowl can lose a substantial amount of heat. At low air temperatures, on the other hand, only a small fraction of the total heat loss is of this character—at 40° F. about 20 per cent and at 20° no more than 15 per cent.

Increased heat production, from whatever cause, increases the amount of heat lost as heat of vaporization. At high temperatures, especially when relative humidity is also high, fowls soon reach the limit of normal physical regulation and must resort to panting to facilitate vaporization of water as the only means of losing heat rapidly enough to keep the body temperature from rising. This condition exists whenever the surrounding air temperature equals or exceeds the skin temperature so that heat can no longer be dissipated by radiation. If the air temperature rises still higher, vaporization must also serve to rid the body of heat absorbed from the hot environment. This obviously cannot continue for long, and the fowl dies from heat exhaustion. Panting is nothing but a very marked increase in the respiration rate as the fowl attempts to get rid of more and more heat by this means. The amount of water vaporized increases slowly at temperatures of 75° to 80° F., and very rapidly thereafter, provided the humidity of the inspired air is low enough

---

* Each quart of water vaporized at body temperature dissipates about 2150 B.t.u. of heat. B.t.u. means British thermal unit—the amount of heat required to raise the temperature of 1 pound of water 1° F. Water vapor is commonly measured in grains. One grain is equal to .0648 gram or 1/7000 of a pound.

to permit.   With inspired air at very low relative humidity but at temperatures of 105° F. or above, some records indicate a short-time evaporative moisture loss of 25 to 30 grams per hen per hour, along with very watery droppings.   If the inspired air is both warm and saturated, the hen is completely unable to avoid collapse and death. The difficulty of eliminating excess heat, while maintaining other body processes, begins to show at air temperatures of about 85° F. Egg size decreases, egg shells become thinner, and production is reduced.

Death losses from heat prostration are often severe in the humid sections of the country, and they are also a serious problem in hot,

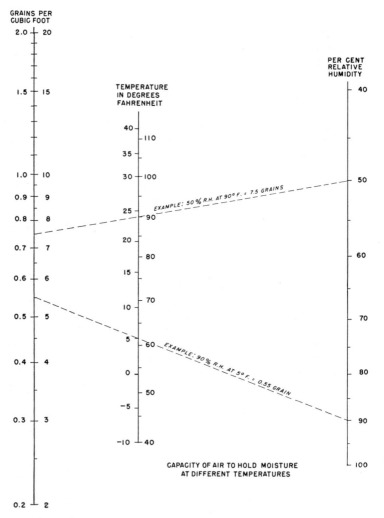

FIG. 7–6.—Chart for quick determination of the amount of moisture air can hold at different temperatures and relative humidities.

dry areas where maximum daily temperatures range from 105° to 115° F. or higher. Survival under such conditions is closely related to the availability of drinking water and to the persistence with which fowls consume it. Losses can also be reduced by intermittent spraying of the fowls and the interior of the houses. Fine mist sprayers are especially helpful in dry areas. The amount of water used is low, about one gallon per hour for each nozzle, and the fine mist promotes evaporative cooling. When humidity is high, cold water can be used to lower the body temperature by contact. Tests at the Beltsville Research Center showed that when no method of cooling was provided, hens were able to survive a temperature of 90° F., provided the relative humidity did not exceed 75 per cent. At 95° they survived at humidities below 60 per cent, but at 100° F.

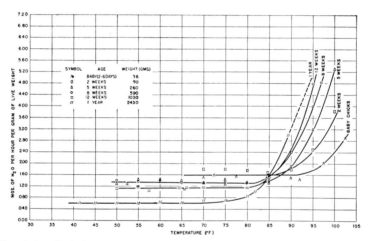

Fig. 7–7.—Relation of water of respiration to environmental temperature. (After Barott and Pringle.)

they survived only if the humidity was 30 per cent or lower. Very fat hens succumbed first, perhaps because the air sacs were constricted and therefore unable to function efficiently in evaporating water from the body tissues.

At low temperatures, on the other hand, the heat loss due to vaporization of water shows little change from normal. Most of the heat loss is then in the form of sensible heat, by radiation and convection, and it is therefore available for warming the air in the hen house. When laying hens are on full feed, the excess heat available for maintaining the normal body temperature is adequate for air temperatures above 40° F. When such hens are active, as during the day, and are producing additional heat because of muscular activity, the critical temperature is lowered to about 20° or perhaps even to 15° F.

At temperatures below 15° or 20° F. hens must draw on stored or food nutrients for the heat energy necessary to maintain normal body temperature, and egg production will therefore be lowered. Combs begin to freeze at about 6° above zero in dry air, and at 9° to 10° above zero in moist air.

It is clear that the compensatory range above the "comfort zone" of thermoneutrality (in which the animal feels neither hot nor cold) is much less than the range below and that fowls, like other farm animals, have more defenses against cold than against heat. They are, however, handicapped by their small size, because they have more body surface per unit of weight. The effects of a sudden drop in temperature are therefore more severe than with larger animals. In a 5-pound hen about 95 per cent of the total body tissue is within $\frac{3}{4}$-inch of the surface of the body. By contrast, in a 1000-pound steer only about 25 per cent of the total body tissue is so exposed.

VENTILATION

The total air breathed by fowls at rest in a comfortable environment is about 1 cubic foot per hen per hour—slightly less for small hens and slightly more for large ones. For 100 $4\frac{1}{2}$-pound hens this would be about 2,400 cubic feet every twenty-four hours. Measured by air change in the average hen house, built for the convenience of the caretaker and not simply to accommodate the hens, this is a very small requirement. It is entirely overshadowed by the rate of air change necessary to remove moisture from a tightly built house. In most instances, if ventilation is adequate to keep the house dry, it will much more than meet the air requirements of the fowls. Under conditions of heat stress, that is, when both air temperature and relative humidity are high, the respiration rate is very rapid and the total volume of air breathed may be eight or ten times normal.

The amount of air which must be moved through a poultry house to carry out excess moisture will depend upon the inside and outside temperatures and the difference between them, and on the relative humidity of the inside and outside air. Raising the temperature increases the capacity of air to hold moisture. In the range of 30° to 75° F., each rise of 1° in temperature means an increase of about 5 per cent in moisture-holding capacity of the air. The amount of water vapor in a pound of saturated air at 5° F. is doubled at 20°, and redoubled successively at about 36°, 55°, 76° and 99°. For every grain or gram or pound of water vapor which air can hold at 5° F., it can hold 32 times as much at 99°.

If, for example, the relative humidity of outside air at any given temperature is 70 per cent, while inside the poultry house at the same temperature it is 80 per cent, the outside air contains $12\frac{1}{2}$ per cent less moisture than the inside air, and forced ventilation of the outside air through the building will remove the excess moisture. But if the relative humidity of both the inside and the outside air is at 80 per cent, no amount of air change will do any good. Either the temperature of the outside air must rise so that it can hold more moisture, or its humidity must drop, if mere air circulation through the house is to remove any moisture.   This state of near equilibrium between inside and outside humidity, often with an excess on the outside, is common in many poultry houses during mild winter weather, often for several days in succession.   Since no change can be effected in the outside air, dampness in the house can be reduced only by (1) providing some means of absorbing moisture, such as built-up litter, (2) raising the inside air temperature by a small amount of artificial heat, or (3) providing sufficient insulation to retain the heat which the hens themselves produce.

Suppose, however, that the outside temperature is 15° F. with a relative humidity of 75 per cent, while the inside temperature is 35°, and that one wishes to keep the inside relative humidity from going above 75 per cent.   If outside air is moved through the hen house at a not too rapid rate, it will be warmed to 35° and its capacity for carrying moisture will be more than doubled.   At 15° and 75 per cent relative humidity, it would be carrying 0.75 grain of moisture per cubic foot (see Fig. 7–6).   After being warmed to 35° it can carry 1.8 grains at the same relative humidity.   Each cubic foot passed through the house can therefore pick up an extra grain of moisture, provided the rate of air movement is slow enough to prevent an appreciable drop in the temperature of the inside air.   (If the incoming air is saturated, it will carry 1.0 grain per cubic foot at 15° F. It can then pick up but 0.8 grain more at 35° and 75 per cent relative humidity.   But at a maximum of 85 per cent relative humidity, it could still pick up 1 grain per cubic foot.)

Assume that the foregoing conditions exist in a 40 × 40 foot pen or house 7 feet high and containing 500 4½-pound hens. The respiratory moisture given off by the flock, calculated at 0.6 milligram per hour per gram of live weight (see Fig. 7–7), will amount to 226,300 grains in twenty-four hours.   If moisture released from the droppings is taken as 6 pounds per 100 hens per day, this will amount to additional 210,000 grains each twenty-four hours, making a total of 436,300 grains of moisture to be removed.   At one grain per cubic foot of air, it will take 18,100 cubic feet per hour, over 36 cubic feet per hen per hour, or 1.6 complete changes of air per hour, to remove the water vapor.   This is a very moderate rate of air movement. In tightly constructed windowless houses which have pressurized ventilation systems, it is not unusual to provide as much as 6 or 8 cubic feet of air change per hen per minute.   The hens in such houses are usually in cages, and the total air space per layer may be no more than 8 cubic feet.   With pressurized ventilation there is no evidence of drafts inside the house.

INSULATION

The heat production of a fasting hen at rest is about 2.75 gram calories per hour per gram of live weight.   For a 4½-pound (2041-gram) hen this amounts to 5613 gram calories or 22 B.t.u. per hour.

11

Normal activity will cause an increase in heat production, and feed consumption will cause an additional increase proportional to the amount of dry matter consumed. The activity increment is usually estimated at about half the basal heat production, though for hens in cages it may be no more than one-third. A 50 per cent increase would add 11 B.t.u. per hour in this example. For hens laying at a high rate—75 or 80 per cent—and consuming about 24 pounds of feed per 100 hens per day, the increase in heat production due to feeding would be about 11 B.t.u. per hen per hour. This calculation assumes 91 per cent of dry matter in the feed and a heating effect of 68 kilocalories per 100 grams of dry matter consumed. Adding the three values $(22 + 11 + 11)$ brings the total heat production of such hens to 44 B.t.u. per hour. For hens in cages we would have $(22 + 7 + 11 =)$ 40 B.t.u. per hour.

This is of necessity an approximation because of the variation in activity and feed consumption among individual hens, because of the regular diurnal variation in basal heat production with a minimum at about 8 P.M. and a maximum at 8 A.M., and because of reduced heat production during the variable roosting period. Furthermore, a reduction must be made to allow for the latent heat of vaporization, because of moisture in the expired air, which is not available for warming the air of the poultry house. At winter temperatures of 30° to 40° this is about 8 per cent of the total heat production. Deducting this from 44 leaves a figure of 40.5 B.t.u. per hen per hour, or 97,200 B.t.u. per 100 hens per day, which will be used in the examples to follow.

The lower total heat production of 4-pound hens is, in practice, partly offset by common procedure of keeping more such hens in a house or pen of given size. If hens are laying at a lower rate than is here assumed, the total feed consumption will be less, and the total heat production will therefore be lower. On the other hand, the amount of moisture to be removed by ventilation will also be lower.

Insulation Needed

In a 20 × 20 foot house 7 feet high, the combined wall and roof area is about 960 square feet. Adding 40 square feet to allow for the extra heat loss through the usual window area gives 1,000 square feet of exposed area, or 10 square feet per hen. The heat production just calculated amounts, then, to 4 B.t.u. per hour per square foot of combined wall and roof area. If walls and roof consist of a single layer of siding and roll roofing, the insulating value is about 2. By definition, this means that with a difference in temperature between inside and outside air of only 2° F., and with no direct ventilation, that is, with the house tightly closed, the heat loss will be 1 B.t.u. per hour through each square foot of exposed area. A flock of 100 hens on full feed could therefore maintain the inside air temperature of such a house at $(2 \times 4 =)$ 8° above that of the outside air. With the necessary minimum amount of ventilation, the difference would be somewhat less, and at winter temperatures of 15° F. or below, the hens would be very uncomfortable.

If the outdoor temperature is likely to average around 5° for days at a time, and if the minimum inside temperature is to be held at 40°, it will be necessary to increase the insulating value from 2 to (35/4 =) 8.7 in order for the hens to be able to maintain this greater temperature difference without the aid of artificial heat. Furthermore, this assumes a tightly closed house, with no consideration of the problem of moisture removal.

It is well to remember that insulation alone sometimes creates a ventilation problem which did not previously exist, and that it is much easier to work out the practical relationships with large flocks than with small ones. If, for example, we apply the foregoing assumed conditions to a flock of 500 hens in a 40 × 40 house instead of to 100 hens in a 20 × 20 house, we will have (500 × 40.5 =) 20,250 B.t.u. per hour for 2,880 square feet of combined wall and ceiling area, or 7 B.t.u. per square foot instead of 4. Conversely, with a flock of 25 hens in a 10 × 10 house, the heat available would be only 2.6 B.t.u. for each square foot of wall and ceiling area, thus making the insulation problem very much more difficult.

POULTRY HOUSE DESIGN

To combine the data on heat production, moisture removal, and insulation for the purpose of hen house design, it is necessary to include at least one other factor, namely, the amount of heat required to warm the outside air used for ventilation. At temperatures in the 35° to 40° range, it will take 1 B.t.u. per degree of rise for each 50 cubic feet of air. Hence, if the volume of air moved through a hen house in one hour is 5,000 cubic feet, and if the difference in temperature between inside and outside air is 10° F., there must be sufficient heat available to permit 1,000 B.t.u. per hour to be used in warming the outside air, or the inside air will soon drop to the same temperature as the incoming air.

It is possible to combine all the foregoing related factors into a heat balance equation or formula as follows:

Let H = the heat available, in this case the B.t.u. of sensible heat produced per hen per hour

D = the difference between inside and outside air temperature in degrees Fahrenheit

A = the combined wall and ceiling area exposed to heat loss, in square feet per hen, with due allowance for glass area

R = the insulating value of the walls and ceiling (or roof)

V = the volume of air change in cubic feet per hen per hour

50 = the cubic feet of air warmed 1 degree F. by 1 B.t.u.

For balanced conditions, the sum of $VD/50$ and AD/R must not exceed the value of H. Hence, $H = VD/50 + AD/R$, or $H/D = V/50 + A/R$.

Since the unknown factor is often the amount of air change permissible for a given temperature difference, the formula can be transformed to read $V = 50(H/D - A/R)$. In our example of 500 hens in a 40 × 40 house 7 feet high, assuming an insulating value (R value) of 8 and a temperature difference of 25 degrees, we would have $V = 50(40.5/25 - 5.76/8)$, or 45 cubic feet of air per hen per hour. The total volume of air in the house amounts to 22.4 cubic feet per hen, and therefore $(45/22.4 =)$ 2 changes per hour can take place without decreasing the specified 25° difference in temperature. Since we have already found that 1.6 changes, or 36 cubic feet per hen per hour, will be sufficient to remove the calculated amount of moisture, no further computations are necessary.

If, however, we should decide to put 1,000 hens in the 40 × 40 house, allowing only 1.6 square feet of floor area per hen, as is often done with large flocks, most of the figures will change. Respiratory moisture will double to 452,000 grains in twenty-four hours, and moisture from the droppings will also double to 420,000 grains, making a total of 872,000 grains. At one grain per cubic foot, 3.25 changes per hour or 36,333 cubic feet per hour will be needed to remove the water vapor. Note that this is still 36 cubic feet per hen per hour. In the heat balance equation we will have $V = 50(40.5/25 - 2.88/8)$, or a maximum of 63 cubic feet of air per hen per hour which can be drawn from the outside without lowering the air temperature inside the house. The volume of air per hen is now 11.2 cubic feet, permitting 5.6 changes per hour.

The heat balance equation can be used in other ways. Suppose, for example, that we have a 40 × 40 house 7 feet high with an overall R value of 12, and that we want to know what temperature can be maintained inside by a flock of 1,000 $4\frac{1}{2}$-pound hens when the outside temperature falls to 0° F. Our transformed equation will be $D = H/(V/50 + A/R)$. Using the values already calculated, we can substitute them in the equation so that it will read $D = 40.5/(36/50 + 2.88/12)$. Solving this gives 42° as the answer we were after.

Similarly, we might want to determine the required R value under some assumed set of conditions. For a specific example, assume a building that is 30 × 150 feet and 7 feet high, that we want to keep in it a flock of 3,000 $4\frac{1}{2}$-pound hens, and that we want to be able to maintain indoor temperatures in winter at 40° F. above the outdoor temperature. For simplicity, we can use the values that we have previously calculated for the $4\frac{1}{2}$-pound hen, and we will set up the equation in the form $R = A/(H/D - V/50)$. When we substitute known values it will read $R = 2.34/(40.5/40 - 36/50)$. Solving, we arrive at an R value of 8.

Metric Units

To see what some of these relationships look like when expressed in metric units, assume a flock of 400 2-kilogram hens in a windowless house that is 10 × 10 meters and 2.4 meters high. The volume of air would be 240 cubic meters, or 0.6 cubic meter per hen. The floor area would be 0.25 square meter per hen, and the total area exposed to heat loss would be 196 square meters, or 0.49 square meter per hen. Call it 0.5 for easy calculation.

Total feed intake of a flock of 400 2-kilogram hens laying at the rate of 75 to 80 per cent, and fed a typical high-energy ration, will be about 44 kilograms a day. The amount of manure voided will therefore be about 53 to 57 kilograms. If we use the midpoint between these two values and assume that 20 per cent will become free water in the hen house, there will be about 11 kilograms of water a day to create dampness.

Total air breathed by fowls at rest in a comfortable environment is about 28 cubic decimeters (.028 cubic meter) per hen per hour. For 400 2-kilogram hens this would be about 270 cubic meters every twenty-four hours.

The respiratory moisture given off by such a flock, calculated at 0.6 milligram per gram of live weight per hour, will amount to 11,520 grams in twenty-four hours. If moisture from the droppings is taken as 11 kilograms and added to the respiratory moisture, there will be a total of 22,520 grams to be removed. At 2.3 grams per cubic meter (the equivalent of 1 grain per cubic foot which we used previously), it will require 410 cubic meters per hour, equal to one cubic meter per hen per hour, or 1.6 complete changes of air per hour, to remove the water vapor.

The heat production of fasting hens at rest is about 2.75 gram-calories per hour per gram of live weight. For a 2-kilogram hen this amounts to 5,500 gram-calories per hour. Adding 50 per cent for normal activity and 2,810 gram-calories for the heating effect of feed (assuming 91 per cent dry matter in the feed and a heating effect of 68 kilogram-calories for each 100 grams of dry matter consumed), brings the total for each hen to 11,160 gram-calories per hour. Subtracting 8 per cent for latent heat in the expired air leaves 10,175 gram-calories per hen per hour. For our 400-hen flock this will amount to nearly 98,000 kilogram-calories per day.

To adapt the heat balance equation to metric units we will have:

H = heat avilable in kilogram-calories of sensible heat per hen per hour (10.2)

D = difference between inside and outside temperature in degrees Centigrade (specified as 15 in this example)

A = combined wall and ceiling area exposed to heat loss, expressed as square meters per hen (0.5)

R = insulating value. When expressed as the temperature difference in degrees Centigrade that will just permit a heat loss of 1 kilogram-calorie per hour through each square meter of exposed surface, our previous value of 8 in British units becomes 5.34 in metric units.

V = volume of air change in cubic meters per hen per hour

50 cubic feet of air warmed 1° F. by 1 B.t.u. is equivalent to 3.125 cubic meters of air warmed 1° C. by 1 kilogram-calorie.

Instead of $V = 50(H/D—A/R)$ we will have $V = 3.125(H/D—A/R)$. After substituting the new values we will have $V = 3.125$ (10.2/15—0.5/5.34) which gives 1.8 for the value of V. Since the total volume of air in the house is (240/400 =) 0.6 cubic meter per hen, we will have (1.8/0.6 =) 3 changes of air per hour that can occur with no reduction in the 15-degree difference specified as a minimum. This is well above the 1.6 changes required to remove the calculated amount of water vapor.

Under some conditions it may be practical to devise means for making use of artificial heat instead of building such well-insulated houses. This is apparent if one considers the fact that the sensible heat produced by a flock of 500 hens in twenty-four hours is no more than the calculated heat of combustion of 40 pounds of good coal. Such a comparison neglects the practical problem of heat distribution, and it makes no allowance for flue losses, but it helps to emphasize the fact that it is impossible for a flock of hens to keep a poorly insulated house warm and dry in severe winter weather.

The application of the foregoing discussion to practical conditions may be summed up in the following recommendations for procedures which will aid in keeping hens comfortable in cold weather, without the use of artificial heat. They are listed in their approximate order of importance.

1. Build large houses rather than small. Make them 30 or 40 feet deep instead of 20. Use long houses with several pens rather than several smaller houses, and thereby reduce total exposed area subject to heat loss. For large flocks, use 2-story or 3-story houses for the same reason.
2. Insulate the ceiling or roof in order to reduce heat loss in winter and lessen the absorption of solar heat in summer. In a large single-story house, the ceiling or roof represents a much higher percentage of the total area exposed to heat loss than it does in a small house.
3. Use deep or built-up litter as an aid in temporary absorption of moisture given off by the hens. (Does not apply to cage installations.)
4. Control ventilation so that heat is conserved during the period of low night temperatures while the hens are relatively inactive. Humidity will rise, but it can be corrected during the daytime when the sun's heat will help dry out the house.

The aim of the foregoing procedures is to maintain hen house temperatures above freezing at all times, and to maintain a minimum difference between inside and outside temperatures of 20° F. A secondary consideration is to keep the relative humidity down to 80 or 75 per cent, and the moisture content of the litter down to

40 per cent. These latter conditions are more important from the standpoint of preventing dirty eggs than from their effect on egg production.

HOUSE CONSTRUCTION

The purpose in building a poultry house is to furnish the greatest possible comfort to the flock at the least possible cost per bird. Just where the law of diminishing returns comes in with reference to the grade of lumber and the class of skilled labor employed for the construction, is a matter of judgment in individual cases.

F ɪɢ. 7–8.—A two-story hen house with a 6-inch fill of wood shavings for insulation in side walls and roof. When outside temperatures ranged from 0° to 20° F,. the inside temperature was maintained at 45° to 55°. (Courtesy of Minnesota Agricultural Experiment Station.)

It is, of course, possible to err in creating an unjustifiable overhead by building an expensive house, as is not infrequently done. Just as possible and as frequent is an overeagerness to save money on first costs by using poor material and unskilled labor which is usually followed by an undue depreciation and an unsatisfactory house.

Factory-Built Houses

The easiest way to acquire a poultry house is to purchase one, complete with insulation, a ventilating system, and all equipment, and have it erected by the manufacturer. This is one of the recent developments in egg farming, especially in parts of the country where complete control of environment is essential to successful flock management. It is also becoming a common practice in some broiler areas.

One important reason for the growing interest in such plans is that a flock owner can be sure of the full cost in advance instead of having to depend on his own or a contractor's estimate. A second reason, important to many operators, is that financing is often easier to arrange because the entire transaction is carried out with one supplier. This can also be an advantage to the buyer when something goes wrong within the guarantee period. Furthermore, the factory-built house is likely to go up in less time than will be involved with local contracting. The cost of such a house will vary with size as well as with the type and amount of equipment included, but in 1965 the average cost was about $3.00 per hen capacity, with a range of perhaps 50 cents above and below that figure.

Many poultrymen, however, prefer to build their own houses and to select and install the necessary equipment. Some of the important considerations in poultry house construction will therefore be presented briefly in the following pages.

Foundations

A good foundation must be solid enough to support the building, deep enough to prevent heaving by frost, and high enough above grade to keep out surface water. In order to leave room for the opening and shutting of doors where a deep litter is used, the top of the foundation must be at least 6 inches above the floor level. This brings the tops of the door sills 8 or more inches above the floor. If for some reason it is necessary to locate the house where the texture of the ground is such that it tends to hold moisture, a tile placed even with the bottom and just at the outside of the foundation, and furnished with a suitable outlet is a necessary precaution if the house is to be dry.

Floors

The hen-house floor must be moisture proof, free from cracks, and easily cleaned. It should be rat-proof and durable. A board floor, if properly laid, is free from cracks and is easily cleaned and disinfected. It is not a durable floor when compared with concrete, and it is not rat-proof unless raised well off the ground. While the air space below such a floor effectively stops capillary moisture, there are many times during the year when circulation of cold air beneath the house may make the floor so cold as to cause condensation of moisture from the warmer air inside the house. This "sweating" of the floor is a common cause of wet litter.

Concrete floors are dry if properly constructed. They are sanitary, durable and rat-proof. They are not cold when properly bedded with litter. In many parts of the country they have a valuable equalizing effect on the temperature inside the poultry house. The temperature of a wood floor remains within about 2° F. of the outside air temperature, for a temperature range of 25° to 95° F. A concrete floor, on the other hand, may be from 5° to 7° warmer than the air at low temperatures, and as much as 15° cooler than the air temperature when the latter is 90° to 95° F. This is a point of considerable importance in keeping fowls comfortable during hot weather.

In recent years the slat floor has become popular in some sections of the country.   Slats may be used for the entire floor area, or they may cover only about half the floor, usually in a strip down the center of a long house.   In any case the slat portion is raised high enough above a subfloor to provide a pit for the accumulation of manure. Such pits are often equipped with mechanical scrapers for periodic removal of manure.   In some of the larger installations they are deep enough to permit removal of manure by the use of a tractor with scraper blade.

Dirt floors and deep litter are sometimes used in broiler houses. They are much less expensive than other types of floors, and many growers have been well satisfied with them.   The entire accumulation of litter and manure is removed after each lot of broilers is sold or, in some instances, only after three or four lots have been grown.

Fig. 7–9.—A custom-built windowless, pressure-ventilated house for 70,000 broilers. (Courtesy of Bill Brown Company, Rogers, Arkansas.)

Walls and Partitions

The walls and partitions must be solid enough to support the roof and withstand heavy winds.   Wide variation is possible in the use of construction materials, depending on availability, cost, and the insulating value desired.   The recent trend has been to eliminate partitions in many of the larger houses, thereby making larger pens. This makes it necessary to give particular attention to strength of the overall structure in order to avoid danger of collapse from heavy snow loads or in windstorms.

Insulation

It has become common practice to use some type of insulation in the construction of houses built for flocks of commercial size.   Roof insulation helps in both summer and winter.   Wall insulation is added in the colder parts of the country, the kind and amount depending on the length of the winter season and the expected minimum temperatures.   Insulation values for various types of wall

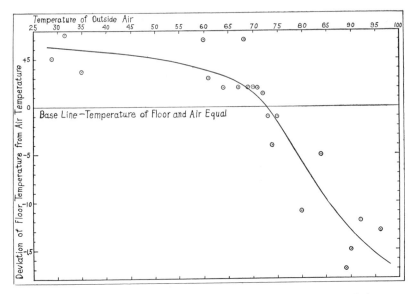

F IG. 7–10.—Curve showing difference between floor temperature and air temperature in a house with a concrete floor. (Courtesy of Maryland Agricultural Experiment Station.)

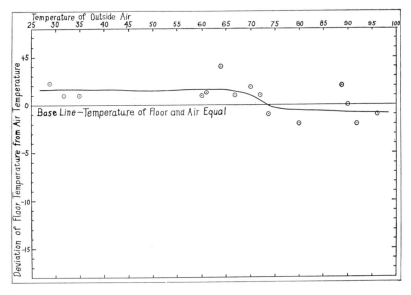

F IG. 7–11.—Curve showing difference between floor temperature and air temperature in a house with a board floor. The temperature of a wood floor tends to follow closely the temperature of the outside air. (Courtesy of Maryland Agricultural Experiment Station.)

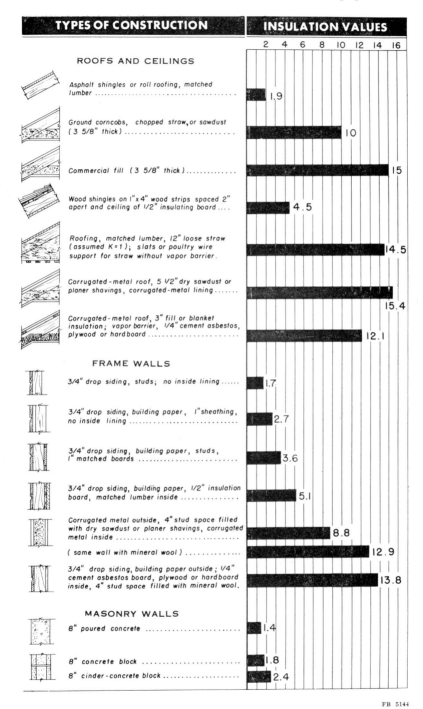

TYPES OF CONSTRUCTION

INSULATION VALUES

2 4 6 8 10 12 14 16

ROOFS AND CEILINGS

Asphalt shingles or roll roofing, matched lumber 1.9

Ground corncobs, chopped straw, or sawdust (3 5/8" thick) 10

Commercial fill (3 5/8" thick) 15

Wood shingles on 1"x4" wood strips spaced 2" apart and ceiling of 1/2" insulating board 4.5

Roofing, matched lumber, 12" loose straw (assumed K=1); slats or poultry wire support for straw without vapor barrier. 14.5

Corrugated-metal roof, 5 1/2" dry sawdust or planer shavings, corrugated-metal lining 15.4

Corrugated-metal roof, 3" fill or blanket insulation; vapor barrier, 1/4" cement asbestos, plywood or hardboard 12.1

FRAME WALLS

3/4" drop siding, studs; no inside lining 1.7

3/4" drop siding, building paper, 1"sheathing, no inside lining 2.7

3/4" drop siding, building paper, studs, 1" matched boards 3.6

3/4" drop siding, building paper, 1/2" insulation board, matched lumber inside 5.1

Corrugated metal outside, 4" stud space filled with dry sawdust or planer shavings, corrugated metal inside 8.8

(same wall with mineral wool) 12.9

3/4" drop siding, building paper outside; 1/4" cement asbestos board, plywood or hardboard inside, 4" stud space filled with mineral wool. 13.8

MASONRY WALLS

8" poured concrete 1.4

8" concrete block 1.8

8" cinder-concrete block 2.4

FB 5144

FIG. 7–12.—Insulation values (R values) for some common types of wall and ceiling construction. (Prepared by the U. S. Department of Agriculture.)

and roof construction are shown in Figure 7–12. The numerical values refer to the difference in degrees Fahrenheit which can exist between the warm and cold sides of a wall while just permitting 1 B.t.u. of heat to pass through an area of one square foot in one hour. This is commonly referred to as the "R" value, for resistance to heat loss, and some types of insulating material are stamped by the manufacturer to show the R value. For technical purposes, engineers commonly use what is known as the "U" value, or co-efficient of heat transfer. It is the reciprocal of the R value. R values of 2, 4, 8 and 12 are equivalent to U values of .5, .25, .125 and .0833, respectively. R values commonly recommended in the several temperature zones shown in Figure 7–1 are:

Zone	Walls	Ceiling
1-N	15	20
1-S	10	15
2-N & S	8	12
3-N & S	2–3	8
4-N & S	1	4

Vapor Barriers

Condensation of moisture within an insulated wall greatly reduces the insulating value, and may permanently injure certain types of insulating material. It is therefore important to use a vapor barrier of some sort on the inner or warm side of the insulation in order to prevent condensation at such times as the temperature falls below the dew point. This may consist of lightweight roll roofing, aluminum foil, polyethylene film and asphalt-coated paper, or two coats of asphalt or aluminum-flake paint. Some types of commercial insulating material are made with a vapor barrier surface on one side. It is important that these be installed with the vapor barrier on the inside (warm side) of the wall or ceiling, and that the barrier not be torn or damaged during application.

Windows and Ventilators

It is customary to use windows in a poultry house for both light and ventilation. Cross ventilation is especially important during warm summer weather. Proper ventilation by means of windows alone is often very difficult in cold weather.

Most commercial poultrymen today use ventilating fans to insure adequate air circulation during warm weather, and to control the rate of air change in cold weather. The capacity of fans should be sufficient to supply 6 or 7 cubic feet of air per minute per hen at $\frac{1}{8}$ inch static pressure. It is easy to make the mistake of installing fans that are too small. A common type in use in large houses is 36 inches in diameter with direct drive. Another popular type is a 24-inch turnabout fan rated at 4,000 cfm at $\frac{1}{8}$-inch static pressure.

Motors should be totally enclosed, and they should be equipped with thermal-overload circuit breakers.

Both pressurized and exhaust ventilation systems are satisfactory. With a pressurized system, fans are commonly located in an attic so that they force air into the main part of the house through holes distributed over the ceiling. Exhaust fans, on the other hand, are commonly located in the side walls of the house, usually near the ceiling. It is very important to keep exhaust fans free of dust and feathers. This applies not only to the motor housing and blades but to the screened opening as well. Intake fans are less of a problem in this respect, and this is one reason why pressurized systems are preferred by many flock owners.

Standby generators, either self-powered or tractor-driven, provide excellent insurance against costly drops in egg production resulting from power failure. It is particularly important that ventilation systems in windowless houses continue to operate without interruption, but the standby unit can also be used to keep lighting systems, automatic feeders, water systems, and egg collection belts in operation. Any standby generator should be checked regularly to make sure that it will function properly if a power failure should occur.

Roofs

Composition roll roofing is the material most commonly used for poultry house roofs. It is draft and moisture proof, is easy to apply, and is relatively inexpensive. It must be properly laid, and it needs regular attention and occasional recoating, if it is to last more than a few years. It makes a house extremely hot in summer unless the roof is insulated or the roofing is coated with a reflecting type paint.

Aluminum roof coatings, including exterior type aluminum foil, are being successfully used to reduce interior summer temperatures. Differences of 5° or 6° become important when exterior temperatures are high.

Built-up roofs, which consist of several layers of roofing paper cemented down with hot asphalt, are popular in some parts of the country, especially for roofs which have a very slight pitch.

Metal roofs are increasing in popularity because of their lasting quality. Less lumber is needed to support a metal roof than for composition roofing. It is advisable to use insulation under a metal roof in order to make the house cooler in summer, and to prevent moisture condensation in winter.

Remodeling

It is often more economical to remodel an existing barn or other building than to build a new hen house, and some of the most practical hen houses in use for both farm and commercial flocks are of this sort. If the remodeled building meets the requirements stated earlier in this chapter it may be just as satisfactory as a new house, and much less expensive.

POULTRY-HOUSE EQUIPMENT

Those pieces of equipment which are built in as a part of the house should be simple, few in number, adequate in size, removable for cleaning, and conveniently and systematically placed so that their care will take a minimum of labor.

Fig. 7–13.—One-story house for layers, with bulk feed tanks conveniently located. (Courtesy of Creighton Brothers, Warsaw, Indiana.)

Nests

The desirable qualities of a nest are that it be roomy, easily cleaned and sprayed, dark, cool and well ventilated, and conveniently located.

Dark nests are preferred because the hen likes seclusion for laying. Dark nests also reduce the likelihood of egg eating. Some arrangement for shutting the fowls out at night prevents them from roosting in the nests and fouling them. This they are prone to do, especially at molting time, in order to escape being crowded by other birds on the perch.

Some poultrymen like the "community" type of nest, which is really a covered box about 2 feet wide and 6 feet long. It has no partitions, and there is an opening at each end through which the hens may enter and leave. A sloping cover is hinged for convenience in gathering the eggs. Such nests are often built on legs so that the entire unit can be moved out from the wall for better ventilation during hot weather. Each community nest will replace 10 or 12 individual open nests.

Community type nests are available as commercial units about four feet long, with wire mesh floors. At least one manufacturer provides an automatic device for closing the nests in late afternoon, gently pushing out any hens that may be occupying the nests as roosting quarters.

Trap Nests.—These differ from open nests in that each one is provided with a trap door by means of which a bird shuts herself

FIG. 7–14.—This two-story windowless house with aluminum siding accommodates 40,000 layers.   (Courtesy of New York State College of Agriculture at Cornell University.)

FIG. 7–15.—Slatted floor house on the farm of Franklin Steury, Berne, Indiana.
(J. C. Allen and Son Photo.)

FIG. 7–16.—Part litter and part slatted floor is another common arrangement. (Courtesy of Automatic Poultry Feeder Company.)

FIG. 7–17.—Interior of a windowless, insulated, power-ventilated and fully automated house with slat floor. (Courtesy of Chore-Time Equipment, Inc., Milford, Indiana.)

in when she enters.   They are the accepted means of securing accurate individual egg records and are an essential part of the equipment for pedigree breeding where more than one female is continuously mated with one male.

They are of many different styles.   First in importance is their dependability as to accuracy, though it is hardly less important that they be comfortable and attractive, if floor eggs are to be avoided.

No trap nest is a comfortable place in extremely hot weather unless every effort has been made to have it abundantly ventilated. This may even require nest floors of hardware cloth and the discarding of the use of nest bedding for a time, allowing the birds to lay on the bare wire.   There should be one trap nest for every 3 hens.

Perches

In order to insure comfort the perches should allow from 8 to 10 inches of room for each bird and be 15 to 18 inches apart.   The most common material used for perches is 2 by 3 or 2 by 4 inch lumber. This may be laid on the side or placed on edge.   In either case it is well to round the upper edges.

Fig. 7–18.—One type of automatic feeding equipment.
(Courtesy of Chore-Time Equipment, Inc.)

Feeding Equipment

The design of feeding equipment varies considerably on different farms and in different parts of the country. No matter what style of construction is used, the feeding devices should be easy to fill, easy to clean, built to avoid waste, so arranged that the fowls cannot roost on them, and constructed in such a manner that so long as they contain any feed at all the fowls will be able to reach it. From the standpoint of practical results it is essential that ample feeding space be provided. A safe rule to follow is to have 1 foot of hopper feeding space for every 5 hens.

Automatic or mechanical feeders are standard equipment on large commercial egg and broiler farms. They save a great deal of labor and keep fresh feed available to the fowls at all times. Uninterrupted service is as important with feeders as with lights and ventilating fans, and some sort of standby generating equipment should be provided for use in the event of power failures.

Fig. 7–19.—Interior arrangement of a 70 × 360 slat floor house for 25,000 layers, as used by Creighton Brothers, Warsaw, Indiana. (Courtesy of Chore-Time Equipment, Inc.)

Watering Devices

A perfect watering device should keep the water clean and cool in warm weather, and be of such construction that it may be easily cleaned and that freezing will not destroy its usefulness. To keep water clean the watering equipment should be high enough so that litter will not be scratched into it, and so located that the fowls cannot contaminate it with droppings.

In houses which lack sufficient insulation to prevent freezing, soil heating cable may be used to protect water pipes. A thermostat should be used to shut off the current at some predetermined point, say 35° F., to prevent needless use of electric current. Proper installation, with suitable ground connections, is highly important from a safety standpoint.

FIG. 7–20.—Community-type nest with egg conveyor located along the front. The system can be extended to a complete loop in a 350-foot house. Note the panel which is time-clock controlled to close the nests in late afternoon. (Courtesy of Storm Industries, Inc., Dassel, Minnesota.)

Fig. 7–21.—Egg collection belts in a single-deck installation in California. (Courtesy of Jamesway Division, Butler Manufacturing Co.)

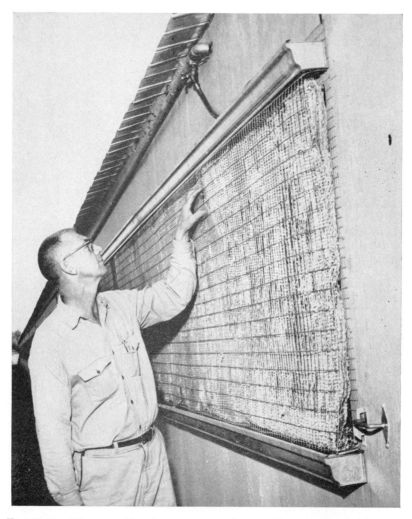

FIG. 7–22.—Water trickles down over this 36-inch high excelsior pad through which air is drawn into a 60 × 380 foot house for 33,000 layers on the ranch of Herb den Dulk, Ripon, California. Eighteen 36-inch fans of 10,800 cfm capacity can effect a complete air change in one and one-half minutes. (Courtesy of Pacific Poultryman.)

FIG. 7–23.—Mechanical removal of droppings helps to reduce moisture in a large hen house. Creighton Brothers Poultry Farm, Warsaw, Indiana. (J. C. Allen and Son Photo.)

FIG. 7–24.—This long bin is used with an electric stirrer for drying poultry manure on a California farm. (Courtesy of Pacific Poultryman.)

Automatic watering devices are important from the standpoint of saving labor. Shallow V-shaped troughs running the entire length of the hen house and carrying a constant flow of water are very satisfactory for large flocks.

Laying Cages

There are some sections of the country where more layers are kept in cages than in the conventional type of house with litter or slat floors. Some installations provide a single cage for each hen. Others are designed for two, three or four layers per cage, and a few are of the community-cage type, with as many as 25 layers in each cage.

Fig. 7–25.—Shade is provided by a lattice connecting the eaves of two 34 × 228 foot cage houses in California. (Courtesy of Pacific Poultryman.)

In some houses there is a single tier or deck of cages over the entire floor area, while in others the cages are two tiers high. Automatic watering equipment is essential, but feeding may be either automatic or manual. Eggs commonly roll to the front of the cages where they are collected by hand, but some installations have egg collecting belts.

With single deck installations, manure accumulates on the floor and is removed at regular intervals. Tiered cages may be provided with belts for conveying manure to one end of the house, or with platforms that can be cleaned with mechanical scrapers.

In some parts of southern California, where freezing temperatures are the exception and little protection from cold is needed, outdoor laying cages have become popular. As many as one-fourth of all layers in some areas are housed in this manner.

FIG. 7–26.—Pipe with foggers rests on gravel between two cage houses in California. Such equipment is very important for keeping layers comfortable during hot weather. (Courtesy of Pacific Poultryman.)

FIG. 7–27.—This 2000-gallon vacuum tank can be filled with liquid manure in four minutes. Such equipment must have a full-opening, non-restricted slide valve. In the field, the load is blown out against a baffle to spread a strip 16 to 20 feet wide. (Courtesy of New York State College of Agriculture at Cornell University.)

FIG. 7–28.—This spinner-type sprayer has an auger in the bottom. When used with a tractor and power take-off, it will handle either liquid or semi-liquid manure, spreading a strip 20 feet wide. (Courtesy of New York State College of Agriculture at Cornell University.)

FIG. 7–29.—Three-wheel manure cleaning machine used under cages by Willis Hollowell, Ramona, California. (Courtesy of Pacific Poultryman.)

All that is necessary in the way of construction is a roof over the cages and some kind of framework to hold the cages off the ground. Many variations in watering and feeding arrangements are possible, but most are aimed at making it possible to do the necessary labor of caring for the hens and gathering the eggs in a minimum amount of time. Some operators have been able to keep labor time down to 0.7 hour per hen per year, but the average is nearer one hour, which compares favorably with the time required under conventional methods of housing.

Fig. 7–30.—Manure cleaning machine in use to scrape manure from beneath cages on Willis Hollowell ranch, Ramona, California. (Courtesy of Pacific Poultryman.)

Certain management problems, such as cannibalism, damp litter and trap-nesting are completely solved by the use of laying cages. On the other hand, there are certain new problems to meet. The percentage of cracked eggs is sometimes rather high. There will be few very dirty eggs, but a large number may be slightly soiled.

Protection from excessive heat is often a problem where the outdoor cages are used, and rather elaborate sprinkling systems are sometimes necessary to prevent serious death losses when summer temperatures often range from 95° to 105° in the middle of the day.

One of the interesting and important practical findings in the management of caged layers is that there are marked differences between strains of fowls in their adaptability to close confinement in laying batteries. Without doubt this is a limiting factor in the profitable operation of such plants. Numerous engineering problems in connection with lighting, ventilation, heating and humidity have also been met and not all of them have as yet been completely solved.

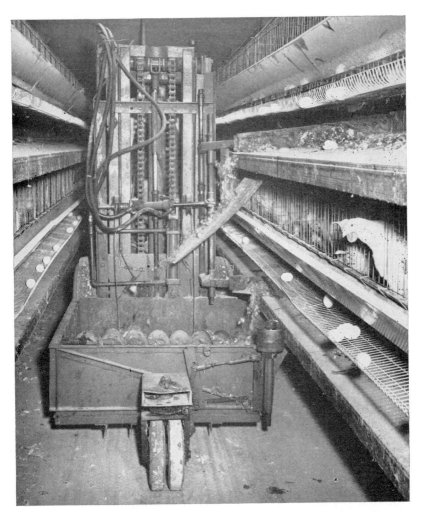

Fig. 7–31.—Machine used by Ray Fisher, Lathrop, California, for cleaning under double-deck cages. (Courtesy of Pacific Poultryman.)

Fig. 7–32.—Poultry manure is composted in this insulated steel drum 100 feet long and 10 feet in diameter, with a capacity of 250,000 pounds of material. The drum revolves slowly, completing the composting in five to seven days, with an end-product that contains about 3 per cent nitrogen, 6 per cent phosphoric acid and 2 per cent potash. (Courtesy of Pacific Poultryman.)

CARE OF THE HOUSE

A successful poultry house must be clean, reasonably dry, well ventilated and, above all, comfortable for the hens. Good management aimed at maintaining these conditions will pay dividends in sustained production.

Types of Litter

An important point in maintaining comfortable conditions in the poultry house is having the right kind of litter. Many different materials are used for this purpose, depending largely on what is locally available. Among the materials in common use in different sections of the country are straw, shavings, ground corn cobs, cotton-seed hulls, peat moss, shredded corn stalks, shredded sugar cane, oat hulls, and sawdust. Ground corn cobs head the list of desirable farm-produced litters.

In a series of tests at the Delaware station, in which more than 66,000 broilers were used, sawdust was consistently lowest in cost per 1,000 broilers, of the twelve litter materials tested. It was readily available in the area—an important practical consideration—but its moisture content frequently was too high at the time of purchase to make it wholly satisfactory. Peanut shells, ground corn cobs, peat moss and sugar cane fiber were all ranked above sawdust except for cost. Pens containing mineral-type litters were often dusty.

Built-up Litter

When all grain is hopper-fed it is important to have a litter which does not pack readily. Ground or crushed cobs, shavings, and sawdust meet this requirement, and are well adapted to use as deep or built-up litter. Built-up litter provides a warm floor. For this reason it is especially well adapted for use in the northern sections of the country. If kept in good condition, it will absorb considerable moisture on days when the humidity is high, and release it on following dry days. Maintaining deep litter takes much less labor, in spite of necessary stirring, than is required to renew shallow litter at frequent intervals in order to keep it reasonably dry. Finally, there is some advantage to be gained by the fact that fowls can pick up from the litter some products of intestinal synthesis which may simplify the feeding problem. Such built-up litter need not be cleaned out oftener than once a year, and some poultrymen continue to use it for two years or longer.

The usual procedure with deep litter is to start in the fall with two to four inches of dry litter, and add to this gradually until the floor is covered eight to ten inches deep by about the first of December. After that no more litter is added, but the old litter is stirred occasionally to keep it in good condition. It may be removed and replaced with clean, shallow litter in the late spring, or it may be left in until the regular fall cleaning.

Adding hydrated lime to deep litter will help to keep it in workable condition so that it is less likely to pack down. The amount of lime used varies from 15 to 25 pounds for each 100 square feet of floor area. It should be distributed evenly and then worked into the litter by stirring. Additional applications can be made from time to time as necessary.

Old built-up litter, whether limed or unlimed, contains fewer yeasts, molds and bacteria than comparatively new litter. This is probably because of its increased alkalinity, pH of 8.0 or more.

Value and Preservation of Poultry Manure

Since poultry manure contains not only the feces but also the excretion of the kidneys, it is much richer in nitrogen than that of other domestic animals. Analyses of the urine obtained from catheterized fowls show that about 64 per cent of the urinary nitrogen is present as uric acid, and therefore very readily available to growing plants. By putrefaction it is very readily changed to ammonium carbonate. This means that as poultry manure is ordinarily handled, much of its nitrogen is liberated as ammonia and consequently lost as far as fertilizing value is concerned. Since the night droppings from 1,000 hens may easily amount to 20 tons a year, substantial savings can be made by proper treatment.

Workers at the New Jersey Station found that fresh manure produced by laying hens contained about 78 per cent moisture, 1 per cent nitrogen, 0.8 per cent phosphoric acid, and 0.5 per cent potash.

Untreated poultry manure lost a large percentage of its nitrogen as ammonia, especially in warm weather.

Superphosphate was the most effective material used to prevent loss of nitrogen, and the recommended rate of application was 100 pounds per ton of fresh manure.

Hydrated lime was the most effective deodorizer. It also had a marked effect in reducing nitrogen losses and in improving the handling qualities of the product. The recommended application is 100 to 200 pounds per ton of manure, or about $1\frac{1}{2}$ pounds per 100 hens per day if scattered over the droppings boards or in the space under roosting racks.

The Minnesota Extension Service recommends that approximately 250 pounds of 20 per cent superphosphate and 20 to 25 pounds of muriate of potash be mixed with each ton of manure in order to balance it for use on crop land. For spreading over the droppings beneath the roosts, it is recommended that $\frac{1}{2}$ pound of a similar mixture be used daily for each 100 hens. Labor can be saved by spreading a little less than 2 pounds of this mixture twice a week.

An egg farm with 100,000 layers will produce over 12 tons of manure a day, well over 4,000 tons a year. Even if the owner has sufficient crop land to make use of all this manure, the labor of handling is considerable. In some areas there are small contractors who make a business of cleaning layer and broiler houses for others at specified times. Some flock owners have developed extensive irrigation systems for handling the manure in liquid form, pumping it to fields through 5-inch or 6-inch pipe under fairly high pressure, and using nozzles for spreading. Others use truck-mounted tanks which discharge the liquid manure in a plow furrow, covering it at the same time, thus controlling the odor problem and solving the fly problem at the same time. A few large operators, mainly in California, have worked out satisfactory methods of drying the manure so that it can be bagged and sold as fertilizer, but this is not a common practice.

Chapter 8

The Principles of Poultry Nutrition

THE transformation of plant, animal and mineral matter into forms highly prized as a source of food for man is the primary basis for the poultry industry. From a nutritional standpoint, the nutrients contained in a poultry feed are as useful to man as to a laying hen. However, as eggs or poultry meat, these nutrients are in a much more palatable form. For profitable poultry production, the conversion of feed to eggs and meat must be done efficiently and economically. To formulate rations that will do this, it is necessary to know something of the food nutrients and their use by the fowl.

THE NUTRIENTS

Many microorganisms have very simple nutrient requirements. If they are given several mineral elements, water, a source of nitrogen and a simple source of energy, they can synthesize all the chemical compounds they require for growth and reproduction. Fowls, as is the case with all higher animals, have much more complex nutrient needs. More than 40 specific chemical compounds or chemical elements are nutrients that need to be present in the diet to support life, growth and reproduction. These nutrients can be divided into six classes, somewhat according to their function and chemical nature: (1) water, (2) proteins, (3) carbohydrates, (4) fats, (5) vitamins and (6) minerals.

Most of the nutrients are absolutely essential for life. A ration must supply every known essential nutrient in the proper amounts. A ration containing all the nutrients except one will not support life. If an insufficient amount of the nutrient is present, the ration may support life but only very slow growth in the young, or not support reproduction in the adult.

The same nutrients found in a ration are also found in the body tissues and eggs of the fowl. There is not, however, a direct transfer of nutrients from the feed to the animal tissue. The nutrients must be digested, absorbed and rebuilt into the characteristic tissue of the animal. Poultry feeds are characteristically high in carbohydrates and relatively much lower in protein and fats. Body tissue and eggs, however, are composed chiefly of protein and fat with only very small amounts of carbohydrate. Thus the nutrients supplied in feed must undergo extensive processes of digestion and metabolism in the animal body.

Water

Water plays a highly important part in the digestion and metabolism of the fowl. (1) It is a constituent part of the body and of the contents of the egg, comprising from 55 to 75 per cent of the former and more than 65 per cent of the latter; (2) it serves to soften the feed in the crop, preparing it for maceration in the gizzard; (3) it aids and takes a part (hydrolysis) in the processes of digestion and absorption; (4) as an important constituent of the blood and lymph it serves as a carrier, transporting the end-products of digestion from the digestive tract to all parts of the body, and waste products from all parts of the body to the points of elimination; (5) it serves to cool the body by evaporation through the air sacs, lungs and skin, and to equalize the temperature of the various regions and parts.

Water usually forms from 8 to 12 per cent of the air-dry weight of most poultry rations. Water is also formed in the body by oxidation of the hydrogen of the organic nutrients. These sources combined, however, furnish but a small fraction of that required, which points to the necessity of a liberal supply beyond that furnished in the feed.

Proteins

Proteins are complex organic compounds containing carbon, hydrogen, oxygen, nitrogen and sulfur. They are made up of more than 20 individual organic compounds called amino acids. A protein molecule can be visualized as a long chain or several chains of amino acids joined together by linkages termed peptide bonds. Since an average protein contains about 16 per cent nitrogen, the protein content of a feed or carcass can be estimated by multiplying the nitrogen content by 6.25. Protein determined in this manner is often referred to as crude protein.

The properties of a protein molecule are determined by the number, kind and arrangement of the amino acids that make up the protein. With over 20 amino acids normally found in proteins, the possible arrangements into specific proteins are almost infinite. Proteins are also found combined with carbohydrates, fats, minerals, and other compounds that help to add to the complexity of proteins found in nature.

In feeding poultry, the products produced consist mainly of protein. On a dry-weight basis the carcass of an eight-week-old broiler is more than 65 per cent protein and the egg contents are about 50 per cent protein. Typical broiler rations will contain from 22 to 24 per cent protein and a laying feed about 16 to 17 per cent. There is a concentration of protein from diet to product in poultry feeding.

From the standpoint of nutrition, the amino acids that make up the protein are really the essential nutrients rather than the protein molecule itself. During digestion, dietary protein is broken down into individual amino acids which are then absorbed and rearranged into specific proteins found in body tissues or in egg proteins. Body and egg proteins are made up of the same amino acids as found in dietary proteins, although the proportion of the amino acids in tissue proteins may be quite different from that in the diet.

The tissues of the chicken have the ability to synthesize some of the amino acids found in proteins, provided they have a satisfactory source of dietary nitrogen. Many of the amino acids cannot be synthesized by body tissues and must be provided in the diet. The amino acids that must be provided in the diet are often referred to as *essential* amino acids, while those that can be synthesized are termed *non-essential*. This terminology refers only to their dietary essentiality because all are needed to make body and egg protein. The essential and non-essential amino acids are listed in Table 8–1.

Table 8–1.—The Amino Acids Required by the Growing Chick, and Their Classification as Dietary Essentials

Essential	*Non-essential*
Arginine	Alanine
Cystine	Aspartic acid
Histidine	Glutamic acid
Isoleucine	Glycine
Leucine	Hydroxyproline
Lysine	Proline
Methionine	Serine
Phenylalanine	
Threonine	
Tryptophan	
Tyrosine	
Valine	

Two of the amino acids listed as essential can actually be synthesized by body tissue. Cystine can be synthesized from methionine, and tyrosine from phenylalanine. They cannot come from simpler compounds, however.

Certain other amino acids can be shown to be dietary essentials under special conditions. Glycine, for example, can be synthesized but not at a rapid enough rate to support maximum growth of a young chick. When a dietary protein low in glycine is fed to young chicks, their growth is improved if more glycine is added to the diet. When a highly purified diet is fed that contains no protein and only essential amino acids, glutamic acid must be added to supply nitrogen in the best form for synthesis of non-essential amino acids. Under similar conditions dietary proline may be helpful because the rate of synthesis may be too slow.

The amino acid requirements of growing chickens and laying hens are met in practice by proteins from plant and animal sources. The quality of a protein for animal feeding is determined by how closely the amino acid composition of that protein meets the dietary amino acid requirements of the animal. Usually it is necessary to choose more than one source of dietary protein, and combine them in such a way that the amino acid composition of the mixture meets the dietary requirements of the animal.

The amino acids most difficult to supply in proper amounts from feed proteins are lysine, methionine and cystine, and tryptophan. They are sometimes referred to as critical amino acids because special attention must be given to meeting the requirements when formulating rations.

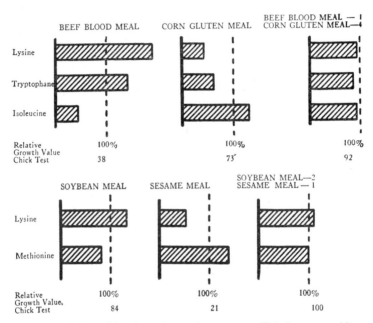

Fig. 8–1.—Careful combination of protein sources will help to provide proper amino acid balance. (After Almquist. Courtesy of U.S. Industrial Chemicals, Inc.)

Although cereal grains are low in protein, they make up a large proportion of a usual poultry ration. Their proteins are particularly deficient in lysine and often in tryptophan. Protein sources to be used with cereal grains must be chosen so that they make up the deficiency of lysine and tryptophan in grain proteins.

Two examples of supplementary action between different proteins are shown in Figure 8–1. Beef blood meal is a rare example of a protein deficient in isoleucine, although it contains lysine and tryptophan in appreciable amounts. Corn gluten meal, on the other hand, contains a surplus of isoleucine, but a deficiency of both lysine and tryptophan. When the two are combined in the ratio of 1 part of blood meal to 4 parts of corn gluten meal, the mixture is nicely balanced with respect to all three amino acids, and in feeding tests it has proved to be much more effective in promoting chick growth than either blood meal or corn gluten meal alone. The second example involves lysine and methionine, as provided by soybean meal and sesame meal.

When formulating poultry rations the diet must supply all the essential amino acids in ample amounts, and sufficient total nitrogen for the chicken to synthesize the other amino acids needed.

An amino acid deficiency always is accompanied by slow growth or poor egg production. Feathering is often poor and usually fat makes up a larger proportion of the carcass than in an adequately nourished chick. Many amino acids are used for other purposes in the body

Fig. 8–2.—Arginine deficiency in a chick four weeks of age resulting in poor feathering and subnormal growth.

in addition to being a component of protein. Tryptophan can be used to form the vitamin, nicotinic acid; tyrosine is needed for synthesis of the hormones, thyroxin and adrenalin, and formation of melanic pigments. Methionine is a methylating agent and can replace some of the dietary choline.

Carbohydrates

Carbohydrates are compounds of carbon, hydrogen and oxygen in which the hydrogen and oxygen are almost always in the same mutual proportion as in water (H_2O). They are plentiful in plants, appearing usually in the form of sugars, starches, pentosans or cellulose. As protein predominates in the fowl's body, so carbohydrates predominate in the structure of the plant.

Starch is the form in which most plants store their reserve energy. The starches stored in the kernel of corn and the potato tuber are familiar examples.

Starch is the only complex carbohydrate which chickens can readily digest. The structural carbohydrates of plants consist largely of cellulose and pentosans which are indigestible for chickens. Cellulose and other complex carbohydrates are usually classified as crude fiber in feedstuffs. Carbohydrates are the major source of energy in rations for all classes of poultry but only ingredients in which the carbohydrate is mainly starch, sucrose, or simple sugars, can be efficient sources of energy. Lactose, the sugar found in milk, cannot be used by chickens because they do not possess the digestive enzyme lactase in their digestive secretions.

Fats

True fats are glycerol esters of long chain fatty acids. These are compounds of carbon, hydrogen and oxygen but they contain a much lower percentage of oxygen than carbohydrates. Because of this, and their high content of hydrogen, fats have over twice as much energy value per unit weight as do carbohydrates. They are the most concentrated sources of dietary energy used in poultry feeding.

When fats contain a high percentage of saturated fatty acids, they are usually solids at room temperature. Fats such as beef tallow and lard are in this category. Other fats contain a high percentage of unsaturated fatty acids and are usually liquid at room temperature. Vegetable oils such as corn oil, soybean oil and cottonseed oil are in this category.

Fat makes up over 40 per cent of the dry egg contents and about 17 per cent of the dry weight of a market broiler. Feeds are much lower in fat, most feed ingredients containing only 2 to 5 per cent fat. Fats have also been an economical source of energy for poultry rations and are frequently added to broiler and laying feeds today.

Fat is the form in which energy is stored in the body and in the egg. The percentage of fat seldom falls below 6 in the very lean animal, while it may rise as high as 40 in the very fat animal.

Other compounds are frequently found associated with fats in feeds and in the body. These include steroids, waxes and phospholipids. Several vitamins fall in this category. Only the true fats, however, are good sources of energy for animals.

Fats contain several different fatty acids, most of which can be synthesized by the animal body. However, one fatty acid cannot be synthesized by body tissue. This fatty acid, linoleic acid, must be present in the diet of young growing chicks or they will grow poorly, have an accumulation of liver fat, and be more susceptible to respiratory infection. Laying hens fed diets severely deficient in linoleic acid will lay very small eggs that will not hatch well. Arachidonic acid, which can be synthesized from linoleic acid, can alleviate these deficiency symptoms if included in the diet. Linoleic and arachidonic acid are considered essential fatty acids because at least one of them must be present in the diet. The best sources of essential fatty acids are vegetable oils such as corn oil, soybean oil, or safflower oil. Practical rations for poultry usually contain sufficient amounts of essential fatty acids.

Vitamins

Unlike the other classes of nutrients discussed, vitamins as a group have few chemical characteristics common to all members. The classification of a substance as a vitamin is usually based on several criteria. They are organic compounds, not synthesized by body tissues, that are required in very small amounts in the diet. They are not major structural components of the body and most commonly function as coenzymes or regulators of metabolism. The 13 vitamins required by poultry are usually classified as fat-soluble or water-soluble. The fat-soluble vitamins include vitamins A, D, E, and K and the water-soluble vitamins are thiamin, riboflavin, nicotinic acid, folic acid, biotin, pantothenic acid, pyridoxine, vitamin B_{12}, and choline. Poultry do not require vitamin C in their diet because their body tissues can synthesize this vitamin.

All these vitamins are essential for life and they must be provided in proper amounts for chickens to grow and reproduce. The egg normally contains sufficient vitamins to supply needs of the developing embryo. For this reason, eggs are one of the best animal sources of vitamins for the human diet.

In the following paragraphs some of the important characteristics of the individual vitamins will be discussed, together with symptoms of deficiency.

Vitamin A.—All animals require some dietary source of vitamin A or one of its precursors. Vitamin A is probably concerned with the synthesis of an important constituent of the epithelial tissues of the body. One of the visual pigments in the eye contains vitamin A and most of us have learned that vitamin A helps to protect against night blindness. Deficiency symptoms in chicks include muscular incoordination, uric acid deposits in the ureters and kidneys, and general unthriftiness. Hens receiving insufficient vitamin A show poor egg production, and eggs produced frequently do not hatch.

Vitamin A is found in large amounts in fish liver oils, but the major sources found in nature are the plant precursors.

Chickens, like other animals, are able to transform the carotenes in plant tissues (fresh green forage, alfalfa meal and the like) into vitamin A. They can also make similar use of the pigment cryptoxanthin in yellow corn. Vitamin A can now be readily produced by chemical synthesis. Vitamin A and its precursors are chemically unstable and can be readily oxidized to inactive compounds during storage of feeds or ingredients. It is a common practice to add commercially produced stabilized forms of vitamin A to rations for all classes of poultry today to prevent vitamin A deficiency.

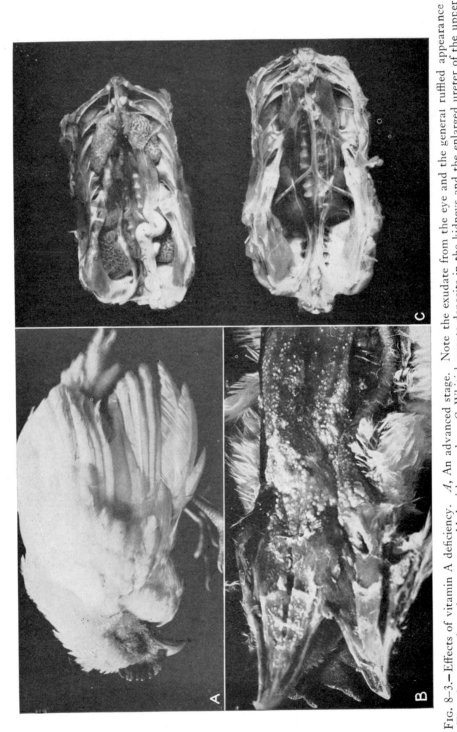

Fig. 8–3.—Effects of vitamin A deficiency. A, An advanced stage. Note the exudate from the eye and the general ruffled appearance B, The pharynx and esophagus are studded with pustules. C, Whitish urate deposits in the kidneys and the enlarged ureter of the upper specimen are compared with the normal condition below. (Courtesy of the National Research Council.)

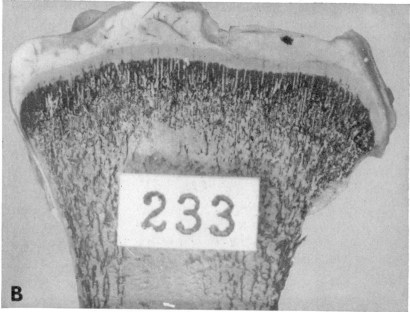

FIG. 8–4.—Section of tibia of vitamin D deficient chick *A* and a normal chick *B* after staining with silver nitrate and exposure to light. The bone from the rachitic chick has large areas of uncalcified cartilage.

Vitamin D.—The primary function of vitamin D is to promote normal absorption and deposition of calcium. The effects of a deficiency of vitamin D are particularly severe in the young animal. Chicks receiving rations lacking or low in vitamin D soon develop rickets similar to that resulting from a deficiency of calcium or phosphorus. Growing bones fail to calcify normally, and chicks are retarded in growth, unthrifty and often unable to walk.

Hens fed diets deficient in vitamin D lay eggs with progressively thinner shells until production ceases. Embryo development is interfered with, probably because the embryo cannot efficiently use calcium from the egg shell.

If animals are exposed to ultraviolet light from sunlight or even from fluorescent lights, they will not develop vitamin D deficiency even though they are receiving none in their diet. A steroid precursor of vitamin D present in secretions of the skin is converted to vitamin D by the ultraviolet radiation on the surface of the skin and is then reabsorbed through the skin or taken in by mouth as the chicken preens. Not over 0.1 per cent of the sun's radiant energy in many parts of the country has antirachitic value, but even this small amount need not be available to chicks for more than ten minutes daily to provide them with sufficient vitamin D.

Vitamin D occurs in several different chemical forms, the most common of which have been designated D_2 and D_3. Vitamin D_2 is formed from the irradiation of ergosterol, a steroid found in plants, while D_3 is formed by irradiation of 7-dehydro-cholesterol, a steroid found in animal tissues. Vitamin D_3 is more than 30 times as efficient for preventing rickets in chickens as vitamin D_2. In poultry feeding, sources of vitamin D should be used whose potency has been assayed in chick experiments.

Present day poultry rations are supplemented with sources of vitamin D of known potency such as irradiated animal sterols, fish liver oils, or vitamin A and D feeding oils. Even though sunlight can provide vitamin D to chickens, present practices of brooding, rearing and housing of laying hens, or broilers, make exposure of chickens to direct sunlight relatively rare.

Vitamin E (Tocopherols).—A deficiency of vitamin E manifests itself in a wide variety of ways, primarily because several other dietary factors can affect the requirement of vitamin E.

In growing chicks, a deficiency can result in (1) encephalomalacia or "crazy chick disease," (2) exudative diathesis, an edema caused by excessive capillary permeability, or (3) muscular dystrophy. Encephalomalacia occurs when the diet contains unsaturated fats that are susceptible to rancidity. Several antioxidant compounds, in addition to vitamin E, are also effective against encephalomalacia. Exudative diathesis is prevented by dietary selenium, and muscular dystrophy is a complex disease influenced by vitamin E, selenium and the amino acids methionine and cystine.

Normally, these vitamin E deficiency diseases can be observed only under special dietary conditions produced in the laboratory.

Fig. 8–5.—Chick with encephalomalacia caused by vitamin E deficiency.

Under farm conditions in the United States, encephalomalacia is the only vitamin E deficiency disease that has been found in growing chicks.

Poor hatchability of fertile eggs is sometimes noted when rations for breeding hens are deficient in vitamin E. To prevent possible vitamin E deficiency, rations for growing chicks and breeding hens are usually supplemented with a source of vitamin E or a suitable antioxidant. Vitamin E can be chemically synthesized or isolated from vegetable oils. Supplements of vitamin E of guaranteed potency are available for feed supplementation. The most potent natural sources of vitamin E are whole grains and dried alfalfa meal.

Vitamin K.—The function of vitamin K is intimately associated with normal clotting of blood. Chicks fed a ration deficient in this vitamin are likely to have severe hemorrhages following a bruise or injury to any part of the body, and may bleed to death from such minor injuries as those incidental to wingbanding. Mature fowls are not so easily affected, but when breeding hens are fed rations deficient in vitamin K, the chicks hatched from their eggs have very low reserves of the vitamin and are therefore susceptible to severe bleeding because of greatly prolonged blood-clotting time.

Although vitamin K is usually abundant in alfalfa meal, meat scraps and fish meal, vitamin K deficiency has occasionally been observed under field conditions. Some modern poultry rations may have rather low levels of alfalfa meal and fish products, and may contain certain feed additives that increase vitamin K requirements. Vitamin K is usually added to rations for growing chicks and breeding hens as the synthetic water-soluble form of vitamin K, menadione sodium bisulfite.

Riboflavin.—This water-soluble vitamin is the one most likely to be deficient in rations made up of ingredients normally found in poultry feeds. For this reason all poultry rations should be supplemented with a source of riboflavin. Chicks receiving rations deficient in this vitamin grow poorly and often show a peculiar lameness called curled-toe paralysis. Breeding hens need supplements of riboflavin in their rations or their eggs will not hatch properly.

Riboflavin is chemically synthesized or produced during the production of antibiotics or other compounds by industrial fermentation processes. Concentrates of riboflavin from these sources can be used to supplement poultry rations. The most potent food sources of riboflavin are milk products, green forages and fermentation by-products.

Thiamin.—This is the vitamin formerly designated as B or B_1. A ration deficient in thiamin is inadequate for growth and brings on nervous disorders in both young and old birds, culminating in paralysis of the peripheral nerves (polyneuritis).

The chicken has a rather high requirement for this vitamin, but since it is found in abundance in whole grains which make up the major part of most poultry rations, the effects of a deficiency are not observed under practical conditions. Special sources of this vitamin are not normally added to a poultry ration.

Nicotinic Acid.—This vitamin is essential for the normal growth and development of the chick. Since corn contains very little nicotinic acid, rations containing high percentages of corn may be deficient in this vitamin. Corn is also low in tryptophan, so there is little opportunity for conversion of this amino acid into nicotinic acid. A deficiency of the vitamin in young chicks results primarily in an enlargement of the hock joint and perosis. There is also a dark inflammation of the tongue and mouth cavity, loss of appetite, poor feathering, and the chicks become nervous and irritable With lowered feed consumption, growth is greatly retarded. Chemically synthesized nicotinic acid is generally added to rations for starting chicks and breeding hens. Among feed products, good sources of nicotinic acid include liver, yeast, wheat bran and middlings, fermentation by-products and most grasses.

Pantothenic Acid.—Young chicks fed a ration deficient in pantothenic acid show slow growth and extremely ragged feathering. Scabby lesions appear at the corners of the mouth, on the edges of the eyelids and around the vent. In severe cases, they also are seen on the feet. A deficiency in the ration of breeding flocks results in lowered hatchability, and chicks that hatch frequently show high

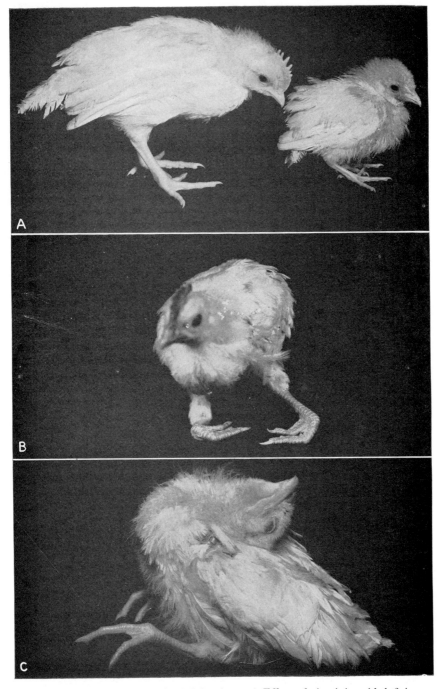

Fig. 8–6.—Effects of vitamin deficiencies. *A*, Effect of nicotinic acid deficiency on chick growth. *B*, Riboflavin deficiency in a young chick. Note the curled toes and the tendency to squat on the hocks. *C*, Head retraction caused by a deficiency of thiamin. (Courtesy of the National Research Council.)

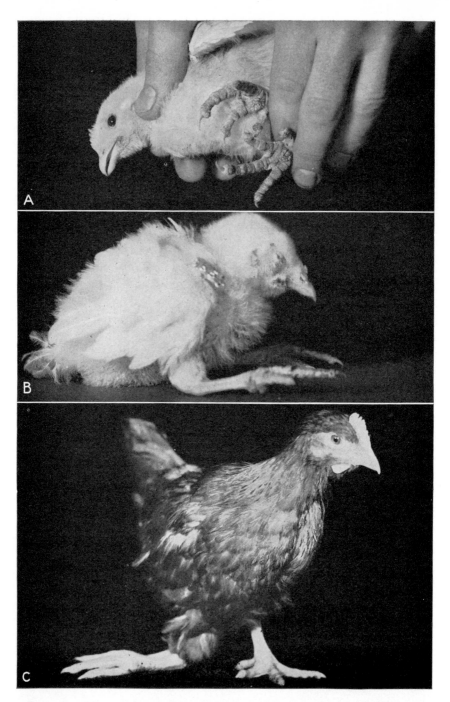

Fig. 8–7.—Effect of vitamin deficiencies. *A*, Biotin deficiency. Note the severe lesions on the bottom of the feet, and the lesions at the corner of the mouth. *B*, An advanced stage of pantothenic acid deficiency. Note the lesions at the corner of the mouth, and on the eyelids and feet. *C*, Perosis or slipped tendon resulting from a deficiency of manganese. This condition may also be caused by a deficiency of choline, biotin or folic acid. (Courtesy of the National Research Council.)

early mortality. Pure calcium pantothenate is often added to rations for starting chicks and breeding hens. In feeds the best sources are brewers yeast, alfalfa, fermentation residues and milk products.

Vitamin B$_6$ (Pyridoxine).—This term is now used to include pyridoxol, pyridoxal and pyridoxamine, all of which serve essentially the same function in metabolism. A severe deficiency results in jerky movements, aimless running about, followed by convulsions, complete exhaustion, and death. In mature fowls there is loss of appetite, followed by rapid loss of weight and death. Partial deficiency causes lowered egg production and poor hatchability.

Since grains, wheat and rice by-products, milk products, meat and fish products, alfalfa, and many other feeds contain appreciable quantities of pyridoxine, a deficiency in ordinary rations is very unlikely.

Biotin.—A deficiency of biotin in the ration of young chicks results in skin lesions quite similar to those observed in pantothenic acid deficiency. The feet become rough and calloused and later crack open and become hemorrhagic. Eventually, similar lesions appear at the corners of the mouth, and the eyelids may become granular.

When chicks are fed raw egg-white, they develop biotin deficiency because biotin is inactivated by avidin, one of the proteins in egg-white. An excess of biotin must be supplied under such conditions. Cooked egg-white has no such unfavorable effect.

Biotin is also involved in the prevention of perosis, and is essential for good hatchability of eggs. The amount needed for good health and egg production in mature hens is apparently very small.

Biotin is rather widely distributed, and deficiencies are not likely to occur under practical feeding conditions. Among the good sources are grains and their by-products, dried yeast, alfalfa meal, milk products, and green pasture grasses.

Choline.—Along with manganese, folic acid, nicotinic acid and biotin, choline is necessary for the prevention of perosis (slipped tendon) in young chicks. It is required in much larger amounts than other vitamins, but it is present in many commonly used feed ingredients. A lack of choline in rations for young chicks results in retarded growth, poor feed utilization and perosis. Hens seem to be able to synthesize all the choline they require. Along with methionine it serves as an important source of methyl groups which are necessary in metabolism. Rations for starting chicks may contain marginal amounts of choline and choline concentrates are sometimes added, especially for broilers. Good sources of choline include fish solubles, fish meal, soybean meal and distillers' solubles. It is also present in appreciable amounts in meat scrap and dried milk.

Folic Acid (Pteroylglutamic Acid).—Folic acid must also be included in any complete list of vitamins needed by the chicken. When young chicks are deprived of it they show retarded growth, poor feathering and perosis. Colored plumage will be lacking in normal pigmentation.   A characteristic anemia is also present. Practical rations are rarely, if ever, lacking in adequate amounts of folic acid.

Vitamin B$_{12}$.—Although the needs of the growing chick and the breeding hen are most critical, vitamin B$_{12}$ is required by all classes of poultry.   It is found in nature only in animal products or products of bacterial fermentation, and is not found in plants.   Therefore, rations which contain only small amounts of animal products, such as fish meal or meat scrap, will be very low in vitamin B$_{12}$.   This vitamin is usually included in rations for starting chicks and breeding hens in the form of a commercially available vitamin B$_{12}$ concentrate, especially if the ration is low in animal protein products.

Vitamin B$_{12}$ contains cobalt and is the only form in which cobalt is useful in the rations of non-ruminant animals.   Ruminants are able to produce their own B$_{12}$ by the action of microorganisms in the rumen, provided some source of cobalt is included in the ration.

Minerals

In addition to the carbon, hydrogen, nitrogen and sulfur found in the organic constituents of an animal body, many other chemical elements are required nutrients.   These are usually designated as minerals.   The elements known to be required in the diet of poultry are: calcium, phosphorus, sodium, potassium, magnesium, chlorine, iodine, iron, manganese, copper, molybdenum, zinc and selenium. Cobalt is required only as a constituent of vitamin B$_{12}$.   Non-ruminant animals cannot synthesize vitamin B$_{12}$ using an inorganic source of cobalt.

Calcium, phosphorus, sodium, potassium, magnesium and chlorine are usually designated as the major elements required since they must be present in the diet in relatively large quantities.   Calcium, for example, is required in amounts up to 1 per cent of the diet for growing chickens and over 3 per cent for laying hens, while magnesium is needed at about 0.03 to 0.05 per cent of the diet.   The remaining elements are needed in only trace amounts, and requirements for them are usually expressed in parts per million or milligrams per pound of diet.   Although they are required in small amounts, the lack of a trace element in the diet can be just as detrimental to an animal as a lack of one of the major elements.

Calcium, Phosphorus and Magnesium.—These elements are important constituents of bone.   The ash of a bone contains about 25 per cent of calcium, 12 per cent of phosphorus, and 0.5 per cent of magnesium.   Lack of enough dietary calcium or phosphorus results in poor mineralization of bone.   Deficient chicks have soft, easily bent bones that fracture readily.   Marked deformity of the skeleton can be produced.   This condition is called rickets in growing animals, and can result from a deficiency of either calcium or phosphorus.   The shell of a large egg contains about 2 grams of calcium in the form of calcium carbonate.   For this reason, calcium needs of laying hens are higher than for any other animal species. Lack of sufficient calcium in the diet of laying hens results in soft-shelled eggs and cessation of egg production.

In addition to the need for calcium and phosphorus as structural constituents, they also have other important functions. Phosphorus is essential in energy metabolism, as a constituent of nucleic acids and for the activity of several enzyme systems. Calcium is also important in blood clotting and muscle contraction. Much of the body magnesium is found in bones but it is also very important as an activator of a large number of enzyme systems, particularly those involved in energy metabolism.

Sodium, Potassium and Chlorine.—These elements are the principal inorganic ions of body fluids. Sodium is found chiefly in fluids outside cells, such as blood, lymph and extracellular fluid. Potassium is found chiefly inside the cells. These elements are important in maintaining acid-base and fluid balance of body tissues. Chlorine is also a constituent of the hydrochloric acid secreted by the proventriculus. A deficiency of any of these elements results in poor growth, dehydration of the body and usually death, if the deficiency is sufficiently severe.

Trace Minerals.—These are used in a great number of ways by the body. In general, they are considered to be components or activators of enzymes. Many enzyme systems contain a mineral element as a part of the enzyme-protein structure, and others require a specific inorganic ion for their activity. Iron is a constituent of hemoglobin, which is the oxygen carrier of the blood and also a constituent of related compounds found in muscle and in oxidative enzyme systems.

The lack of a trace element in the diet often leads to rather specific deficiency symptoms. Iron deficiency produces an anemia, zinc deficiency results in enlargement of the hock joint, shortening of bones and characteristically poor feather development. Manganese deficiency results in a characteristic twisting of the leg called perosis.

A deficiency of any one of several trace elements in the diet of a breeding hen affects the hatchability of eggs and often results in characteristic abnormalities in the developing embryo. Many other elements are found in the animal body but have not been shown to be nutritionally essential. As techniques for study of trace elements improve, other essential mineral elements may be recognized.

Mineral Sources.—In feeding poultry, special attention must be given to supplying sufficient calcium, phosphorus, sodium, chlorine, manganese and zinc in rations. The rest of the required minerals are widely distributed in ingredients used in poultry feeds so that no special supplements of these are needed. Calcium may be furnished as calcium carbonate in the form of limestone or marine shells. Phosphorus can be obtained from inorganic phosphorus sources such as dicalcium phosphate or by using ingredients high in phos-

FIG. 8–8.—Zinc deficiency. Chick A received a diet very deficient in zinc; chick B, a diet only slightly deficient; and chick C, a normal diet. A severe nutrient deficiency may result in characteristic deficiency symptoms; a milder deficiency may cause only slightly impaired growth rate.

phorus, such as meat and bone scraps or fish meal. Sodium and chlorine can be supplied by common salt (sodium chloride), while zinc oxide or carbonate is the usual source of zinc, and manganese sulfate or oxide the usual source of manganese. By their use, precise amounts of the required nutrients can be added to poultry feeds.

Feed Additives

Poultry feeds often contain substances which are added for purposes not directly concerned with nutrient requirements of the animal. An antioxidant, for example, may be used to prevent rancidity of the fat in the diet, or to protect nutrients from being destroyed by oxidation. Certain estrogenic compounds may be added to increase carcass fat deposition. A large number of poultry diseases may be treated or prevented by including certain medications in the feed.

Some feed additives are used to stimulate growth rate of young chickens although these substances are not nutrients. The most important growth-stimulating compounds used are the antibiotics.

Antibiotics are used widely in human medicine, as well as in the treatment of certain animal diseases. It has been demonstrated many times, however, that their addition to diets for poultry will often improve the rate of gain and feed efficiency of young growing chicks. The growth response obtained from these antibiotics appears to be related to the control of unidentified, weakly pathogenic bacteria that reside primarily in the digestive tract. For this reason, the influence of the antibiotic is often referred to as a disease level effect. When chicks are grown in clean quarters in which chicks have not been housed before, or under germ-free conditions in the laboratory, the usual growth improvements from the use of antibiotics are not obtained.

The growth-stimulating levels of antibiotics are usually considered to be from 5 to 10 grams of an antibiotic per ton of feed. Use of feed additives in poultry feeds is closely regulated in the United States by the Food and Drug Administration of the Department of Health, Education and Welfare. In other countries comparable regulatory agencies exist. The various feed additives as well as the conditions under which they may be used are closely prescribed, and care must be taken that they are used properly. Other compounds that affect the disease level of the organism are also used as growth stimulants; the most widely used of these are certain arsenic compounds.

DIGESTION

Digestion is the process during which food is converted to a form that can be absorbed through the intestinal wall and pass into the blood stream to be used by the body. The digestive process is primarily one of splitting large molecules such as proteins, fats and carbohydrates into simpler components by chemical processes which involve the addition of a molecule of water to the bonds which are broken when these simpler substances are released. Therefore, digestion is primarily a process of hydrolysis.

Mechanical Processes

The mechanical processes involved in digestion, some of which have been mentioned in discussing parts of the alimentary tract, include prehension of food, mechanical disintegration of the food, intimate mixing of the resulting particles with the digestive enzymes, exposure of the final products to a large absorptive surface, propelling of the food along the alimentary tract, and discharge of the digestive residues and other excretory products. All but the first and last of these processes are accomplished by smooth or involuntary muscles.

Enzymes and Enzyme Action

The importance of enzymes in digestion is clear when it is realized that the changes in nutrients that take place in the animal body are brought about at ordinary temperatures, and in nearly neutral solutions that are extremely dilute. To hydrolyze proteins in the laboratory requires several hours of constant boiling with strong acids, and yet the digestive enzymes accomplish it easily in a very short time. The chemist cannot readily make fat from sugar in the laboratory, but the body does it easily.

The action of these digestive enzymes is chiefly hydrolytic. Very little heat is liberated by their action, hence little energy is lost by the animal. Certain *exogenous* enzymes, bacteria, yeasts and

14

molds taken in with the food play a part in digestion. They cause a wide variety of reactions, in many of which there is loss of energy unless the body is in an environment such that it can make use of the heat liberated.

Proteins

Feed proteins as such cannot be used by the cells of the body. In fact, if injected directly into the blood stream, they may be harmful. They have to be broken down into amino acids which can pass through the membranes of the intestine into the blood. The blood distributes the amino acids to all parts of the body where they are used for the construction of body tissues and their products.

Carbohydrates

The starches and even the sugars, such as maltose, cannot pass through the intestinal membranes until they have been broken down into simple sugars referred to as the monosaccharides.

Carbohydrate digestion in the fowl consists chiefly in the hydrolysis of starch to maltose, and then to glucose, which is absorbed rapidly from the intestine. Glucose, fructose and galactose are the only monosaccharides to get into the liver through the portal system, and glucose is the primary carbohydrate of the blood stream.

Fats

During digestion, fat must become partially soluble in water before the processes of digestion and absorption can take place efficiently. Bile, produced in the liver and secreted through the bile ducts, plays a large role in dissolving fat so that it can be acted upon by digestive enzymes and absorbed through the intestinal walls. Bile, fatty acids, and partial degradation products of fats are important in producing conditions whereby fat can be made soluble in the intestinal tract. Not all the fatty acids in a neutral fat are hydrolyzed during digestion, but sufficient hydrolysis takes place so that the products of digestion can be made miscible with water. Fat is absorbed into the blood stream and also into the lymphatic system.

Crude Fiber

Food materials used in poultry feeding nearly all contain some crude fiber. As determined in the laboratory, this consists of cellulose, lignin, cutin and some pentosans. In the ruminant some of this material is broken down by the action of exogenous enzymes taken in with the food, as well as by bacterial action. With fowls, however, bacteria have little opportunity for action. Very soon after food passes from the gizzard to the intestine it is mixed with the bile, which inhibits bacterial development. The rectum is so short that there is no appreciable amount of bacterial action possible there. This leaves the ceca as the only place in which bacteria have an opportunity for effective action.

Because of the short time required for feeds to pass through the digestive tract of the fowl, very little digestion of crude fiber can occur even in the ceca. It has been shown that the ceca slowly fill with the fluid contents of the intestine, and then empty themselves at intervals ranging from eight to twenty-four hours, depending upon the nature of the food consumed. This would suggest ample time for bacterial action, but the amount of food material to find its way into the ceca is apparently not very large in proportion to the amount consumed.

Minerals and Vitamins

Minerals are usually absorbed from the intestine without change in composition, and cannot be said to undergo digestion in the ordinary sense of the term. Many vitamins must be released from bound forms in which they are found in feed during digestion.

The Final Nutritive Materials

The usual diet of the fowl is made up of a great number of feeds of a very heterogeneous character. The proteins and carbohydrates in particular are extremely variable from time to time. Under the action of the digestive enzymes this great mixture of substances is broken down to a small number of comparatively simple chemical compounds that can be used by the cells of the body. This process, which we call digestion, and which in a technical sense really occurs outside the body, renders the animal more or less independent of the particular kinds of feed that happen to be available, and furnishes the cells with an essentially constant supply of uniform nutritive material.

METABOLISM

One of the properties of cells is the assimilation of the end products of digestion as these are carried to them by the blood and lymph. If digestion is looked upon as including all changes taking place from the time the food is consumed until it is in proper form and condition to be assimilated by the tissues of the body, metabolism may be considered as including all processes that the nutritive materials undergo from the time they enter the blood stream until the end products are eventually excreted from the body.

Carbohydrate Metabolism

As has already been stated, the carbohydrate of the blood stream is all glucose. Glucose may be used to form the carbohydrates of the cells, it may be used as fuel, or it may be used in the formation of glycogen or fat. The total carbohydrates in the cells of the body can never be large, so that quantitatively the use of glucose for this purpose is relatively unimportant. Its oxidation for fuel is physiologically the most important use.

As soon as there is a surplus of glucose above the fuel needs it is used for the formation of glycogen. This occurs in the liver. Glycogen is animal starch, and is the proximate form of carbohydrate storage. It is stored in various parts of the body, particularly in the liver. When necessity arises, the liver glycogen is changed to glucose of the blood stream and is carried to various parts of the body for energy purposes. The concentration of glucose in the blood is maintained at a nearly constant percentage by certain endocrine glands, through their control over the synthesis and hydrolysis of glycogen and glucose utilization.

Finally, if there is still a surplus of glucose, it may be used in the formation of fat, which is the ultimate form of carbohydrate storage.

The important uses that the body makes of carbohydrates are indicated diagrammatically in Figure 8–9.

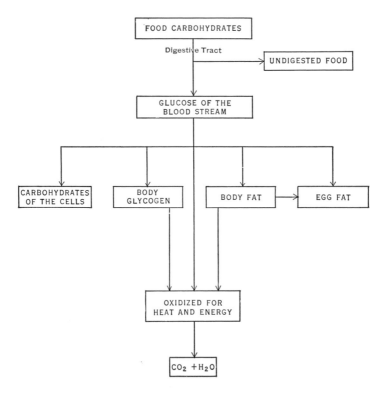

Fig. 8–9.—Diagram showing the normal uses which the body makes of carbohydrates.

Fat Metabolism

The sources of stored fat in the body are: (1) ingested fats which, after digestion and absorption, are found in a form that is more nearly like body fat than they were when eaten; and (2) carbohydrates that are used in the manner already described. The fat formed from carbohydrates is, for a given species, always the same. That formed from ingested fats is dependent to some extent on the character and amount of the ingested fat. When large amounts of dietary fat are consumed, the body and egg fats may have a fatty acid composition similar to that of the consumed fat.

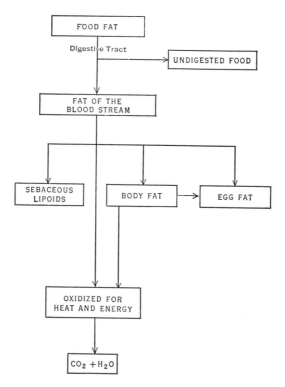

FIG. 8–10.—Diagram showing the normal uses which the body makes of fats.

Fat once absorbed from the intestine is never excreted, except for the small amount of sebaceous lipoids in the skin. There is no physiological limit to the storage of fat, but there is a very definite limit to the storage of carbohydrate as glycogen. When the glycogen stores are at a maximum, the excess carbohydrates are stored in the form of fat, as has already been explained. The important uses that the body makes of fats are indicated diagrammatically in Figure 8–10.

Protein Metabolism

Proteins are not stored in the sense that the other nutrients are. They make up much of the organic structure of the body, and all of the enzymes needed in metabolism are proteins. Excess amounts of dietary protein can be used for energy. Because of price, they are not so economically used for this purpose as are the carbohydrates, and hence, in practical feeding operations, it is usually desirable to reduce the level of feeding of the more costly protein feeds to a reasonable minimum as indicated by the requirements of the animals being fed.

Before the excess amino acids can be used for other than structural purposes they must be deaminated. The nitrogen that is thus split off is excreted by way of the kidneys, chiefly in the form of uric acid. The non-nitrogenous portion may be oxidized immediately to CO_2 and H_2O, or part of it may be stored in the form of glycogen or fat, if conditions make that necessary. The important uses that the body makes of proteins are indicated diagrammatically in Figure 8–11.

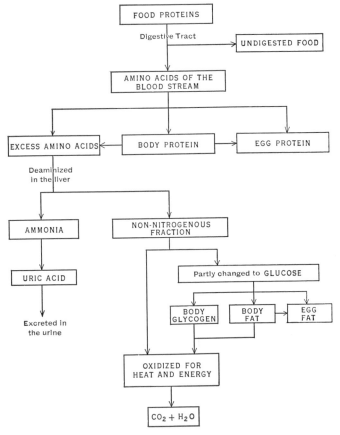

FIG. 8–11.—Diagram showing the normal uses which the body makes of proteins.

Minerals and Vitamins

The metabolism of minerals and vitamins differs from the metabolism of carbohydrates, fats and proteins, in that these nutrients are not used as energy sources but are necessary to the animal for the proper metabolism of the major classes of nutrients. Some of the major minerals, such as calcium and phosphorus, must be built into the bone crystals or into the calcium carbonate of eggshells. Other trace minerals are metabolized by being incorporated into the structure of a protein molecule in an important enzyme system. Many of the vitamins must be changed to their coenzyme forms before they can be active in metabolism, and excesses of the vitamins might be metabolized by the body into CO_2 and water or changed into excretory products which are excreted via the urine.

Chapter 9

The Feeds

THE nutrients required by poultry must be supplied in rations by ingredients available in sufficient quantity, at economical prices. Ingredients vary in the nutrients they contain, and in the availability of these nutrients to poultry. Some attention must be given to ways in which their potential usefulness for a poultry ration can be determined.

EVALUATION OF FEED INGREDIENTS

Modern analytical methods make it possible to analyze feed ingredients for a large number of nutrients required by poultry. The carbohydrates, fats, vitamins, minerals and amino acids present help to determine the potential usefulness of an ingredient when used in a poultry ration. However, these analyses alone do not give sufficient information about the relative value of several possible feed ingredients. Some estimate of the ability of an animal to digest and absorb the nutrients contained in the feedstuff is still required.

One of the oldest but still widely used laboratory methods for predicting the value of a feedstuff for animals is a system of chemical analysis termed "proximate analysis." By appropriate analytical procedures, the components of a feedstuff can be divided into six categories: crude protein, crude fiber, nitrogen-free extract, crude fat (ether extract), ash, and moisture. This classification can give some information about the potential usefulness of a feed ingredient. For example, ingredients high in crude fiber and low in nitrogen-free extract are unlikely to be very useful because fiber is largely undigested by chickens. Feeds high in crude protein are potentially good protein sources, and ingredients with a high content of nitrogen-free extract or crude fat are potentially good sources of energy.

Nutrient composition tables have been prepared which list the average quantity of many nutrients contained in a wide variety of feedstuffs. If the ingredients are known, it is possible to calculate the nutrient composition of a poultry feed by using values obtained from these tabulations. A recent and comprehensive summary of the nutrient composition of feedstuffs is found in the Joint United States-Canadian Tables of Feed Composition (Publication 1232 of the National Academy of Sciences—National Research Council, 2101 Constitution Ave., N. W., Washington, D. C. 20418).

(216)

The protein and metabolizable energy content, and the amount of fat, fiber, calcium and phosphorus in some common poultry feed ingredients are shown in Table 9–1, as an illustration of a table of nutrient composition. Similarly, the amounts of crude protein and the amino acids lysine, methionine, cystine, and tryptophan, are given for these ingredients in Table 9–2.

Table 9–1.—Average Composition of Some Common Poultry Feed Ingredients

Ingredient	Protein	Metabolizable Energy	Fat	Fiber	Calcium	Phosphorus
	percent	kcal/lb			per cent	
Grain and grain products						
Barley	12	1290	2	6	0.1	0.4
Corn, yellow, No. 2	9	1560	4	2	0.0	0.3
Hominy feed, yellow	11	1300	6	5	0.0	0.5
Milo	11	1480	3	2	0.0	0.3
Molasses ·	3	890	0	0	0.9	0.1
Oats	12	1190	5	11	0.1	0.3
Wheat	13	1500	2	3	0.0	0.4
Wheat flour middlings	17	1200	4	5	0.1	0.8
Wheat standard middlings	17	820	5	8	0.2	0.9
Fats						
Grease, stabilized	0	3500	100	0	0.0	0.0
Tallow, feed grade	0	3500	100	0	0.0	0.0
Vegetable oils	0	4000	100	0	0.0	0.0
Protein supplements						
Corn gluten meal	43	1510	2	4	0.1	0.4
Cottonseed meal	41	830	3	13	0.2	1.0
Fish meal	60	1350	8	1	5.5	2.8
Liver and glandular meal	65	1300	16	2	0.7	1.1
Meat and bone scrap	50	900	10	2	10.6	5.1
Peanut meal, dehulled	50	1200	3	4	0.2	0.5
Poultry by-product meal	55	1350	13	2	3.0	1.7
Soybean meal	45	1020	1	6	0.3	0.7
Soybean meal, dehulled	50	1150	1	3	0.3	0.6
Miscellaneous						
Alfalfa meal	17	620	3	24	1.6	0.3
Corn distillers' solubles	27	1320	9	4	0.4	1.4
Whey, dried	13	830	1	0	0.9	0.8
Yeast, brewers' dried	45	1000	5	4	0.1	1.4

Table 9–2.—Amino Acid Composition of Some Ingredients Commonly Used in Poultry Rations (Expressed as a percentage of ingredient)

Ingredient	Crude Protein	Lysine	Methionine	Cystine	Tryptophan
Barley	12	0.5	0.17	0.20	0.15
Corn, yellow, No. 2	9	0.2	0.18	0.18	0.10
Hominy feed, yellow	11	0.4	0.18	0.18	0.10
Milo	11	0.3	0.13	0.15	0.12
Oats	12	0.4	0.18	0.22	0.16
Wheat	13	0.4	0.17	0.22	0.16
Wheat flour middlings	17	0.7	0.16	0.19	0.19
Wheat standard middlings	17	0.7	0.16	0.19	0.19
Corn gluten meal	43	0.8	1.00	0.70	0.21
Cottonseed meal, solvent	41	1.6	0.60	1.00	0.50
Fish meal	60	6.0	1.80	0.94	0.83
Liver and glandular meal	65	4.8	1.30	1.00	0.60
Meat and bone scrap	50	3.5	0.70	0.60	0.30
Peanut meal	50	2.3	0.40	0.70	0.50
Poultry by-product meal	55	4.1	1.00	1.00	0.45
Soybean meal	44	2.9	0.67	0.75	0.58
Soybean meal	50	3.2	0.74	0.83	0.64
Alfalfa meal	17	0.9	0.29	0.32	0.21
Corn distillers' solubles	27	0.9	0.60	0.30	0.20
Whey, dried	13	1.1	0.20	0.30	0.20
Yeast, brewers' dried	45	3.0	0.70	0.50	0.50

Evaluation by Feeding Experiments

The chemical evaluation of poultry feed ingredients cannot accurately predict the usefulness to an animal of the nutrients chemically detected in a feed. For this reason other measurements of the value of a particular ingredient must be made in actual feeding studies.

For most animals it is possible to determine the digestibility of most of the classes of nutrients in a feed which have been determined by proximate analysis. By measuring the amount of crude protein in the diet, and the amount that appears in the feces per unit of diet, the digestible crude protein can be estimated. Similarly, estimates can be made of the digestible crude fiber, the digestible crude fat, and the digestible nitrogen-free extract. However, determinations of digestibility are difficult to perform with poultry because the urine and the feces are mixed in the cloaca before they are excreted.

Metabolizable energy values are more useful biological measures of feeding value of a feedstuff for poultry than measurement of digestible nutrients. When starch is oxidized to carbon dioxide and water by burning, the amount of energy released as heat is the same as the amount of energy made available in the animal body when starch is metabolized to carbon dioxide and water. For this reason, the potential energy available to an animal in a feed ingredient can be estimated by measuring its combustible energy. However, not all this energy is useful to the animal because not all of a feed can usually be digested, absorbed and metabolized. Gross or combustible energy determinations can be corrected for the energy loss which occurs in feces and urine following ingestion of a diet. When this correction is made, the remaining portion of the gross energy value is termed the metabolizable energy. Metabolizable energy values have been determined for a large number of poultry feed ingredients, some of which are shown in Table 9–1. These values are usually expressed in kilogram calories per pound of feedstuff.

The metabolizable energy value of a feed ingredient gives an overall estimate of its useful energy. To have a high metabolizable energy value, a feed ingredient must be highly digestible. Conversely, those ingredients with a low metabolizable energy value are poorly digested and of considerably less value for poultry. The usefulness of knowing the energy value of various feed ingredients will become even more apparent when actual formulation of poultry feeds is discussed.

CLASSIFICATION OF FEED INGREDIENTS

In discussing the many ingredients which may be useful in poultry rations, it seems logical to group them on the basis of the nutrients which they contain. The classification used here will be (1) cereal grains and by-products, (2) fats, (3) protein sources, (4) mineral sources, (5) vitamin sources, and (6) water.

The Cereal Grains and By-Products

Grains are used in poultry feeds primarily as a source of energy. They contain relatively low amounts of poor quality protein that is particularly low in the essential amino acids lysine and tryptophan. Poultry rations made up largely of grains must be supplemented with suitable sources of protein. Grains are also deficient in minerals, particularly sodium, calcium and available phosphorus.

Of the grains fed to poultry, corn and grain sorghums are used in greatest amounts. In 1964, according to USDA estimates, these two feeds made up 98 per cent of the cereal grains fed to broilers. Nearly 92 per cent of the total was corn. Corn and grain sorghums made up 73 per cent of the grains used in feeding laying hens, with the remainder made up of wheat, barley, oats and rye.

Corn has the highest metabolizable energy value of the common grains. Wheat and milo, a grain sorghum, are only slightly lower. The choice of grains used in feeding poultry is based primarily on relative cost per unit of metabolizable energy provided. Corn is used extensively in the United States because of its high energy value, large supply and relatively low cost. Use of certain grains also depends on the area of the country. Grain sorghums are more widely used in the Southwest and West where they are grown. Barley and wheat are used in considerable quantities in the West and Northwestern United States.

By-products of wheat milling, such as wheat standard middlings or flour middlings, are used in poultry feeding to a limited extent. They contain more protein and are lower in energy value than the original wheat. The protein in these by-products is of poor quality and cannot be used to supply a large portion of the protein needed in a poultry feed.

Fats

Considerable quantities of fats are used in poultry feeding, primarily as potent sources of energy. Fats normally contain two to three times as much metabolizable energy per unit of weight as grains. The main limitation on the use of fats in feeding, other than cost, is the physical nature of the ration containing fat. Rations very high in fat tend to cake and do not flow readily. The usual practical limit for adding fats is 3 to 5 per cent of the diet, although with special techniques pelleted diets may contain as high as 7 or 8 per cent added fat. The major fats available for feeding are the animal fats produced as by-products of meat packing. Those that are based primarily on fat obtained from slaughter of cattle are tallows, whereas those containing considerable quantities of softer fats such as lard are termed greases. Various other fats available for animal feeding come from the processing procedures commonly used in production of edible fats or soap. These are often described as hydrolyzed animal fat or animal and vegetable fats. Various vegetable oils which are available for animal feeding are normally more expensive than animal fat. They are somewhat more digestible than animal fats, and have a slightly higher metabolizable energy value.

Protein Sources

Since all grains and grain by-products are deficient both in amount and quality of protein, it is necessary to supply protein to poultry rations from other sources. The common ingredients for this purpose are the oil seed meals and certain animal protein concentrates. The relative importance of the various high protein feeds is shown by the following figures for total consumption by all livestock, excluding work animals, for the years beginning October 1, 1949, 1954, 1958, and 1965. The choice of a specific protein supplement used in a feed will depend upon its relative cost and its amino acid composition. The combination of protein sources contained in the diet must adequately meet the amino acid needs of the animal.

	1949	1954	1958	1965
		1,000 Tons		
Soybean cake and meal	4,514	5,428	8,938	9,266
Cottonseed cake and meal	2,375	2,405	2,198	2,710
Tankage and meat meal	842	1,339	1,484	1,932
Corn gluten feed and meal	926	1,034	1,044	1,406
Fish meal and solubles	261	395	512	618
Linseed cake and meal	670	488	417	300
Copra cake and meal	204	182	148	100
Peanut cake and meal	93	18	75	79

The sources of animal protein most commonly used in poultry feeding are meat packing by-products, fish meals, and by-products of poultry processing. The plant sources of protein are obtained chiefly from certain oil-bearing seeds such as cottonseed, peanut, and soybean, as well as from by-products of corn milling such as corn gluten meal.

Meat Scraps.—Meat meal or meat scrap consists of dry rendered residue from animal tissues. It should not contain more than traces of hair, hoof, horn, hide trimmings, blood meal, manure, or stomach contents. If a meat meal contains more than 4.4 per cent of phosphorus, it is designated either meat and bone meal, or meat and bone scrap. The usual meat product in poultry feeding is meat and bone scrap containing about 50 per cent protein.

The proteins of meat products are good sources of lysine but are somewhat deficient in methionine, cystine, and tryptophan. Because of a high content of mineral matter, meat and bone scrap is relatively low in energy. However, rations for growing chicks containing fairly high amounts of meat and bone scrap often need little further supplementation of calcium and phosphorus. Meat and bone scrap can be used in poultry feeds at levels up to eight or nine per cent of the ration. The use of higher levels should be avoided because the calcium and phosphorus content of the ration would become too high.

Fish Meal.—Fish meal is made from the tissues of undecomposed whole fish or fish cuttings which may or may not have had some of the fish oil removed. Fish meals usually contain 60 to 70 per cent of proteins which are good sources of lysine and methionine. They supplement proteins from cereal grains particularly well, and provide considerable calcium and phosphorus in a ration. The metabolizable energy value of good quality fish meal is about 1,300 kilocalories per pound, which is higher than most other common protein sources. Fish meal can be made from many kinds of fish such as menhaden, sardine or pilchard, herring, anchovy, salmon, white fish, crab or shrimp.

Poultry By-Product Meal.—The official definition describes this product as the "ground dry rendered clean wholesome parts of the carcass of slaughtered poultry, such as heads, feet, undeveloped eggs and intestines, exclusive of feathers except in such trace amounts as might occur unavoidably in good factory practice. It should contain not more than 16 per cent ash and not more than 4 per cent acid insoluble ash." Considerable quantities of this material are now available for poultry feeding. It contains about 55 per cent protein, and is a good source of tryptophan and lysine. Poultry by-product meal can also be a good source of calcium and phosphorus.

Other Animal Protein Sources.—In addition to the main sources of animal proteins, a number of other animal products are available to a limited extent as protein sources in animal feeds. These include blood meal, liver and glandular meal, hydrolyzed feather meal, tankage, and certain milk products. The use of some of these animal products is limited because of their protein quality, amount available, or relative cost compared with the major sources of protein discussed above.

Cottonseed Meal.—This is the high protein residue remaining after extraction of the oil from the cottonseed. Its use in feeding poultry is limited by the presence of a compound called gossypol, which can depress growth rate of young chicks or cause a characteristic discoloration of yolks laid by hens fed cottonseed meal. A degossypolized cottonseed meal (in which the gossypol has been inactivated) is now available. In addition, new varieties of cotton produce seeds without the pigment glands containing gossypol. As these varieties gain commercial importance, the usefulness of the meal for feeding poultry should increase.

The cottonseed meal used in poultry feeding normally contains 41 to 43 per cent of protein, relatively low in the essential amino acid lysine. If appreciable amounts are used, another protein source rich in lysine must be used to provide sufficient quantities of this essential amino acid in the ration.

Peanut Meal.—This is the residue remaining after removal of most of the oil from peanut kernels by a mechanical or solvent extraction process. Expeller-processed peanut meal usually contains approximately 45 per cent protein, whereas solvent-extracted meal contains about 50 per cent. The protein in peanut meal is somewhat low in the essential amino acids methionine and lysine, and if it is used in poultry rations, other proteins or sources of these amino acids must be provided to properly balance the amino acid composition of the final protein mixture.

Soybean Meal.—This is by far the most important protein source used in poultry feeding today. It is produced by removing the oil from soybeans by a solvent extraction process. If soybean meal contains most of the soybean hull, it usually contains 44 per cent of protein, while dehulled soybean meal normally contains 50 per cent of protein. The dehulled meal is most commonly used in poultry feeding because it has a higher energy value than the meal containing 44 per cent protein. Soybean meal is unique among major plant protein sources in that it is a good source of lysine. For this reason, soybean meal can be used in combination with cereal proteins to provide a high quality protein mixture for animal feeding. It is somewhat low in methionine and cystine and rations composed mainly of corn and soybean meal often must be supplemented with methionine.

Soybean meal contains a number of substances which are growth-inhibiting unless the meal is properly heat-treated. Heat treatment is a standard practice in the commercial production of soybean meal, to insure a satisfactory source of protein for animal feeding.

Corn Gluten Meal.—This is a by-product of the manufacture of corn starch or syrup by a wet milling process. It is the portion of the corn grain remaining after extraction of most of the starch and germ and removal of the bran. Corn gluten meal is normally marketed containing 41 to 43 per cent of protein. Proteins in corn gluten meal are very deficient in lysine and tryptophan but are good sources of methionine. The use of this protein source is limited in rations already containing considerable protein from grains. Much of the pigment in the corn grain is concentrated in corn gluten meal. Large amounts of this ingredient are used as a source of yellow pigment for broiler skin and legs, and for egg yolks. A corn gluten meal containing 60 per cent of protein and high amounts of pigment is also available for animal feeding.

Other Plant Protein Supplements.—In addition to the four plant protein sources just described, several other high protein materials from plant oil seeds are available in limited amounts. These include safflower meal, sesame meal and sunflower seed meal. All are rather deficient in lysine, but sesame meal is often used to supply methionine.

Amino Acids

In addition to using protein supplements as sources, it is possible to include amino acids in poultry feed as the individual chemical compounds. The amino acid methionine is commercially produced for use in supplementing poultry rations. It is available as DL-methionine or methionine hydroxyanalog. Lysine is also commercially produced and may eventually become important as a feed additive.

Mineral Supplements

The mineral elements most likely to be deficient in rations for poultry are: calcium, phosphorus, sodium, chlorine, manganese and zinc. Rations composed of normal feed ingredients may be deficient in these elements unless special sources are supplied.

Calcium and Phosphorus Supplements.—The most commonly used sources of calcium in a poultry ration are ground limestone and marine shells. Both of these are primarily calcium carbonate. Limestone especially intended for animal feeding should be used instead of agricultural lime. Certain limestones contain impurities that may prove detrimental when consumed in large amounts. Magnesium, present in large quantities in dolomitic limestone, is the major impurity found in limestone deposits.

Another widely fed source of calcium carbonate for laying hens is oyster shell, although other marine shells of similar composition are equally valuable. Often, both of these calcium supplements are used: ground limestone included in a laying feed to supply part of the calcium needed by the hen, and oyster shell offered on a free-choice basis to supply the remainder of the calcium required. It is becoming increasingly common, however, to include all the calcium required by laying hens as an integral part of the laying mash.

The most important phosphorus sources in poultry feeding are dicalcium phosphate, defluorinated rock phosphate, and steamed bone meal. All these are calcium phosphates which can supply both calcium and phosphorus.

Sodium Chloride.—Plant materials used in animal feeding are usually quite low in sodium and chlorine. Rations for nearly all farm animals are supplemented with a source of these elements. Sodium chloride, added as common salt, is usually included in poultry feeds at 0.25 to 0.50 per cent of the diet. Feed ingredients grown in certain areas of the United States will contain relatively low amounts of iodine; a possible deficiency of iodine can be avoided by the use of iodized salt.

Trace Mineral Supplements.—The elements manganese and zinc are normally supplied as manganese sulfate or manganese oxide and zinc carbonate or oxide. It has become common practice to supplement rations for all classes of poultry with these two trace elements. Other trace minerals required by poultry are not likely to be deficient in rations made up of the usual feed ingredients.

Vitamin Supplements

All the vitamins that may be deficient in poultry feeds can be added to the diet as chemically synthesized vitamins, or vitamins produced by fermentation processes. The vitamins are commercially available in pure form or as vitamin concentrates at relatively low cost and they can be added to a poultry feed by means of a premix which supplies specified amounts of each vitamin.

Certain ingredients available for poultry feeding are potent sources of vitamins. These include yeasts, fish solubles, distillers' solubles, liver meal, alfalfa meal and milk by-products.

Unidentified Growth Factors

When all the known nutrients are included in highly purified form in diets for young chicks or poults, some investigators have still reported improvements in the growth rate of animals fed certain complex feed ingredients. Those that will improve growth rate under these conditions are usually called sources of unidentified growth factors. It is a fairly common practice to include sources of unidentified growth factors in rations for starting chicks, broilers, and breeding hens. These sources include distillers' dried solubles, condensed fish solubles, various fermentation by-products, dried whey, and dried yeast.

Water

This highly important part of all poultry rations has been discussed as a nutrient. It must be further emphasized that a suitable and constant supply of clean, cool water is essential to the best feeding practice. To provide water that is always clean and cool is a summer problem which must be met by the feeder's ingenuity if he is not so fortunate as to have running water available.

In the northern and central states a constantly available supply of water during the winter also presents its problems. This is particularly true if the feeding plan includes the use of artificial lights. It is fully as essential to have water available when the lights are turned on as it is to have feed. An increased consumption of both is one object in using lights. Water heaters of various styles are available. Many are so designed as to involve little or no fire hazard and have ample capacity for heating the water sufficiently to prevent its freezing in the coldest weather.

15

Chapter 10

The Nutrient Requirements of Poultry

Nutrient requirements are known more precisely for poultry than for any other species of animal. This has come about because of the economic importance of the poultry industry and also because a chick is an excellent experimental subject for nutrition studies. Proper poultry rations can be devised only by application of the nutritional information known about the class of poultry to be fed. The application of this information to poultry feeding requires knowledge of the nutrients, the feedstuffs available to supply these nutrients, and the amount of nutrient needed for the particular productive purpose. In this chapter, the requirements of the nutrients will be considered, particularly with regard to their application in formulating rations.

THE REQUIREMENTS FOR ENERGY

The largest single dietary need of an animal is for a source of energy. Energy is required for all physiological processes in the animal—movement, respiration, circulation, absorption, excretion, the nervous system, reproduction, temperature regulation—in short, all the processes of life.

Energy Requirements for Maintenance

Animals kept for productive purposes must be fed to maintain life whether they are producing or not. A considerable part of the feed consumed by all classes of poultry must be used for maintenance.

The maintenance requirement for energy includes the need for basal metabolism and normal activity. The basal metabolism is the minimum energy expenditure or heat production under conditions when the influence of feed, environmental temperature and voluntary activity are removed. The basal heat production varies with the size of the animal and in general, as size increases, basal heat production per unit of body weight decreases. The minimum heat production of day-old chicks is about 5.5 small calories per gram of live weight per hour, while the figure for adult hens is about half of this. As an extreme example, the resting metabolism of a hummingbird expressed as oxygen consumption is 15 cc. per gram of live weight per hour. The corresponding figure for an elephant is 0.15 cc.

The energy required for activity can vary considerably but is usually estimated as about 50 per cent of the basal metabolism. This is probably influenced by housing conditions as well as breed of chicken used. Housing in cages where activity is greatly restricted may result in lower energy expenditure for activity compared with the less restricted conditions prevailing in floor pens.

In spite of the fact that larger animals require less energy per unit size for maintenance, the total energy required by larger animals is more than by smaller ones. From the practical standpoint, this means that the smallest body size for a laying hen consistent with

Table 10-1.—Estimated Feed Required per Day and per Dozen Eggs by 100 Hens of Different Weights and Egg Production (pounds)

| | Feed consumed by | | | | | |
| | 4-pound hens | | 5-pound hens | | 6-pound hens | |
Eggs/100 hens/day	per day	per doz. eggs	per day	per doz. eggs	per day	per doz. eggs
0	15.8	—	18.6	—	21.2	—
10	16.7	20.1	19.6	23.6	22.1	26.6
20	17.6	10.5	20.4	12.2	22.9	13.7
30	18.4	7.4	21.3	8.5	23.9	9.6
40	19.3	5.8	22.2	6.7	24.7	7.4
50	20.2	4.8	23.1	5.5	25.6	6.1
60	21.1	4.2	24.0	4.8	26.5	5.3
70	22.0	3.8	24.9	4.3	27.5	4.7
80	22.9	3.4	25.8	3.9	28.1	4.2
90	23.8	3.2	26.7	3.6	29.2	3.9
100	24.7	3.0	27.6	3.3	30.1	3.6

Feed assumed to contain 1,350 kilocalories of metabolizable energy per pound of diet.

good production, egg size and livability will be the most efficient for converting feed to product due to a low energy expenditure for maintenance. For broiler production the animal that reaches market weight in the shortest possible time is the most efficient in converting feed to product because the longer an animal must be fed to reach market weight, the greater the maintenance cost.

The data in Table 10-1 illustrate the effect of body weight and rate of egg production on feed required by laying hens. The feed required to maintain a non-laying hen is more than half that needed for full production. The feed needed to maintain a 4-pound hen is considerably less than for a 5- or 6-pound hen. In terms of amount of feed required to produce a dozen eggs, high production is much more efficient than low production because the maintenance feed is spread over more eggs.

The same principle applies to broiler production. Broilers that reach market weight in eight weeks require considerably less feed per unit weight than those requiring twelve weeks to reach the same weight. Each increment of growth must be maintained longer in slow-growing birds.

Effect of Temperature.—Because of the ability of warm-blooded animals to maintain a constant body temperature that is normally several degrees above the environmental temperature, the animal is constantly losing heat to its surroundings. This loss of heat means a loss of energy that must be supplied in the feed. Heat production must equal heat loss if the animal is to maintain its normal temperature, and this means that there is a rapid increase in the metabolic rate whenever the environmental temperature falls below the critical point. Thus, the maintenance energy required at low environmental temperature is greater than that required at a more comfortable temperature.

The minimum rate of heat production in day-old male chicks occurs in an environmental temperature of 95° F. Heat output is more than doubled at a temperature of 75° F, in order to compensate for increased heat loss. For the adult hen the minimum basal heat production occurs over a range of about 10°, between 65 and 75° F. These values are for fasting chickens at rest. Feeding an animal will increase its heat production and the higher the level of feeding the more heat is produced during the assimilation of the feed. A flock of hens on full feed will be better able to withstand the effects of cold weather than will a flock which is being restricted in its feed intake. There are also other adaptive mechanisms, such as greater feather cover which may help in resistance to cold weather. However, when the temperature of a laying house falls much below 55° F, considerable food energy must be converted to heat to maintain body temperature. This can have a marked effect on efficiency of conversion of feed to product during the cold winter months.

Energy Requirements and Food Intake

Most egg-type laying hens and growing broilers are allowed to consume as much feed as they wish. The amount of feed that poultry will consume under these conditions is primarily related to the energy requirements of the animal at that time. When other nutrients are present in adequate amounts, the amount of feed consumed is determined primarily by the energy level of the ration. Energy consumption measured in terms of kilocalories of metabolizable energy consumed per day is more likely to be constant than total feed consumption, if rations containing different amounts of metabolizable energy per unit of ration are fed. This is clearly illustrated by some data from experiments conducted at the University of Arizona, which are shown in Table 10–2. In these experiments five rations containing from 1,060 to 1,550 kilocalories of metabolizable energy per pound of diet were fed to laying hens for a total

Table 10–2.—The Effect of Metabolizable Energy Content of the Diet and Environmental Temperature on Energy Consumption, Feed Intake, and Feed per Dozen Eggs

Metabolizable energy per pound of diet	Average total eggs/ hen	Feed consumed/ 100 hens/ day	Feed/ dozen eggs laid	Metabolizable energy consumed/ hen/day	Protein consumed/ 100 hens/day
kcal		lbs	lbs	kcal	lbs
		Entire experiment (336 days)			
1060	216	30.3	5.66	321	4.8
1200	215	25.0	4.69	300	4.0
1350	223	22.3	4.03	301	3.6
1450	218	20.7	3.83	300	3.3
1550	197	18.9	3.87	293	3.0
		112 coolest days (maximum 69° F, mean 55° F)			
1060	81	35.5	5.90	375	5.8
1200	84	29.5	4.73	354	4.7
1350	84	25.6	4.10	346	4.1
1450	83	24.1	3.90	350	3.8
1550	77	22.2	3.88	345	3.6
		112 hottest days (maximum 98° F, mean 86° F)			
1060	64	24.5	5.14	260	3.9
1200	61	19.8	4.37	238	3.2
1350	64	18.0	3.79	243	2.9
1450	63	16.7	3.56	242	2.7
1550	55	15.2	3.73	237	2.4

Heywang, B. W. and M. G. Vavich: Poultry Science, *41*, 1389–1393, 1962.

of 366 days. When feed consumption was measured in terms of kilocalories of metabolizable energy consumed, the energy consumption per hen, averaged for the whole experiment, was about 300 kcal per day for all diets. The marked effect of temperature of the environment on energy consumption is also shown by this experiment. The calories consumed per hen per day for the 112 hottest days, which had an average temperature of 86° F, was more than 100 kilocalories less than the mean energy consumption for the 112 coolest days during which the temperature averaged 55° F. Even though the energy consumption for the hot days and cool days was markedly different, within each of these periods the energy consumption per hen per day was nearly the same regardless of the level of metabolizable energy contained in the diets. This experiment demonstrates that laying hens do not regulate feed consumption according to the total amount of feed they are able to consume. Hens on the lowest energy ration consumed nearly 50 per cent more feed than hens fed the highest energy ration. These data also show that a high energy ration is more efficient in terms of feed consumed per dozen eggs produced. This is because less total feed is needed to provide the energy needs of the laying hen.

The same general principle applies to growing chicks, *i.e.*, a young chick tends to regulate feed consumption to consume a given quantity of energy. An experiment conducted at Cornell University (shown in Table 10–3) illustrates the type of data obtained with growing chicks. In this experiment, the energy content of a diet was varied from 3.2 to 3.9 kilocalories per gram by including increasing quantities of soybean oil in the diet. The first diet contained only 1.2 per cent soybean oil and the last 16 per cent. Young growing chicks are not able to regulate their caloric intake as closely as laying hens. Energy consumption increased slightly as the energy content of the diet increased. The energy consumption was relatively constant, however, compared with total feed intake on the various diets. As the energy level of the diet increased, feed required per unit gain was markedly decreased. These data show that even with young chicks there is a remarkably constant consumption of metabolizable energy over wide ranges of energy content of the diet.

Table 10–3.—Effect of Energy Content of the Diet on Energy Consumption, Feed Consumption and Feed per Unit Gain of Growing Chicks

Energy content of diet	Gain 1–4 weeks of age	Feed consumed/chick, 1–4 weeks of age	Metabolizable energy consumed	Feed/gain
kcal/gm	gm	gm	kcal	
3.2	468	836	2648	1.79
3.4	498	800	2725	1.61
3.6	519	765	2785	1.47
3.9	514	730	2816	1.42

Energy Requirements for Growth

Energy requirements cannot be stated as precisely as amino acid, vitamin and mineral requirements. Good growth rate can be achieved with a wide range of energy levels because of the ability of the chick to adjust the amount of feed consumed to maintain a fairly constant energy intake. Generally, maximum growth rate will not be achieved with rations for starting chicks containing below 1,200 kilocalories of metabolizable energy per pound. Broilers are usually fed rations higher in energy content than are replacement pullets. In broiler production, maximum growth rate is usually essential so that broilers can reach market weight in the shortest time, while with replacement pullets very rapid growth rate is less critical. In practice, rations for starting chicks intended as replacement pullets usually contain from 1,250 to 1,350 kilocalories of metabolizable energy per pound of diet while broiler starter rations contain higher levels of energy, ranging from 1,400 to 1,550 kilocalories per pound.

Energy Requirements for Egg Production

The net energy required by a high producing hen consists of energy expended for the basal metabolic rate, activity requirements and energy stored in the egg. If the basal metabolic rate is estimated as 68 kilocalories per kg of body weight$^{0.75}$, the activity increment is considered as 50 per cent of the basal metabolism, and a large egg contains 90 kilocalories of energy, a 4-pound (1.8 kg.) hen in a comfortable environment, producing an egg a day, would have a net requirement of 250 kilocalories of energy per day. The efficiency of using dietary metabolizable energy for these purposes is probably about 75 per cent, so that the metabolizable energy intake required to supply the energy needed would be about 330 kilocalories of metabolizable energy per day. This would require an intake of about 0.24 pounds of feed containing 1,350 kilocalories of metabolizable energy per pound. These assumptions formed the basis for the estimates of feed consumption in Table 10-1. When a hen produces an egg only eight out of every ten days, the energy put into an egg would be reduced to 72 kilocalories per day and correspondingly less for lower rates of production.

Available evidence suggests that pullets coming into peak production, with a body weight between 3.5 and 4 pounds and housed in a comfortable environment, will consume about 280 kilocalories of metabolizable energy per day. As their body weight increases to slightly over 4 pounds and egg size improves, similar hens in good production probably consume from 310 to 320 kilocalories per day. Environmental factors, as discussed above, may alter these estimates markedly.

Because of the capacity of hens to alter consumption of feed in response to the energy content of a ration, the energy requirement of hens cannot be expressed in terms of a specific number of kilocalories of metabolizable energy per pound of ration. However, the minimum level of energy in a laying ration should not be below 1,200 kilocalories of metabolizable energy per pound to ensure maximum rate of production. When hens are subjected to a cold environment, the level of energy should not fall below 1,250 kilocalories of metabolizable energy per pound. The level of energy actually used in a ration will depend to a large degree on price of feed ingredients available.

REQUIREMENT FOR PROTEIN

Protein needs for maintenance are relatively low, and therefore the requirement depends primarily on the amounts needed for productive purposes. To properly meet the protein requirement, the essential amino acids must be supplied in the proper amounts, and the total level of nitrogen in the diet must be high enough and in the proper form to permit synthesis of the non-essential amino acids.

Once the minimum amount of protein required to support maximum growth rate or egg production is supplied, additional protein is oxidized for energy. Protein is not stored in the body in appreciable amounts. Since protein is usually the most expensive component of a ration, it is not economical to feed excess protein to animals. For this reason, protein levels in rations for animals are usually kept closer to the minimum requirement than are other nutrients.

Protein Requirements for Growth

Protein and amino acid requirements for young growing chicks are particularly critical. The largest portion of the dry matter increase with growth is protein. Deficiency of either total protein or an essential amino acid will reduce growth rate. Protein synthesis requires that all the amino acids needed to make up the protein be present in the body at nearly the same time. When an essential amino acid is absent, no protein is synthesized at all. Incomplete proteins cannot be made. Amino acids that cannot be efficiently used for protein synthesis are converted to carbohydrates or fat that can be readily oxidized for immediate energy needs or stored in adipose tissue. The carcasses of animals fed rations deficient in protein or amino acids usually contain more fat than

Table 10–4.—Amino Acid Requirements of Chicks and Laying Hens

Amino acid	Starting chicks		Laying hens	
	Per cent of diet	Per cent of protein	Per cent of diet	Per cent of protein
Arginine	1.2	6.0	1.0	6.0
Lysine	1.1	5.5	0.8	5.0
Methionine	0.75	3.8	0.58	3.6
or				
Methionine	0.4	2.0	0.32	2.0
and Cystine	0.35	1.8	0.26	1.6
Tryptophan	0.2	1.0	0.16	1.0
Glycine	1.0	5.0	—	—
Histidine	0.4	2.0	0.3	1.9
Leucine	1.4	7.0	1.2	7.5
Isoleucine	0.75	3.8	0.8	5.0
Phenylalanine	1.3	6.5	1.0	6.4
or				
Phenylalanine	0.7	3.5	0.7	4.4
and Tyrosine	0.6	3.0	0.32	2.0
Threonine	0.7	3.5	0.55	3.5
Valine	0.85	4.3	0.8	5.0

Chick requirements are for a diet containing 20 per cent protein, from National Research Council Nutrient Requirements of Poultry. Requirements for layers are for diet containing 16 per cent protein, from Cornell University Extension Stencil #205.

those from animals fed adequate amounts of a well-balanced protein.

Much of our present-day knowledge of amino acid requirements of growing chicks has been obtained from experiments in which individual crystalline amino acids have been used to formulate amino acid mixtures adequate to support rapid growth. Today highly purified diets containing mixtures of crystalline amino acids have been developed that will support rates of chick growth that are nearly the same as obtained from diets containing good-quality intact protein.

An estimate of the amino acid requirements of starting chicks is given in Table 10–4. These amino acid requirements are based primarily on recommendations of the National Research Council. Many factors influence amino acid requirements when they are stated as percentages of the diet, and no such table of requirements can be considered constant for all conditions.

The most important consideration in expressing amino acid requirements is the amount of feed consumed. A fixed amount of total dietary protein and essential amino acids is needed to support a given rate of gain of body tissue of constant composition. However, when the protein requirement is expressed as a constant percentage of the diet, the absolute daily intake of protein will depend upon feed consumption. Energy level in the diet is probably the most important consideration in determining food intake. For

Table 10–5.—The Effect of Substitution of Fat for Carbohydrate in a High Protein Purified Diet for Young Chicks

	Lot A	Lot B
The ration		
Protein-vitamin-mineral premix	49 parts	49 parts
Glucose	34	—
Corn oil	7	21
Total	90 parts	70 parts
Protein, by analysis, per cent	33.4	42.3
Metabolizable energy, kcals/gram	3.82	4.91
Total protein in 90 grams of Ration A	30.0 grams	—
Total protein in 70 grams of Ration B	—	29.6 grams
Metabolizable energy in 90 grams, kcals	343.8	—
Metabolizable energy in 70 grams, kcals	—	343.7
Results		
Average weight after 28 days, grams	439	438
Total feed consumed per chick, grams	545	439
Feed per gram of gain, grams	1.52	1.22
Total protein eaten per chick, grams	182	186
Protein per gram of gain, grams	0.51	0.52

this reason, requirements expressed as a percentage of the diet are usually related to the energy content of the diet.

The results of an experiment with two highly purified diets differing widely in energy content, shown in Table 10–5, illustrate the influence of energy content of the diet on protein intake. Previous experiments showed that 30 per cent protein was necessary in this particular diet to obtain maximum growth. Diet A consisted of 49 parts of a protein-vitamin-mineral premix, 34 parts of glucose and 7 parts of corn oil. This mixture provides 33.4 per cent of protein and 3.82 kilocalories of metabolizable energy per gram. Diet B contained 49 parts of the premix and 21 parts of corn oil; the carbohydrate was all replaced by corn oil. It provided 42.3 per cent of protein and 4.91 kilocalories of metabolizable energy per gram. After twenty-eight days, chicks fed diet A had consumed 545 grams of feed and weighed 439 grams each. Those fed diet B had consumed only 439 grams but weighed 438 grams each. It took 1.52 grams of diet A for each gram of gain but only 1.22 grams of diet B. The total amount of protein consumed by chicks fed diet A was the same as that consumed by chicks receiving diet B but the percentage of protein in the two diets differed markedly. Voluntary feed intake decreased 19.4 per cent over the feeding period when the caloric density of the ration was increased from 3.82 to 4.91 kilocalories per gram. To insure the same protein intake, the percentage of protein had to be increased to compensate for the reduced feed consumption. Since the amino acid composition of the protein used in diets A and B was the same, amino acid intakes also remained constant even though the percentages of the amino acids in the diets differed greatly.

The protein content of diet A could be expressed as 8.7 grams per 100 kilocalories of metabolizable energy, and similarly that of diet B 8.6 grams. This method of expression of protein requirements helps to insure similar protein intake on a wide range of energy levels in a diet. In quite common usage, protein requirements have been expressed as a calorie-protein ratio, an expression obtained by dividing the kilocalories of metabolizable energy per pound of diet by the percentage of protein. By keeping the calorie-protein ratio constant over a wide range of dietary energy levels, the expected intake of protein can be maintained at a nearly constant absolute level.

Of course, as protein intakes change, intake of individual amino acids also changes. Amino acid requirements could all be expressed in terms of energy level in the same manner as total protein. If, however, amino acid requirements are expressed as a percentage of the protein (as in Table 10–4), a balanced protein fed at the proper level will also insure an adequate amino acid intake. Further complication of such calculations by expressing each amino acid in relation to energy level separately from total protein probably is unnecessary. The approximate protein requirement for starting chicks is as follows:

Metabolizable energy content of diet kcal/lb	Percentage of dietary protein
1200	20.0
1300	21.6
1400	23.3
1500	25.0

These are expressed as a percentage of a diet at specific energy levels to illustrate how the requirement can change as energy content of the diet changes.

Effect of Age.—Protein requirements of young chicks decrease with age. As a chick grows, a greater percentage of the diet consumed must be used for maintenance and less for growth. Since the quantity of protein needed for maintenance is relatively low compared with that needed for growth, the protein requirement, expressed as a percentage of the diet, usually falls.

The change in rate of growth during the growing period is shown graphically in Figure 10–1. Growth rate is shown by three different measures for a group of crossbred males from hatching time to sixteen weeks of age. The average weekly increases in body weight are shown in the shaded columns of the table. The weekly increment in gain increases regularly till a maximum gain is reached during the eighth week. The weekly increments of gain become less with each succeeding week. The total cumulative gain or attained weight is shown as a solid line rising from left to right. A different scale is used here to get both measures on the same graph. Finally the rate of growth is shown as the percentage which each weekly gain is of the weight at the beginning of that week. This measure of rate of growth continually decreases following hatching time. Similar data are given in tabular form for a flock of broilers from hatching to nine weeks of age, in Table 10–6. The feed consumption, shown with these data, increases each week even though growth rate plateaus or becomes less. This results in a steady increase in

Table 10–6.—Growth Rate and Feed Consumption of Broiler Chicks

Weeks of age	Average weights gm	Weekly gain gm	Rate of gain per cent	Feed eaten gm/wk	Weekly feed/gain
0	40				
1	91	51	128	73	1.4
2	204	113	124	199	1.8
3	363	159	78	318	2.0
4	545	182	50	363	2.0
5	772	227	42	500	2.2
6	1021	249	32	499	2.0
7	1294	273	27	636	2.3
8	1566	272	21	681	2.5
9	1816	250	16	726	2.9

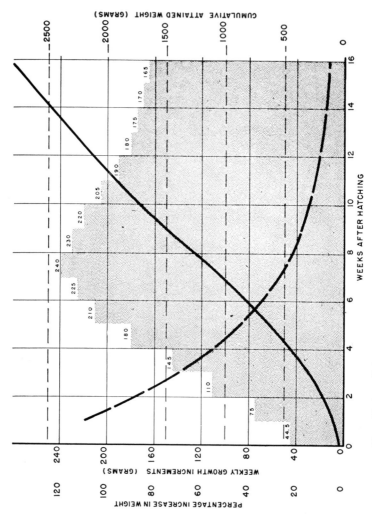

FIG. 10–1.—Chickens make rapid growth if given the right kind of feed. See text for description.

the weekly ratio of feed consumed to weight gain. The protein composition of the gain remains fairly constant during the growth period. Since feed consumed per gram of gain increases as chicks grow, less protein is required per unit of diet consumed.

It is common practice to reduce the protein content of diets for broilers by 3 to 4 percentage units at about six weeks of age. Protein requirements of replacement pullets are relatively low. With diets of moderate energy level, no more than 15 per cent protein is required between 12 and 22 weeks of age for egg-type replacement pullets. Although protein requirements probably fall continuously with age, it is normally not feasible to change protein levels of diets often enough to take into account the constantly changing protein needs.

Protein Requirements of Laying Hens

With each large egg laid, a hen produces about 6.7 grams of protein. This is equivalent to the amount of protein deposited daily by a growing broiler gaining at the rate of about 37 grams per day. Although hens do not always lay an egg every day, if the protein needs for maintenance are also considered, the daily protein needs for high-producing laying hens are fully as great as for a fast-growing broiler.

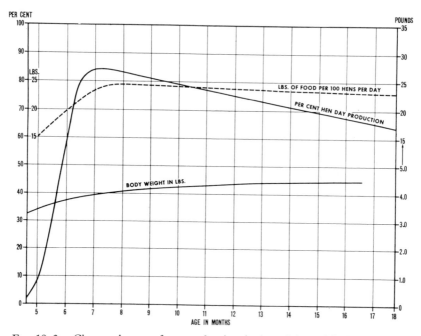

Fig. 10-2.—Changes in rate of egg production, body weight and feed consumption expected for high-producing laying hens during the production year. (Courtesy of Kimber Farms, Inc.)

Protein requirements of laying hens may vary considerably depending primarily on the rate of production and needs for body weight gains. Average egg production, feed consumption, and body weight curves of a modern, high-producing strain of layers are shown in Figure 10–2. In a typical flock, egg production would be expected to begin at twenty-two weeks of age when body weight is only 3.5 pounds. During the next few weeks, egg production rises rapidly to a maximum, while body weight continues to increase as the hen completes her body growth. As the production year advances and mature weight is reached, rate of egg production begins to fall gradually.

In terms of protein needs for laying hens, the greatest amount of protein is required whenimaximum rate of production is reached while the hen is still gainng in body weight. For many years a usual feeding program for laying hens consisted of feeding one laying ration throughout the production year. More recently, however, the critical need for adequate amounts of high-quality protein during the early months of production has been recognized and many feeding programs for laying hens include several different rations varying in protein content, to be used at different stages of the production year.

A typical feeding program might include 3 different laying rations. The formula used during the early production period, when maximum rate of lay is reached, contains 18 to 19 per cent of protein. When mature body weight is reached, and number of eggs produced begins to decrease, the protein content of the diet is reduced to 16 to 17 per cent. An even further reduction in protein level is sometimes made when egg production decreases to a still lower level.

As discussed previously, when protein requirements are expressed as a percentage of the diet, many additional factors influence the protein requirement. In the experiments summarized in Table 10–2, the rations fed contained 16 per cent protein. The protein intake varied tremendously, depending on the feed consumed, from 2.4 lbs per 100 hens per day for the highest energy ration in hot weather, to 5.8 lbs per 100 hens per day for the lowest energy ration in cold weather. To avoid deficiency or waste of dietary protein, rations for laying hens must be formulated to take into account the factors affecting feed consumption and protein needs. During very hot weather, hens at a given stage of production should receive more protein as a percentage of the diet than comparable hens during colder weather.

Some reports from Cornell University have summarized the changes in protein requirements of laying hens that can be expected as a result of the factors discussed above. These are listed for three stages of production in Table 10–7. The protein requirements listed in the early stage of production are based on a requirement of about 17 grams of a well-balanced protein per day. For the second stage the requirement is estimated as 16 grams of protein per day and for the third period, 15 grams per day. The expected feed consumption

Table 10-7.—Protein Requirements of White Leghorn Hens as Related to Environmental Temperature, Stage of Production, and Metabolizable Energy Content of the Diet

Metabolizable energy of diet	Cool climate		Hot climate	
	Expected feed consumption/ 100 hens/day	Protein required	Expected feed consumption/ 100 hens/day	Protein required
kcal/lb	lbs	per cent of diet	lbs	percent of diet
	22 to 40 weeks of age			
1250	22.0	17.0	20.5	18.0
1300	21.0	17.5	20.0	18.5
1350	20.5	18.0	19.0	19.5
1400	20.0	18.5	18.5	20.0
	40 weeks of age to 65% production			
1250	26.0	14.5	23.5	15.5
1300	25.0	15.0	22.0	16.5
1350	24.0	15.5	21.5	17.0
1400	23.0	16.0	20.5	17.5
	after production has fallen below 65% production			
1250	25.0	14.0	23.0	15.0
1300	24.0	14.5	22.0	15.5
1350	23.0	15.0	21.0	16.5
1400	22.0	15.5	20.0	17.0

listed in the table applies only to laying strains of slightly more than 4 pounds mature weight and under conditions where adequate housing and other management factors have been provided. These figures do illustrate, however, the changes in formulation necessary to insure a proper daily intake of protein under widely varying conditions.

Any statement of protein needs of laying hens must of course assume a proper amino acid balance of the dietary protein. A deficiency of an essential amino acid will result in poor egg production and reduced egg size just as will a deficiency of total protein. Amino aicd requirements of layers are subject to similar variations as are requirements for total protein.

The determination of requirements for individual amino acids for laying hens is considerably more difficult than for growing chicks. Actual feeding experiments to adequately test levels of each amino acid are hard to perform because of the long feeding period necessary to properly evaluate the performance of laying hens. Purified diets containing crystalline amino acids have been successfully devised for laying hens but their high cost makes long-term feeding experiments very expensive. Estimates of the amino acid requirements of laying hens are based primarily on the amino acid composition of egg protein. The proportion of essential amino acids in dietary protein must closely follow the proportion of amino acids in the egg proteins synthesized. The estimated requirements for the essential amino acids for laying hens are given in Table 10–4.

VITAMIN AND MINERAL REQUIREMENTS

Most requirements of poultry for vitamins and minerals are precisely known, particularly for those vitamins and mineral elements likely to be deficient in practical rations. Except for a few of the vitamins or minerals that are not likely to be deficient under practical conditions, dietary levels can be recommended that will provide sufficient amounts to allow efficient growth and production.

Unlike protein, vitamins and trace mineral elements are usually supplied to poultry feeds in excess of their minimum requirements. Thus, requirements for these nutrients are usually not stated in terms of expected rate of feed consumption or energy content of the diet, since sufficient amounts over the minimum requirement are usually included in diets for poultry. However, if only minimum levels are provided, variations in expected feed consumption must be considered, and very high energy rations must be more liberally supplied with vitamins and minerals than low energy rations.

Requirements of Vitamins and Minerals for Growth

Estimates of minimum requirements for vitamins and minerals for young chicks are included in Table 10–8. Rations for young starting chicks and starting broilers are usually very liberally supplied with supplemental vitamins and trace elements. Because of the rapid increase in body mass that occurs at this stage of life, the needs for these nutrients are particularly critical.

Levels of calcium and phosphorus supplied to rations for growing chicks should be kept very close to the stated requirements. Excess calcium may interact with other components of the diet and cause deficiencies of other mineral elements, particularly manganese and zinc, by interfering with their absorption from the intestinal tract. The phosphorus must in large part be supplied in a form that is available to the young chick. The requirement of starting chickens for available phosphorus is about 0.45 per cent of the diet. Phosphorus in plant materials is usually not considered to be more than 30 per cent available to chickens, whereas in mineral supplements and animal products the phosphorus is usually highly available.

Requirements for Egg Production and Hatchability

A very critical test for the nutrient composition of a ration is its ability to support hatchability of eggs. The requirements of vitamins and trace elements for egg production are much less critical than are the requirements for hatchability. The quantity of vitamins and trace elements present in an egg can be modified a great deal by the amount present in the diet consumed by the hen. Rations for breeding hens normally are more liberally supplemented with vitamins, trace elements, and sources of possible unidentified nutritional factors than are rations for laying hens.

Table 10–8.—Vitamin and Mineral Requirements of Chickens (in Percentage or Amount Required per Kilogram of Feed)[1]

	Starting chickens 0–8 wks.	Growing chickens 8–18 wks.	Laying hens	Breeding hens
Vitamins				
Vitamin A activity (U.S.P. Units)	2,000	2,000	4,000	4,000
Vitamin D (Int. Chick Units)	200	200	500	500
Vitamin K_1, mg	0.8*	0.8*	0.8*	0.8*
Thiamin, mg	1.8	?	?	0.8
Riboflavin, mg	3.6	1.8	2.2	3.8
Pantothenic acid, mg	10	10	2.2	10
Nicotinic acid, mg	27	11	11*	27*
Pyridoxine, mg	3	3*	3	4.5
Biotin, mg	0.09	?	?	0.15
Choline, mg	1,300	1,000*	—	—
Folacin, mg	1.2	1.0*	0.25	0.35
Vitamin B_{12}, mg	0.009	?	?	0.003
Minerals				
Calcium, per cent	1.0	1.0	3.0*	3.0*
Phosphorus, per cent[2]	0.7	0.6	0.6	0.6
Sodium, per cent	0.15	0.15	0.15	0.15
Potassium, per cent	0.2	0.16	0.16*	0.16*
Manganese, mg	55	33*	33*	33
Iodine, mg	0.35	0.35	0.30	0.30
Magnesium, mg	500	?	?	?
Iron, mg	40	?	?	?
Copper, mg	4	?	?	?
Zinc, mg	35	25*	25*	35*

[1] Obtained in part from National Research Council Nutrient Requirements for Poultry. Values followed by * are estimates by the present authors. These figures are estimates of minimum requirements, and include no margin of safety.

[2] At least 0.45 per cent of the total feed of starting chickens should be inorganic phosphorus. Approximately 30 per cent of the phosphorus of plant sources may be considered a part of the inorganic phosphorus.

16

Calcium Requirements of Laying Hens

A major nutritional need in the diet of laying hens is calcium. For every large egg a hen lays she must use about 2 grams of calcium in the formation of the eggshell. A hen that lays 250 eggs per year deposits roughly 500 grams of calcium in her eggs, primarily in the form of calcium carbonate. This represents approximately 1,300 grams of calcium carbonate deposited by the hen in the shells of the eggs. Calcium is not efficiently used by the laying hen and probably only 50 to 60 per cent of the calcium consumed is actually retained and deposited in the eggs. To produce the eggshells required, this hen would have to consume about 2,600 grams of calcium carbonate during a laying year, an amount considerably in excess of her body weight. This example illustrates the magnitude of the calcium metabolism that must go on in a laying hen. This is considerably greater than for any other species of animal.

The calcium requirement of laying hens is difficult to state in precise terms. This is because egg production can be maintained at a high level with lower levels of calcium than are required to produce a satisfactory eggshell. Modern marketing and egg-handling conditions require a very sturdy eggshell that will not crack easily during handling. When hens near the end of their production year, the eggshells produced are normally thinner and of poorer quality than those produced by pullets in the early part of the production year. Hot weather will cause a thinner eggshell to be produced. Eggshell quality can also be influenced by respiratory diseases, which seem to affect the oviduct so that abnormal egg-shells are produced. Not all these factors affecting eggshell quality can be corrected by feeding more dietary calcium.

Feed consumption is also important in determining calcium requirements when expressed as a percentage of the diet, for the same reasons discussed previously for protein requirements. It is possible for young pullets in the early stages of production to make good use of their dietary calcium and manufacture satisfactory egg-shells when the calcium content of the diet is less than 3 per cent. Under other conditions, particularly for rations for old hens in hot weather, the calcium content of a laying mash may be raised to as high as 4 to 4.5 per cent, in an effort to improve eggshell quality.

EVALUATION OF FEEDING PROGRAMS

The best estimate of the value of a ration for the production of poultry meat or eggs is the efficiency with which the conversion of food to product is made. A balanced ration may be defined as a combination of feeds furnishing nutrients in such proportions, amounts and form as to properly nourish without waste a given group of birds for a particular purpose. The nutrient requirements for poultry discussed earlier in this chapter must be met with the feed ingredients available so that the final formula provides a balanced ration.

PLATE III

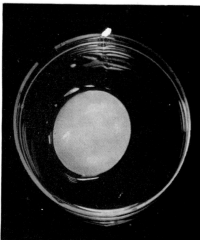

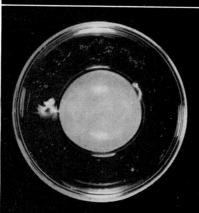

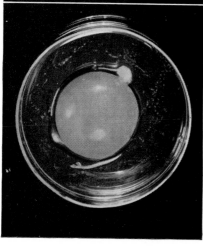

**Yolk Color Is Directly
Influenced by Feed**

———

Extremely Pale Yolk

Produced by hens fed a mixture
of—

Oats 50%
Bran 50%
Occasional table scraps
No green forage

———

Medium-Colored Yolk

Produced by hens fed a ration
of—

Yellow corn 50%
Wheat 25%
Oats 25%
No green forage

———

Deep Orange Yolk

Produced by hens fed a mixture
of—

Corn 52%
Wheat 24%
Oats 14%
Dried milk and soy
    bean meal 10%
Green grass pasture

———

These three examples of the influence of feed on yolk color were
observed in three flocks near
Urbana, Illinois. The spots appearing on the yolks are merely
light reflections.

Courtesy of the Illinois
Agricultural Experiment Station.

For economical poultry and egg production the cost of the ration must also be considered. The most economical feed is one which produces the most product at least cost. This is not necessarily the feed costing the least per pound.

Many poultry producers do not have complete knowledge of the nutrient composition of the feed they are using. They use a commercially produced feed, and have no way to estimate the metabolizable energy content or some of the other important nutrients. Therefore it is essential for a poultry farmer to know the efficiency of his feeding program.

Feed efficiency, measured in terms of amount of feed required to produce a pound of broiler or a dozen eggs, can be affected by a number of factors as seen in previous discussions. The most important of these are (1) rate of growth or egg production, (2) metabolizable energy content of the feed, (3) body size of laying hens, (4) nutrient adequacy of the ration (5) environmental temperature, (6) health of the flock.

When the feed efficiency of a healthy flock of laying hens in high production and housed in a comfortable environment is poor, the feeding program should be evaluated to determine if improvements in feed efficiency can economically be made. Adequate records of production and feed consumption are essential in evaluating a feeding program. Such records make it possible for a good poultry producer to know the pounds of feed required to produce a pound of broiler or a dozen eggs.

Palatability

Chickens have the ability to taste, and appear to prefer certain flavors over others. If two feeds are offered to a group of chickens, one containing a preferred flavor compound and one not, the feed containing the desirable flavor will be consumed to a greater extent than the unflavored one. However, if no choice is given, both feeds will usually be consumed in about the same amount. Palatability, as such, is probably much less important in affecting feed consumption than the nutritional adequacy of the diet.

Rapid changes in rations for laying hens should be avoided, since occasionally a hen will refuse to consume a new ration with a consistency and appearance markedly different from the one she has been previously fed. Mixing the new feed with the old for a few days will usually suffice to make the change smoothly.

Effect on Product

The composition of the feed can in some ways affect the composition of the product. Probably the yellow color of broiler skin and shanks, or of the egg yolk, is the most important characteristic that can be influenced by feeding. Some markets require different degrees of yolk color or skin color in broilers from others. There are special markets in food industries for very deeply colored egg yolks. The color of the skin or shank of a broiler or of the yolk of an egg is primarily due to carotenoid pigments consumed in the feed. The amount of feed ingredients used that are high in these pigments will greatly affect the pigmentation of these products. Corn, alfalfa meal and corn gluten meal are the primary feedstuffs used to contribute these pigments. Many synthetic pigment compounds and other feed sources of pigments have been studied for their usefulness in feeding poultry. Pimento peppers, marigold petals, and algae meal are other feed sources containing high levels of carotenoid pigments useful in producing pigmentation desirable in poultry products.

Chapter 11

Controlling Diseases and Parasites

Losses from disease and from parasites can be very serious, and it is important for the poultryman to be familiar with the most effective means of prevention and control in order to keep such losses at a minimum. Constant vigilance is the price of success in this phase of poultry management.

Various estimates place the monetary loss to the poultry industry at more than $300,000,000 a year. Not all of this loss can be prevented, but ways of reducing it are certainly worthy of special study. Of much more direct concern to the individual flock owner are such losses as 30 or 40 per cent of a flock of young chicks from bronchitis or more than a month's egg production following an outbreak of Newcastle disease.

THE NATURE OF DISEASE

The disease problem may be looked upon as a constant struggle between the host and the invading organisms. The flock owner sits as a sort of referee whose interests and sympathies are entirely with the host but who is too often helpless to do much more than watch a losing battle, while all his profit and some of his capital are hauled away to an incinerator or disposal pit.

If the poultryman is to avoid this unhappy circumstance, he must become, in effect, a health officer for his flock. He must plan and carry out a program of flock management which will turn the tide of battle always, or nearly always, in favor of the host. There are three distinct approaches to such a program. The first is to adopt strict sanitary and quarantine procedures which will keep host and disease organisms apart. For example, it is obvious that if chickens can be kept continuously under conditions such that the cholera organism can never gain entrance, they will not be exposed to or suffer from fowl cholera. Chickens can be kept indoors, in buildings screened against flies and other insects, so that they will probably never become infested with tapeworms. Complete protection against all diseases and parasites is very difficult, if not impossible, to carry out on a commercial scale, but many practices can be adopted that will aid materially in the control of these troubles.

The second general method is to weaken the attacking agent so that it is unable successfully to invade the host and establish itself. This is usually accomplished by placing various sorts of barriers in the way, or by destroying large numbers of the invaders through the use of strong disinfectants. Specific examples are the use of drugs to reduce coccidial infections, the spraying of poultry houses with malathion emulsion to control lice and mites, and the maintenance of high humidity in separate hatchers together with formaldehyde fumigation to slow the spread of pullorum organisms from infected to healthy chicks.

The third method of approach is to strengthen the position of the host so that it is better able to withstand the constant onslaught of invading organisms of various kinds. This objective may be partially accomplished through natural means, such as breeding for increased resistance to specific diseases, improved nutrition which helps to insure the physical well-being of the fowls, and provision for clean and comfortable surroundings. It may also take the form of purely artificial protection, such as vaccination against fowl pox or laryngotracheitis.

In actual practice, all three methods of disease control are used, as well as occasional treatment for specific maladies. As a general rule, medicinal treatment is ineffective, and dependence must be placed on other methods in attempting to reduce or prevent mortality. The poultryman needs information of three sorts in solving this problem:

1. How to avoid disease outbreaks by proper methods of management,
2. How to recognize disease outbreaks when they do occur, and
3. Procedures to follow in obtaining a correct diagnosis and specific directions for control.

Each of these will be discussed briefly in the following pages.

DISEASE PREVENTION

Maintenance of flock health is one of the prerequisites to profitable poultry and egg production, and this implies a need for some knowledge of the more important disease-inducing agents, the methods by which they are spread from flock to flock, and the weak points at which they may be most easily controlled or eliminated. Most of the economically important diseases of poultry are infectious and contagious. They are readily transmitted from one individual to another, though sometimes by widely varying means.

The Causes of Disease

Many diseases are caused by bacteria. Common examples are tuberculosis, fowl cholera, pullorum disease, coryza. Most of them, fortunately, are not transmissible to other farm animals or to man. Effective methods of control include the elimination of carrier fowls, and the adoption of quarantine and sanitation procedures which will help to prevent infection.

Certain important diseases are caused by ultra-microscopic agents called viruses. Some of these are extremely virulent, and the diseases which they cause can be very costly to flock owners. Fowl pox, laryngotracheitis, and the avian leukosis complex are examples. Effective vaccines have been developed for the first two, and constitute a means of providing adequate protection for individuals and flocks.

Two of the most destructive diseases of poultry, coccidiosis and blackhead, are caused by microscopic animal organisms known as protozoa. Chickens develop a certain degree of immunity to coccidiosis following a mild infection.

Fowls are also susceptible to a few mycoses or fungous diseases. These are of much less frequent occurrence than the types of disease already mentioned, but they can cause serious losses on occasion. The two examples most often encountered are aspergillosis and thrush.

Finally, there are numerous parasitic infestations to which fowls are peculiarly subject. These include internal parasites such as the large intestinal roundworm, the cecal worm, and various tapeworms; and external parasites such as body lice, sticktight fleas, roost mites, and the northern fowl mite.

So-called nutritional diseases result chiefly from deficiencies of certain vitamins and minerals. These have been discussed in Chapter 8.

The Spread of Disease

Poultry diseases are spread in many different ways, and the common means by which each particular disease is disseminated must be known before one can proceed intelligently to break the cycle of infection and prevent further losses. In controlling respiratory infections, for example, it is much more important to keep the pullets entirely away from the older hens, i.e., housed separately, than to go to extreme lengths in providing clean quarters. Hens which have recovered may act as carriers and are a constant source of infection for other susceptible individuals.

Similarly, hens which have survived an outbreak of pullorum disease as chicks may become carriers. Many eggs laid by these carrier hens will be infected with the pullorum organism and, in consequence, chicks from such eggs already have the disease when they are hatched.

Certain infections are apparently air borne. Others are readily transmitted by means of contaminated soil or water. Still others are spread by contact. Some may be disseminated by vectors, i.e., flies, mosquitoes, ticks, and the like, which without becoming infected themselves nevertheless transmit infectious material from one fowl to another. Finally, there is always danger of disease dissemination by purely mechanical means—on the shoes and outer clothing of persons who may pass from one flock to another, on feed bags which are re-used without sterilization, in crates which are used to transport fowls, or on the feet of wild birds which fly from farm to farm.

Specific methods of transmission can be guarded against when they are known to be important in connection with a particular disease, but because of the many other possible means of spreading disease, and because the primary method of dissemination is not always known, it is necessary also to make use of those general sanitary and quarantine measures which are effective for almost any type of infection.

Methods of Sanitation and Isolation

The practice of sanitation is not always simple and it is not easy. If carelessly or only partially followed it is of little value, but if rigidly carried out it can be highly effective. An excellent example of the value of a careful sanitation and isolation program is furnished by the results obtained in Maine in a program designed to raise broilers free of specific pathogens. This originated as a research program aimed at control of diseases that cause condemnation of large numbers of broilers in processing plants. In flocks following rigid isolation and sanitation practices, nearly two and one-half million broilers were reared in a 30-month period. With no vaccination 95 per cent of the flocks were free of Newcastle disease. Where chicks were obtained from flocks free of mycoplasmosis only one flock out of 25 showed any evidence of this infection. Infectious bronchitis occurred in 61 per cent of the flocks and was the most difficult to control. Many of the farms under this program completely eliminated respiratory disease, and the weight, feed conversion and livability of the broilers raised were good.

The essential features of the Maine Specific Pathogen Free program of sanitation and isolation reported in Bulletin 633 of the Maine Agricultural Experiment Station included the following points.

1. Houses must not have dirt floors.
2. Houses must be screened against wild birds (maximum of one inch).
3. Houses must be provided with doors that lock and are kept locked at all times.
4. The farm shall have bulk feed facilities with outside filler pipes. No feed delivered shall have been handled in bags.
5. There must be outside oil filling pipes.
6. Poultry houses must be located no closer than 100 feet to public highways and not closer than 1,000 feet to poultry houses on adjacent premises.
7. The farm must have an approved disposal pit or incinerator for dead birds.
8. Houses must be located at least 1,000 feet from poultry litter piles and other vermin-attracting debris.

9. All houses should have a pan with an approved disinfectant and a stiff brush in the grain room next to the door. The disinfectant solution should be changed at least once daily. The caretaker must use this to clean his footwear upon entering or leaving the house.
10. Sawdust should be delivered in clean trucks.
11. The house must be thoroughly cleaned and disinfected with an approved disinfectant prior to the introduction of the baby chicks.
12. Chicks must originate from Pullorum-Typhoid Free flocks.
13. Only one age of birds is permitted on a farm, and no pet birds or other poultry allowed.
14. No visitors, servicemen, feedmen, salesmen, or neighbors are to be allowed into the houses at any time.
15. A log book showing date and time must be kept, indicating any authorized persons entering houses.
16. No domestic animals shall be permitted to enter the poultry house (*e.g.*, dogs and cats).
17. No tractors, dump trucks, or other equipment used in connection with the poultry enterprise can be borrowed from or loaned to other farms.
18. Baby chicks shall be delivered in new or disinfected shipping equipment, directly from the hatchery, by attendants wearing disinfected shoes, freshly laundered coveralls, and caps.
19. Caretakers shall not visit premises where other poultry are kept or poultry products are processed.
20. None of the members of the caretaker's household shall work or provide service where poultry is kept or poultry products are processed.
21. Poultry meat and eggs for home consumption shall be purchased in grocery stores only.

Such a complete program cannot be carried out on all poultry farms, and some special problems occur in laying flocks. However, the principles on which the program is based can be applied in other circumstances. The following procedures could be considered as reasonable steps to be followed in a practical sanitation program for commercial flocks. Certain variations and additions may be appropriate under special conditions.

1. If possible, avoid the introduction of partly grown or adult stock to the farm. When this is not possible, as when started pullets are purchased, buy only from farms where good disease control practices are followed. Be sure to determine what immunizations have been given to the stock purchased, and insist on delivery in clean, disinfected crates and trucks.
2. Isolate and rear chicks away from adult stock. Grow chicks indoors, or provide enough land so that range-grown chicks do not occupy a given area more often than once every three years. If chicks from two or more sources are to be grown at the same time, isolate them from each other during the first two months.

3. Avoid traveling directly from the adult flocks to the chick range, if at all possible. If the business is large enough to make it practical, have separate caretakers for chicks and hens.
4. Keep visitors out of the houses and yards, especially those whose business takes them from farm to farm.
5. Maintain clean, sanitary quarters. Have a clean water supply. Use feeders which reduce waste to a minimum, and prevent contamination of feed by the chickens. Avoid spillage of feed where it will attract wild birds and rodents.
6. House pullets and hens separately. This is not only good management, but it protects the pullet flock from infections which may be spread by "carrier" hens.
7. Follow procedures which will keep the fly nuisance at a minimum. In certain areas it may be equally important to control mosquitoes and other biting insects.
8. Keep the poultry areas sufficiently well fenced to prevent the escape of chickens to neighboring farms, and to prevent chickens from other flocks from gaining access to the premises.
9. If a breeding program is being conducted on the farm, practice rigid selection in order to make use of high-viability families, year after year.

HOW TO RECOGNIZE DISEASE

Since complete protection through sanitation and quarantine is rarely possible under farm or ranch conditions, it is important to be able to recognize disease and parasitic infestations in their early stages. Most poultrymen have to acquire this ability through costly experience, because no amount of written information can take the place of knowledge gained by daily contact with a poultry flock and close observation of conditions as they change and develop from season to season.

Often, one of the first signs of trouble in a flock is a drop in feed consumption. This generally occurs before other obvious signs of disease are evident. In large caged-layer installations, changes in feed consumption are often much easier to detect than subtle changes in the appearance of the hens. Other indications of poor health in a flock, such as general unthriftiness, inactivity and specific disease symptoms, can be detected only by careful attention to the appearance and general condition of a flock by an experienced poultryman.

Since many death losses, especially in fowls of laying age, are of a non-specific type, not known to be related to disease organisms, and therefore not capable of spreading to other fowls in the flock, the poultryman must learn to distinguish between various sorts of morbidity before he can hope to apply control measures effectively. This calls for experience, and can be only partially learned from books.

Pathologists at the California Station, in autopsying about 7000 chickens of laying age, more than two-thirds of which came from commercial flocks, found that more than half of the deaths resulted from pathological conditions quite unrelated to infection, parasitism, or other specific disease manifestations. This non-specific mortality is a serious poultry problem to which there is as yet no completely satisfactory answer. Selection of breeding stock on the basis of family survival offers a most encouraging prospect for successful control.

WHAT TO DO WHEN DISEASE OUTBREAKS OCCUR

A sick or dead bird should be considered as a warning, depending somewhat on conditions, and not merely as something to be disposed of promptly. An attempt should be made to determine the cause of death in order that one may decide what steps need to be taken to prevent further loss. Prompt and accurate diagnosis is absolutely essential to any intelligent plan of disease eradication and control. Many local veterinarians have received special training in the diagnosis and control of poultry diseases, and are in a position to give expert assistance. If such a man is located in the community, by all means make use of his services. If no competent help is available, specimens may be sent to a state laboratory for diagnosis. Obviously, not every chicken that dies should be sent to the laboratory for examination, but any indication of more than a normal loss should be the occasion for getting diagnostic help as soon as possible.

It is, of course, important to remember that mere post-mortem examination is not always sufficient for making a diagnosis. Special tests, bacteriological cultures, or animal inoculations may be necessary. These take time. But effective control measures depend, first of all, on an accurate diagnosis. If specimens have decomposed before arrival at the laboratory it is usually quite impossible to determine the exact cause of death.

To obtain a diagnosis at a laboratory, provide the veterinarian with a representative sample of the birds showing typical symptoms observed in the flock. Select three to five laying hens and five to ten brooder chicks for examination. An autopsy performed on a single bird may not provide accurate information on the rest of the flock. Both live affected birds and those freshly dead from the disease are most helpful to the diagnostician.

It is also important to send along a description of the flock giving the total number and age of birds in the flock, the number affected, how long the disease has existed, what the death loss has been, what the specific symptoms are, together with a brief description of the housing, feeding, and management methods in use. All of this can be helpful in arriving at a correct diagnosis.

Fig. 11–1.—A poultry farm incinerator which is fired by LP gas. Such equipment is essential on many large commercial farms. (Courtesy of Pacific Poultryman.)

COMMON DISEASES OF YOUNG CHICKENS

Poultry diseases may properly be classified and discussed on the basis of cause, *e.g.*, bacterial, virus, protozoan, and the like, but the poultryman is usually confronted with the disease first and the cause later—after a diagnosis has been made. For convenience, they will be discussed here as diseases of young chickens and diseases of hens, with parasites as a third classification.

Pullorum Disease

Probably more has been written about this disease than about any other infection in poultry and no doubt more flock owners are familiar with it than with any other ailment, with the possible exception of colds. Under the provisions of the National Poultry Improvement Plan, millions of hens are tested every year for the purpose of detecting reactors which are the means of transmitting the disease to a new generation of chicks.

The cause of the disease is the microorganism *Salmonella pullorum*. In baby chicks, the disease takes the form of an acute, highly fatal septicemia, and most of the deaths occur during the first two weeks after hatching. In female chicks which survive, the organism frequently becomes localized in the ovary so that eggs laid by such individuals are very likely to be infected. After three weeks in an incubator, under conditions which are almost ideal for bacterial growth, the chicks which hatch from infected eggs are literally teeming with the organism, and early death is almost a certainty. Because of this peculiar method of transmission from generation to generation, elimination of the carrier hens is an important step in controlling the disease. The agglutination test, applied by mixing antigen with a drop of blood under field conditions, or with a small amount of blood serum in the laboratory, is the accepted means of identifying reactors. It is important to use an antigen which will show a reaction with the known variant strains, as well as with the standard strain of *S. pullorum*.

Because the disease is so readily spread from chick to chick at hatching time, it has become common practice to fumigate incubators as a precautionary measure. Either the potassium permanganate or the cheesecloth method may be used. The following practical recommendations are taken from Bulletin 416 of the Kentucky Station entitled "Effect of Formaldehyde Fumigation on Mortality of Chick Embryos."

1. The incubator and eggs should be clean and should otherwise conform to the best practices in sanitation.
2. Fumigation at high concentrations should not be made during the first three days of incubation because the embryos are then most susceptible to formaldehyde.
3. Eggs in the separate hatching compartments of an incubator should be fumigated on the eighteenth to twentieth days of incubation.

4. Eggs may be fumigated at time of hatching, but in no case should fumigation be delayed until the chicks have dried.
5. The formalin should be standard 40 per cent, commercial grade. It should be stored in a well-stoppered bottle.

   WARNING: Do not permit formalin to come in direct contact with the hands, for it may cause serious skin trouble. Wear rubber gloves when handling it.

6. Potassium permanganate should be kept in a colored bottle or moisture-proof container.
7. Just before fumigation the humidity in the incubator should be raised to 92° to 94° F. wet-bulb reading. The fumigation should be performed at normal operating temperature.
8. Fumigation by the permanganate method requires the following items:
   (a) Measuring graduate or bottle for the formalin.
   (b) Small balances or standardized measure for the permanganate.
   (c) Large earthenware or enameled dish for combining formalin and permanganate. A large enameled wash basin or cooking utensil may be used.
9. Effective germicidal fumigation for pullorum organisms by the permanganate method requires about 35 cc. of 40 per cent formalin and 17.5 grams of potassium permanganate per 100 cubic feet. Converted to the standard usually employed by hatcherymen, this proportion is equivalent to 1.2 fluid ounces of formalin and 0.6 ounce permanganate per 100 cubic feet.
10. The dish should be placed on the floor of the incubator (or in the intake air channel), the permanganate placed in the dish, and the formalin poured over the permanganate.
11. Ammonium hydroxide may be used after fumigation to shorten the period in which the disagreeable odor of formaldehyde is present. Some reduction in embryo mortality may occur with its use.
12. Control of mushy-chick disease requires two to three times stronger fumigation than the control of pullorum. Seventy to 100 cc. formalin and 35 to 50 grams permanganate per 100 cubic feet is the concentration recommended for effective control of mushy-chick disease.
    Mortality with three times normal fumigation is not serious, and if necessary the treatment could be increased still more, provided the fumigating is done after the fourth day of incubation.
13. Fumigation by the cheesecloth method requires the following items:
    (a) Measuring graduate or bottle for the formalin.

(*b*) Cheesecloth of appropriate size.

(*c*) Small hooks, tacks, or rods, for holding cloth in place.

(*d*) Bucket or basin in which to immerse cheesecloth in the formalin.

(*e*) Rubber gloves to be worn while handling the cheese-cloth saturated with formalin. *Warning! Serious skin trouble may occur if formalin comes in direct contact with the hands.*

14. When the cheesecloth method is used, pieces of cheesecloth about 1 yard square should be immersed in a sufficient quantity of formalin to supply 20 cc. formalin per 100 cubic feet in incubator space. The cloth should then be hung over rods near the fan and allowed to remain for 3 hours. (This method requires approximately two-thirds the quantity of formalin needed in the permanganate method.)

15. Treatment by either method should last not less than 1 hour nor more than 3 hours.

16. If suitable measuring and weighing facilities are not available the operator should consult his local pharmacist or photographer about the weighing or measuring of the needed materials.

17. The recommendations of the incubator manufacturer should be considered in fumigating with formaldehyde.

Infectious Bronchitis

This is one of the most highly contagious of the respiratory diseases of chickens. Even specially constructed isolation quarters may not keep the virus from entering a flock. When the disease strikes very young chicks, mortality is often very high and usually spreads very rapidly through the entire flock.

Some immunity to the disease is transmitted through the egg to chicks from dams immunized against bronchitis virus. For this reason the disease is now more often encountered among more mature birds than in very young chicks in the first two to three weeks after hatching. When hens contract the disease, egg production drops sharply and often a flock will not return to normal production following an attack of infectious bronchitis. Eggshell quality is often poor in hens that have recovered. Rough, very porous shells are commonly observed.

Once a flock has been infected with the disease, no treatment is effective for control. Recovered birds are usually immune. A properly conducted vaccination program is the best method for control of infectious bronchitis. Modified live-virus vaccines are available that will give immunity to infection. These can be administered on a mass basis using vaccines intended for use as a spray, a dust, or in the drinking water. Periodic revaccination is necessary to maintain immunity for long periods.

Coccidiosis

This is one of the most widespread and destructive diseases of chickens. It is caused by various protozoan parasites belonging to the genus *Eimeria*. One species, *Eimeria tenella*, characteristically invades the lining of the ceca, producing the cecal type of the disease, while others are found in the lining of the small intestine where they cause the intestinal type. The cecal type is usually the more acute, and is often designated by poultrymen as "bloody diarrhea." Most outbreaks occur in chickens ranging from 4 to 12 weeks of age, but older chickens may become infected. A certain degree of resistance is established by mild exposure, but resistance to one species does not protect against infection with any of the other species. Furthermore, the recovered resistant individuals may act as carriers and be a source of infection for other susceptible birds with which they come in contact for some time after their recovery.

The life cycle of the parasite is such that freshly discharged oöcysts, which pass out with the droppings, are not infective if eaten by other chickens. Within a few days, however, under suitable conditions of moisture and temperature, these oöcysts go through a process known as sporulation, after which they are highly infective. Whether eaten soon after sporulation or not for as long as several months, they become activated in the intestinal tract of the chicken and produce the characteristic infection of the cecal or intestinal lining.

Sporulated oöcysts are quite resistant, and ordinary disinfectant solutions have little effect on them. Extreme dryness is destructive to them, and so is excessive heat. It is therefore desirable to maintain dry litter during brooding as an aid in both prevention and control. Outbreaks are particularly common following spells of warm, wet weather which provide ideal conditions for the coccidia to develop.

The fact that some time is required after oöcysts are passed out in the droppings before they can become infective for new hosts, affords an opportunity for breaking the life cycle. If affected chickens are confined indoors, if the house is kept warm and dry, and if the litter and droppings are removed daily, so that reinfection is prevented, the disease will quickly run its course. Wiremesh platforms to support the water and feed containers, and wirescreened roosting sections which prevent the chickens from coming in contact with the droppings are also very helpful in combating this disease. Wire panel floors may be used for the entire brooder house.

Many drugs have been developed for the treatment or suppression of coccidiosis. These drugs, known as coccidiostats, act to depress the development of the coccidia with little harm to the host. The drugs are most commonly administered in the feed although some, especially those used for treatment of disease outbreaks, can be

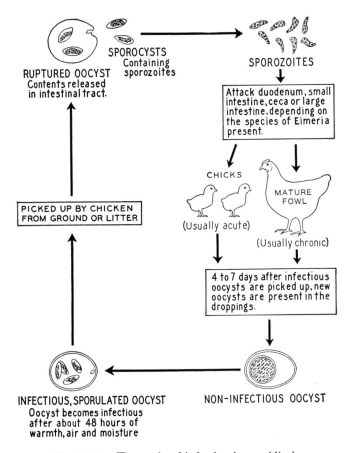

SPOROCYSTS
Containing
sporozoites

RUPTURED OOCYST
Contents released
in intestinal tract.

SPOROZOITES

Attack duodenum, small
intestine, ceca or large
intestine, depending on
the species of Eimeria
present.

CHICKS

MATURE
FOWL

(Usually acute)

(Usually chronic)

PICKED UP BY CHICKEN
FROM GROUND OR LITTER

4 to 7 days after infectious
oocysts are picked up, new
oocysts are present in the
droppings.

INFECTIOUS, SPORULATED OOCYST
Oocyst becomes infectious
after about 48 hours of
warmth, air and moisture

NON-INFECTIOUS OOCYST

Fig. 11–2.—The cycle of infection in coccidiosis.

administered in the drinking water. Coccidiostats are particularly
useful in broiler raising and practically all broiler feeds contain some
drug to aid in the control of coccidiosis. These drugs are not always
one hundred per cent effective, and they should not be used as
substitutes for good management practices. When an effective
coccidiostat is used in conjunction with sound management,
coccidiosis in most instances can be properly controlled.

Following an infection, chickens normally develop a considerable
degree of resistance to coccidiosis. When raising replacement pullets,
some exposure to coccidiosis is desirable to cause development of
immunity. The use of a coccidiostatic drug at lower levels than
would be used for growing broilers often allows a controlled infection
to develop but prevents a "runaway" infection that might cause
serious losses. Controlled doses of mixed cultures of coccidia coupled
with a coccidiostatic drug are sometimes used to encourage the
development of immunity to the disease.

17

Since there are several effective coccidiostatic drugs on the market, manufacturers' directions for the levels used and the methods of administration should be carefully followed.

COMMON DISEASES OF HENS

The most common diseases of hens, in terms of economic loss to the industry, are those caused by viruses. These include the diseases of the avian leukosis complex, fowl pox, laryngotracheitis, and Newcastle disease.

The Avian Leukosis Complex

These diseases, characterized by the growth of lymphoid tumors in many tissues of the body, are among the most costly to the poultry industry today. Recognition of their economic importance led directly to the establishment of the U. S. Regional Poultry Research Laboratory at East Lansing, Michigan. The diseases included in the avian leukosis complex take a wide variety of forms.

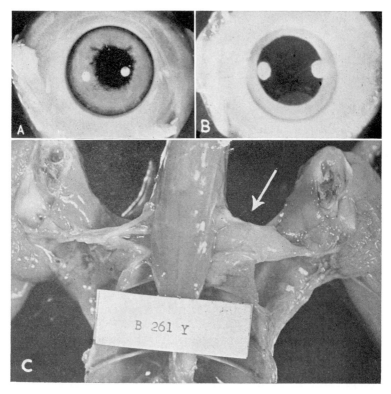

Fig. 11–3.—Common symptoms of the avian leukosis complex. *A*, Distorted pupil characteristic of the ocular type of the disease; *B*, a normal eye; *C*, enlarged nerve trunk characteristic of the neural form of the disease. (Courtesy of U. S. Department of Agriculture.)

This diversity has led to considerable confusion in the past in describing the diseases. In general, however, present-day investigators in this field recognize two apparently separate diseases, Marek's disease and lymphoid leukosis.

Marek's Disease

This disease was formerly called neural lymphomatosis or, commonly, fowl paralysis or range paralysis. It is primarily a disease of younger chickens from 2 to 5 months of age, although birds younger or older than this can be affected.

Paralysis of both legs or wings may be commonly observed in the neural form due to tumors of nerves leading to affected parts. Other tissues may be affected, particularly the visceral organs, the gonads or the eye. In the ocular form of the disease the iris becomes gray and is often distorted in shape. In severe cases, the bird becomes blind.

The infectious agent responsible for the disease has not been isolated but it is probably a virus. Day-old chicks injected with a suspension of tumor cells from an infected bird will show signs of the disease in a few weeks. Many injected chicks will die by the time they are eight weeks of age. Marek's disease has not been shown to be transmitted through the egg but it is readily spread by contact with infected birds. There is no effective treatment of the disease, or any foolproof preventive measures that can be taken. However, losses from this disease can probably be kept to a minimum if good house hygiene and flock management are followed. Young stock should be isolated from old hens during the rearing period to prevent exposure to the virus. Strains of chickens have been developed that show genetic resistance to Marek's disease, and some control may be achieved by eliminating families from breeding stock that show a high incidence of the disease.

Lymphoid Leukosis

Synonyms for this disease are visceral lymphomatosis, or, simply, leukosis. In contrast to Marek's disease, lymphoid leukosis is primarily found in mature birds and is responsible for an appreciable amount of laying-house mortality.

All the visceral organs can be affected by the disease. No one of the organs is exempt from attack, and it often happens that several organs are affected in the same fowl. The liver, spleen, heart, ovary, kidneys and intestines are most frequently involved. The liver in particular may be greatly enlarged and the name, "big-liver disease," has been applied to lymphoid leukosis. The involvement may be generalized throughout several organs, or may be restricted to local tumor areas.

Cells of the blood may be affected, and in this form the disease has been called erythroblastosis. Affected birds may become pale and emaciated, and cease egg production. In some forms the birds become anemic.

Lymphoid leukosis can be spread by transmission of the virus to chicks through eggs from infected hens. In contrast to Marek's disease, spread by contact exposure is rather slow. No effective measures are known for the control or treatment of this disease.

Strict sanitation practices should be followed; infected birds should be disposed of promptly. Attempts are being made to develop flocks free of some leukosis viruses in an attempt to eliminate infection by egg transmission. It is still too soon to determine if this will eventually become an effective method of control.

FIG. 11–4.—Appearance of fowl pox lesions on the comb and wattles about ten days after natural infection.

Fowl Pox

This highly infectious disease, caused by a filterable virus, is also known as chicken pox, avian diphtheria, and sore-head. It shows up in two different forms, commonly designated as the skin or comb form, and the diphtheritic or throat form. Both types may occur in the same individual. In the skin type there are numerous small, raised, blister-like spots on the comb, wattles or face. These soon dry up and form brownish scabs. They may be scattered, and few in number, or they may cover almost the entire surface of the comb, face, and wattles. Light infection may cause little inconvenience to the fowls, but more often it is severe enough to cause loss of appetite, followed by loss in weight and a marked reduction in egg production.

In the diphtheritic form of the disease there are yellowish, raised, necrotic patches in the mouth and throat. They are firmly adherent to the mucous membrane, and may become so extensive as to interfere with eating and with breathing. The eyes are often involved, showing a watery discharge and, later a yellowish pus-like accumulation. The death rate is likely to be greater than with the skin type of the disease.

Treatment is of little value, but vaccination with egg-propagated live virus furnishes almost complete protection against infection. Vaccination actually gives the chicken a mild infection which is sufficient to develop a high degree of immunity. The vaccine is most easily administered by the "stick" method while the chickens are 6 to 16 weeks of age. Vaccination should be a routine annual procedure on farms where the disease has appeared. Pigeon pox vaccine is recommended in the case of fresh outbreaks in laying flocks.

Laryngotracheitis

This disease, known also as chicken "flu," is a highly contagious respiratory infection which often causes high mortality. It is a comparatively new disease in the United States but it has been reported from coast to coast. The cause is a filterable virus to which chickens are extremely susceptible.

The outstanding and most characteristic symptom is gasping. When inhaling, the fowl extends its head and neck upward with the mouth wide open. When exhaling, the head is drawn back and lowered, with the mouth closed. Coughing, rattling, wheezing, and occasional loud cries are frequently heard, as the fowls attempt to dislodge the accumulations of mucus in the air passages.

FIG. 11–5.—Laryngotracheitis. Characteristic position during inspiration. (Courtesy of California Agricultural Experiment Station.)

A vaccine prepared from the membranes of artificially infected embryos applied to the mucous membrane of the cloaca, gives protection against later infection. Another effective vaccine is available which is applied to the cornea of the eye. Since the live virus must be used for vaccination purposes, and since it is capable of causing the disease to break out in virulent form, great care must be taken to see that it is properly used. For this reason, vaccination is ordinarily not recommended unless the disease is prevalent in the community, or occurs regularly on the farm from year to year because of the presence of recovered carriers. If several flocks are housed on a single farm and the disease occurs in one of them, the others may be protected by prompt vaccination. When annual vaccination is practiced, the usual procedure is to apply it when the new crop of chickens is 16 weeks old or older.

Mycoplasmosis

This disease, often called Chronic Respiratory Disease (CRD) or Air Sac Disease, is widespread and causes serious losses to the poultry industry. Young and adult stock may be affected. Those infected with the disease may show nasal discharge, a foamy condition of the eyes and respiratory difficulty. The disease may spread slowly but symptoms may persist for a considerable time.

The disease is caused by an organism known as *Mycoplasma gallisepticum*, which belongs to a group of organisms known as pleuropneumonia-like organisms (PPLO). Field cases of the disease are usually complicated by infection from a virus, especially from infectious bronchitis or Newcastle disease, and one or more species of bacteria, particularly *E. coli*.

Transmission is principally from the hen through the egg to the chick. Contact transmission within a flock occurs, and the speed of spread through a flock depends on factors such as virulence of the organism, dose, and other infections that may be present.

Elimination of the disease can best be accomplished by maintaining breeding flocks free of the organism *Mycoplasma gallisepticum*. Chicks from these flocks may then begin life free of the infection. Vaccines have not proved to be useful and control of the disease by dipping eggs from infected breeders in antibiotic solutions or by administration of antibiotics to affected birds has not been completely effective.

To maintain flocks free of this disease, strict isolation and sanitation practices must be followed that are similar to those outlined earlier in the Maine program for producing Specific Pathogen-Free broilers. These procedures appear to be effective methods for control of the disease if chicks are obtained from breeding flocks free of the infection.

Fowl Plague

The filterable virus which causes fowl plague, or fowl pest, is highly infectious, even in minute amounts. The disease is characterized by an extremely rapid course and high mortality. It is reported to be rather prevalent in Europe, but only two serious outbreaks have occurred in this country, one in 1925 and one in 1929. In both instances the disease was eradicated by prompt action of sanitary officials.

Since the virus is contained in the blood, intimately associated with the red blood cells, there is usually a generalized hemorrhagic condition evident at autopsy. This, together with the rapid onset of the disease and the high death rate, ranging from 50 to 100 per cent, will usually be sufficient for diagnosis. Medicinal treatment is of no benefit whatever. Prompt and complete eradication of affected flocks is essential for the protection of the entire industry. If this disease is suspected, Federal and State officials should be notified immediately.

Newcastle Disease (Avian Pneumoencephalitis)

This virus disease has been known for many years in various parts of the world, but not until the middle forties did it become of major importance in the United States. It is a highly infectious respiratory disease. In young chickens there are varying degrees of muscular incoordination, including many peculiar motions such as

Fig. 11–6.—Eggs laid for some time after an outbreak of Newcastle disease may have soft or thin shells. Affected chickens commonly assume peculiar positions such as those shown here. (Courtesy of Illinois Agricultural Experiment Station.)

walking backward or in circles. In older flocks egg production commonly drops to zero within three to five days after an outbreak. When egg laying is resumed after 4 to 6 weeks, many of the eggs are abnormal in shape with rough and thin shells. Interior quality is also adversely affected. Death losses are usually low among fowls of laying age, but may range up to 25 per cent or more in chicks.

Control of Newcastle disease is possible with vaccines prepared from killed virus or modified live virus preparations. Most vaccination in the United States is done with live virus vaccines. These may be administered by wing web inoculation, intranasal or eye drop methods, in the drinking water, or by spraying or dusting an entire flock. Administration in the drinking water, or by mass dusting or spraying are by far the most popular methods because these require the least labor. The immunity produced by the vaccines is not permanent and must be reinforced by periodic revaccination. Some authorities suggest Newcastle disease vaccination at 4 to 7 days, 4 weeks, 16 weeks, and then every 4 months thereafter.

Immune breeding hens confer some parental immunity on their chicks, but this usually does not last much beyond 10 days of age.

Tuberculosis

Fowl tuberculosis was once very common, especially in the West North Central States. Tests often showed from 10 to 15 per cent of fowls in farm flocks in certain sections to be infected with this disease, but there has been considerable improvement in this respect in recent years.

The cause of the disease is the bacterial organism known as *Mycobacterium avium*, and the symptoms are similar to those of tuberculosis in other animals. Tuberculosis is characteristically slow to develop and chronic in form. Fowls over 18 months of age are much more likely to show infection than are younger members of a flock.

Since the causative organism may remain in the soil of poultry yards for many months, and perhaps years, and since comparatively few cases are found in young fowls, control and eventual eradication can be obtained by the simple procedure of disposing of all fowls as they reach the end of their first laying season, at about 18 months of age, and by keeping all laying flocks confined indoors so that they do not come in contact with contaminated soil. Of course it is likewise essential to raise the young stock on clean ground, away from any lots over which chickens have ranged. This recommendation should not be taken to mean that all poultrymen everywhere should dispose of all laying stock at 18 months of age. There may be economic reasons for doing so, but as far as tuberculosis is concerned, it is recommended only when the disease has become established in a community, or when one has reason to believe that it is present on a particular farm.

The tuberculin test, simply and quickly made by means of a wattle injection, will identify infected fowls. This is an easy method of determining whether or not the disease is present in a flock, and is a means of saving valuable breeding birds from slaughter when the disease is known to be present and old hens are to be disposed of. The possibility of tuberculosis infection is an excellent reason for keeping pullets and older hens in separate houses. No medicinal treatment is of any value.

Since the disease is readily spread by contact with infected carcasses, and since avian tuberculosis is transmissible to swine, diseased carcasses should never be thrown out where other fowls or hogs may have access to them. This is particularly important in those sections of the country where fowl tuberculosis is common and where large numbers of hogs are raised for market. For the same reason, the poultry flock and the swine enterprise should be entirely separated. Many farmers who perhaps are not greatly concerned over a few losses among the chickens, will take an entirely different view of the matter when they realize that allowing the chickens and the pigs to mingle freely may be a cause for retentions or rejections of hog carcasses at the terminal markets.

Infectious Coryza

This is another respiratory disease of chickens, often referred to as the common cold. It is less widespread today than it was during the 1930's and early 1940's. The primary cause is a microörganism called *Hemophilus gallinarum,* but certain other organisms may be associated with it under conditions which increase the severity of the disease. The infection may be of a very mild type, with a slight nasal discharge persisting over several weeks or months, with few other symptoms, or it may be severe and be accompanied by swelling of the face below and behind the eye, or by inflammation and partial occlusion of the respiratory passages. Unfortunately, there is always the danger that the mild type of the disease may change to the severe type at any time.

The organism *Hemophilus gallinarum* does not survive readily outside the bird. Therefore, contact with birds with the disease or those that have recovered from the disease is the chief mode of transmission. Isolation rearing, disposal of old hens at the end of the laying year, and separation of various ages of hens are effective control measures for this disease.

Fowl Cholera

A positive diagnosis of fowl cholera can be made only by a bacteriological examination, because neither symptoms nor lesions are sufficiently characteristic. If the disease is suspected, specimens should be submitted to a diagnostic laboratory at once.

The disease has long been known and is widespread, but by comparison with others which have been described it is of much less economic importance. This may explain why no satisfactory method of treatment or prevention has ever been developed.

Poultrymen are likely to become familiar with it only in the case of an acute outbreak which may occur without warning. Several fowls may be found dead under the roosts some morning when all were apparently healthy the day before. The disease often strikes on farms where excellent management and feeding methods are used, and when flocks are laying at a high rate. The sick birds should be killed and burned along with those dead from the disease. The healthy fowls may be removed to clean and disinfected quarters if any are available. Since recovered fowls may become carriers of the infection, it is usually considered better to dispose of all fowls in the house where the outbreak occurred and, after thorough cleaning and disinfection, to leave the house empty for several weeks or months before restocking it.

Other Diseases of Hens

There are several other infectious diseases of fowls which occur from time to time. They are always serious to the flock-owner affected, but in the aggregate they are of less consequence than the ones which have been described. Among them are fowl typhoid, paratyphoid infections, erysipelas, and so-called blue comb or pullet disease.

Poisons

Fowls frequently have access to poisonous substances and, under certain circumstances they are subject to acute or chronic poisoning. Actually, however, cases of poisoning are not common when considered in relation to the many other ailments of poultry.

Drugs and Chemicals.—Chickens are able to tolerate considerable quantities of arsenic over extended periods, so that there is little danger to them from eating poisoned grasshoppers, or from such drip as may normally occur following the use of arsenical sprays on fruit trees.

Cyanides are extremely toxic for fowls of all ages. In fact, calcium cyanide in both dust and flake forms has been used for the destruction of large numbers of fowls during control work in outbreaks of such diseases as European fowl pest.

Metallic lead consumed in the form of lead shot is poisonous for water fowl and presumably also for chickens. Metallic mercury is also toxic to fowls. If mercurial ointment is used as a treatment for lice, it is important that no excess be left on the feathers where the fowls can pick it off. Mercurial ointment should never be used on breeding hens because the small amount of mercury absorbed by the skin is sufficient to prevent normal hatching of the eggs.

Nicotine sulphate is a violent poison, and extreme care should be exercised in connection with its use.

Certain organic sulphur compounds used for the chemical treatment of seed grains in the routine control of plant diseases may become a potential hazard for poultry. Arasan is an example. If treated seed grain is fed without previous washing to remove the chemical there is danger of retarded growth in chicks, reduced egg production, or of soft-shelled and misshapen eggs not unlike those produced by flocks infected with Newcastle disease or infectious bronchitis.

Common salt is poisonous to fowls if fed in a large enough amount, especially when the fowls do not have free access to water. The minimum lethal dose is about 4 grams per kilogram of live weight. As much as 8 per cent salt in the feed can be tolerated over considerable periods of time.

Plants and Seeds.—Certain plants and seeds to which fowls sometimes have access, or which may inadvertently be included in mixed rations, are poisonous. Corn cockle seed is an example. It is highly unpalatable to fowls and the danger from poisoning is therefore slight unless the seed is present in the mash mixture in fairly large amounts.

The seed of *Crotalaria* and of *Daubentonia*, both of which are grown rather extensively in the southern states, are poisonous to fowls. They should be so handled that chickens do not have access to the seed. Certain other seeds are known to be poisonous, but they normally are not consumed voluntarily by fowls and hence are not of great importance.

Insects.—The rose chafer is definitely poisonous to young chickens, and chickens will feed upon these insects ravenously if given the opportunity. Loss from this cause can easily be prevented under most conditions by so managing the flocks of growing chickens that they do not have access to fields or gardens where rose chafers are numerous during May and early June.

Commercial Feeds.—Poultry workers are confronted every year with numerous cases in which some proprietary feed mixture is suspected of having caused the death of chicks or older fowls. Very rarely are such feeds actually poisonous, as when they have been loaded in cars or trucks which previously were used for some poisonous substance without proper cleaning before re-use. Hundreds of suspected feed samples have been tested by feeding to young chickens and nearly all of them have proved to be harmless. Corn, barley, and wheat grown in certain limited areas in central South Dakota contain sufficient selenium to cause poisoning. Selenium from this source, fed at the rate of 15 parts per million of the total ration, caused hens to lose weight and reduced the hatchability of their eggs to zero.

Cannibalism.—This vice is not properly considered as a disease but it can cause serious problems to a poultry producer. Cannibalism can occur as toe picking in baby chicks, or as feather pulling, vent picking, and head or tail picking in older flocks.

The causes of cannibalism are not well understood. One group of chickens may have considerable cannibalism, while others fed the same ration, housed and managed similarly, may have no difficulty whatsoever.

The lack of some nutrients may result in cannibalism. When chicks are fed diets low in protein or deficient in an essential amino acid, some picking often occurs. Other nutritional deficiencies seem to cause irritability that may result in cannibalism. However, these deficiencies are usually produced under experimental conditions, and are unlikely to be the cause of cannibalism in farm situations. Other factors implicated have been overcrowded housing conditions, insufficient feeding and watering space, or too much light in the house. Properly controlled experiments to determine the causes are difficult to perform.

Many remedies have been proposed for control of cannibalism, most of which probably will not help in most situations. The remedies have included hanging cabbage, beets or other vegetables

Fig. 11–7.—This hen has been properly debeaked.

in the house, painting windows red, darkening the house, using tar or other no-pick salves, adding extra salt to the feed or drinking water, feeding oats, and several others.

The best way to control cannibalism is to prevent it, because once started it may be very difficult to stop. Proper debeaking is probably the simplest and most effective way to prevent chickens from picking each other. Many broiler growers and some egg producers have their chicks debeaked at the hatchery. If this is done properly, it will last throughout the broiler growing period. Layers can be debeaked before housing. This appears to be particularly important if birds are housed in colony cages. Layers should be debeaked by cutting the upper beak midway between the point and the nostrils. This is commonly done with an electric debeaker.

POULTRY PARASITES

Chickens are subject to infestation by a large number of internal and external parasites but, fortunately, only a few of them are of sufficient importance to need special consideration. Certain ones are more important in one section of the country than in another, and some show a seasonal variation in frequency of occurrence. Some are easily kept under control by ordinary good sanitation practices, whereas others require special methods for their elimination.

Internal Parasities

Most important among the internal parasites are the large roundworm of the small intestine, the cecal worm, the gapeworm, and the several varieties of tapeworms.

The Large Roundworm.—This is the common intestinal worm, known to most poultrymen, and usually found in the small intestine. It ranges in length from $1\frac{1}{2}$ to 4 inches, and in numbers from two or three specimens in a single fowl to so many that the bowel is completely filled for a distance of several inches. Prevention is best accomplished by general sanitation, including rotation of lots and ranges, and elimination of low wet areas, or damp spots around the watering devices. Such practices reduce the opportunity which chickens may have for picking up worm eggs. There is no known spray or disinfectant which is effective in killing roundworm eggs.

Tests at the Georgia station, involving 24 lots of broilers over a two-year period, showed that normal sanitary management procedures without the use of any anthelmintics were sufficient to prevent any serious infestation with roundworms. These broilers were grown in pens known to have been contaminated, half on dirt floors and half on concrete.

Various piperazine compounds, such as piperazine citrate, have recently been found to be highly effective, either in individual doses of 300 to 500 milligrams per kilogram of body weight or when added to the drinking water at the rate of 2 to 4 grams per gallon.

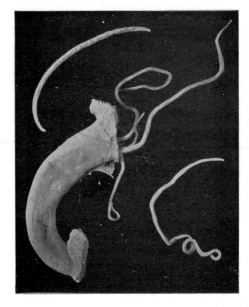

FIG. 11–8.—Section of intestine showing roundworms protruding from a cut end. (Courtesy of California Agricultural Experiment Station.)

The Cecal Worm.—The cecal worm of chickens is very small, not over ½ inch in length, and grayish-white in color. It is frequently found in great numbers in the ceca, where it produces severe inflammation. The life cycle of this parasite is practically identical with that of the large roundworm, and therefore the same methods of prevention and control are effective, namely, general sanitation, rotation of lots and ranges, and strict separation of young and old stock.

Treatment should not be necessary in well-managed flocks, but the drug phenothiazine has been found to be effective in killing and expelling the worms. The dosage is ½ gram per chicken, and flock treatment has been reported to be as effective as individual treatment.

Tapeworms.—These parasites are flat, segmented, ribbon-like worms, which vary in size, depending on the species, from those so small as to be barely visible, to types which are as much as 10 inches long. So far as is known, all tapeworms require an intermediate host for the completion of their life cycle, and this is the key to their prevention and control. If chickens can be so managed that they have no opportunity to eat any of these intermediate hosts, which consist of various beetles, flies, and slugs, there is no possibility of their becoming infested with tapeworms. Prevention is therefore the logical method of control.

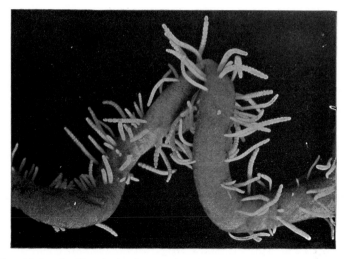

Fig. 11–9.—Inside of a hen's intestine showing attached tapeworms.
(Courtesy of California Agricultural Experiment Station.)

Frequent removal of poultry manure to prevent it becoming a breeding place for flies is important. If roosting racks are used, the manure beneath them should be treated regularly to keep down the fly nuisance. Slugs may be eliminated, or their numbers greatly reduced by the use of certain poison baits when necessary. Earthworms, which may serve as mechanical carriers of the eggs of various parasites, can be kept under control by eliminating wet areas, and seeing that the ranges are well drained throughout.

More than 200 different substances have been tested by many different workers in attempting to find a medicinal agent which would be effective for the removal of tapeworms from chickens. Several different drugs will cause quantities of segments to be detached and removed, but if the heads of the tapeworms remain attached to the wall of the intestine they promptly regenerate so that the infestation is soon as bad as before the treatment was given. Recently, however, a tin compound—di-n-butyl tin dilaurate, sometimes referred to as butynorate—has been shown to be an effective and safe material for the removal of certain species of tapeworms from chickens. The compound was used at the rate of 500 mg. per kilogram of feed (0.05 per cent) or as a single 125-mg. dose by capsule. Removal of the entire tapeworm of several species was accomplished.

External Parasites

The control of external parasites is an important practical problem wherever fowls are kept. In most instances, control measures are comparatively simple and effective, but if they are omitted, the loss caused by parasites may be very serious. It is far better to prevent parasite infestation in poultry houses than to control a serious buildup.

Insecticides.—In recent years insecticides have been developed that can be applied to houses, roosts, nests and birds themselves in mass application for control of most external parasites. These insecticides must be used very carefully so that residues are not found in eggs or poultry meat. Contamination of feed, water and eggs during application of the insecticide should be avoided. Always follow instructions on the label. Only insecticides approved for use in poultry houses should be employed.

Insecticides can be applied in a variety of ways, as dust, spray or mist. Dusts can be applied to individual chickens but a more practical system for large farms is to blow dust at birds in cages or on floors with a crank-type rotary duster. In some cases the insecticide dust can be applied to the litter and birds can treat themselves. Sprays can be applied with hand pump knapsack sprayers, or by large-capacity power sprayers. Electric mist machines are also available that are particularly useful for applying insecticide to caged birds.

Several effective insecticides are available for most parasites encountered. The concentration of insecticide used will depend on the method of application and the particular insecticide.

Lice.—Several different kinds of biting and chewing lice infest chickens. They are permanent parasites in the sense that they live and reproduce on the body of their host. Furthermore, there is a tendency for each species of lice to prefer a certain location on the body of the fowl. Among their special characteristics are flattened bodies, legs which are peculiarly well fitted for clinging to skin and feathers, and a remarkable ability to move about so as to remain out of sight among the feathers.

The three common species of chicken lice are the head louse, the body louse, and the shaft louse. Others are seen occasionally, but cause much less damage. Since one method of treatment may

Fig. 11–10.—Eggs (nits) of the common large louse, attached to the shafts of body feathers.

be used for all, the exact species present is of little consequence to the flock owner.

The older methods of treatment—dusting, dipping and greasing —involved handling of each individual fowl. They are still effective, but they have been replaced by insecticide sprays or dusts in the poultry house. Malathion, carbaryl (Sevin) and coumaphos (Co-Ral) are insecticides recommended for this purpose. These insecticides have the further advantage that they control the red mite or roost mite at the same time with a single spray application.

Roost Mites.—The common roost mite is a familiar pest in all parts of the country. The habits of this parasite are quite different from those of lice. The mites spend most of their time in cracks and crevices about the house, especially the roosts and roost supports, going on the fowls mostly at night. Since they are blood-sucking parasites, they are especially destructive. Insecticide application, as recommended for lice, is a simple and effective method of control.

Scaly-Leg Mites.—These mites are so named because they are responsible for the condition known as scaly leg in fowls. Scaly leg is rarely seen on well-managed poultry plants but it may become serious when fowls are kept for long periods under insanitary conditions. Control is most effectively accomplished by disposing of all mature fowls, giving the house and adjacent yard a thorough cleaning, and then restocking with young pullets. If treatment is to be practiced, it is necessary to find some material which will penetrate beneath the scales of the shanks in order to reach the minute parasites. It must be strong enough to kill the mites without being too irritating to the fowls. Soaking the shanks three times at intervals of 2 to 4 weeks in a 0.5 per cent solution of sodium fluoride is said to be effective, as is also dipping in a mixture of 9 parts kerosene and 2 parts raw linseed oil. Since the mites spread readily from fowl to fowl, treatment of the roosts as for the roost mite is also important.

Northern Fowl Mites.—The northern fowl mite, also sometimes called the feather mite, is a serious pest. Since they may reproduce either on the fowls or in the nests, single treatments are not always sufficient for complete eradication. They are most commonly found around the base of the tail and around the vent, and frequently they prefer male hosts. Their feeding habits are such as to cause the formation of large scabs which spoil the appearance of dressed carcasses. Outbreaks occur sporadically, and often are rather severe before they are discovered. They are sometimes found by reason of the dirty appearance which they give to the plumage of white fowls.

Several methods of control are effective. One of the best, especially in cold weather, is to dust each fowl thoroughly with finely divided orchard spray sulphur. The nests should also be liberally dusted. Since English sparrows harbor this parasite, nests near the poultry house should be destroyed and burned.

18

Nicotine sulphate applied to the skin, one drop below the vent, one on the back of the neck, and one under each wing, has been found highly effective in controlling these mites.

Sprays or dusts of carbaryl (Sevin) or coumaphos (Co-Ral) are often used for treatment, especially when large numbers of birds are involved.

Fowl Ticks.—The fowl tick is common in the southern part of the country and is a serious pest. It is a powerful blood sucker, and its habits are similar to those of the roost mite. The same general methods of control are recommended, but they must be more rigorously applied. Control is difficult not only because the ticks crawl into any deep cracks which are available, but because the seed ticks can live for five or six months, and the nymphal stages for eight to fifteen months without any food. It is necessary to do a very thorough job of cleaning, burning all litter and trash, and even treating nearby trees as well as other outbuildings to which the chickens have access, in order to accomplish complete control. Treatment consists of applying malathion or carbaryl (Sevin) sprays to the hiding places of the ticks on the inside and outside of the infested houses.

Sticktight Fleas.—These parasites are common throughout the southern states, from Florida to California. They attack dogs, cats, and rats, but find chickens an ideal host. They attach themselves to the comb, face, wattles and earlobes in large numbers, and since they are voracious feeders they cause serious injury. Eggs laid by the adult females fall to the floor or ground, and the remainder of the life cycle, through larval and pupal stages to adult is passed there. Control measures must include treatment of the floor of the poultry house and nearby infested soil, as well as the affected fowls.

According to reports from the California Station, sprinkling the yards two or three times weekly for a short period will greatly reduce the breeding of these pests, since they cannot thrive in damp surroundings. The effectiveness of the treatment is increased by scattering salt freely about the yards before wetting the soil.

The Florida Station has reported that complete control was secured by a combination of feeding 5 per cent of commercial sulphur flour in the mash for a period of three weeks and dusting sulphur on the surface soil and in the poultry house at the rate of 2 pounds for each 100 square feet. Neither feeding nor dusting alone was effective.

Malathion dust in dusting boxes or litter has been reported to be effective.

All litter, manure, and other refuse from the house should be burned or spread on distant fields where it can be promptly plowed under. Otherwise the flea larvae will continue to develop and will soon be ready to attack any dogs, cats, or humans in the neighborhood.

Rat control is especially important in preventing flea infestations in the poultry flocks.

Other External Parasites.—Various other parasites occasionally become a nuisance to poultry flocks, and special control methods are sometimes necessary. Chiggers or "red bugs," common bed bugs, Mexican chicken bugs, black flies, and depluming mites may cause trouble at times, but they are usually not a problem on well-managed farms and ranches where sound sanitation practices are continuously followed.

DISINFECTANTS AND THEIR USE

Disinfectants are substances which have the power to kill microorganisms. They are very valuable materials to use under certain conditions, but in good poultry management they are always secondary to scrupulous cleanliness. Not only is cleanliness more important as a means of preventing losses from disease, but it is an essential preliminary to effective disinfection. The action of most disinfectants is greatly retarded in the presence of accumulated organic matter of any kind. Furthermore, the use of copious amounts of water will both wash away infective organisms and dilute them to the point that they are much less dangerous.

Direct sunshine is an effective germicide, and it can often be used to advantage for equipment which is portable and so constructed that it can be fully exposed to the sun's rays.

When disinfection is necessary it is important (1) to do a thorough job of cleaning first, (2) to apply the disinfectant while it is warm or hot if possible, (3) to use it liberally and to apply it thoroughly, and (4) to allow plenty of time for the disinfectant to act.

Steam applied under pressure is probably the most effective of all disinfectants, but it is not available under average farm conditions. Boiling water is also effective, and frequently can be used on the farm.

Chlorine is a good cheap disinfectant that may be used freely. The addition of a wetting agent or detergent when using chlorine solutions will increase their effectiveness.

Quaternary ammonium compounds are very effective against bacteria, but not so satisfactory for viruses. Time is the important factor in cleaning up after a virus infection. Material contaminated with a virus may become safe in as short a time as three weeks after thorough cleaning if moisture and temperature conditions have varied during that period.

Formaldehyde gas is effective in spaces which can be tightly closed, especially if the air is warm and moist. Directions for the use of this material for incubator fumigation have been given in connection with the discussion of pullorum disease.

Common lye (sodium hydroxide) is a powerful disinfectant, especially if applied in a solution of hot water. A 2 per cent solution is made by adding 1 pound of lye to 6 gallons of hot water. Lye must be kept in tightly closed containers because it very soon becomes inactive on exposure to the air.

Saponified cresol solutions are prepared by several different manufacturers and are usually available through local drug and supply houses. The commonly recommended dilution is 4 ounces to a gallon of water. Soft water should be used if available, because the cresol solutions do not mix so readily with hard water.

Since most disinfectants are very irritating, it is important to protect the eyes, face, and hands from contact with the solution being used. If cresol solutions are used in small brooder houses or other confined space, ample time should be allowed for drying before chicks are introduced.

Chapter 12

Marketing Eggs

THE marketing of eggs involves buying and selling, and the physical movement and distribution of eggs between the point of production and the point of consumption. To be effective, marketing must be concerned with those phases of production which influence egg quality, as well as with the preferences of consumers for certain characteristics of the retail product and for the type of package in which it is offered for sale. Between these two extremes come the many details of assembling, grading, standardization, processing, transportation, storage, financing and merchandising. Obviously, the system of purchase, distribution and sale is extensive and complicated, and the costs involved are considerable.

The Marketing Problem

The ultimate objective of the marketing process is to put eggs in the hands of consumers with their original quality unimpaired. In practice this is seldom accomplished in a full and complete sense except where direct marketing from producer to consumer is involved. It will be the purpose of this chapter, however, to emphasize that objective and to point out the ways in which it may most nearly be attained.

The seasonal nature of egg production, though still presenting something of a marketing problem, is not nearly so important as it was thirty or more years ago. In April, 1929, for example, receipts of shell eggs at New York City were nearly four times the receipts in November of that year, and 29 per cent of the year's receipts arrived in the two months of April and May. But in 1959 the difference between April and November receipts was only 5 per cent.

The Geographical Nature of Egg Production

The distribution of poultry flocks does not coincide with the geographical distribution of population, though there has been a growing tendency for market eggs to be produced close to the large centers of population. New York State, with about 9 per cent of the population, produced less than 3 per cent of the Nation's eggs in 1964, while California, with about 10 per cent of the population, produced over 12 per cent of the eggs.

Not all eggs produced in the United States are available for human consumption. Some are used for hatching and many are used for a variety of other non-food purposes such as the production of therapeutic vaccines. The total of non-food uses amounts to nearly 7 per cent of all eggs produced. If 1964 production totals by states are adjusted to allow for non-food uses, and if consumption in all states is assumed to be the same as the U. S. average of 314 eggs per capita, some states have a large surplus production, while others do not produce anywhere near enough to fill their own needs. In Table 12–1 are shown the ten states having the greatest surpluses in 1964 and the ten having the greatest deficits. Of the ten leading states in total population, only California produced a surplus of eggs.

Table 12–1.—Surplus and Deficit States in Egg Production, 1964. Based on Population Estimates by the Bureau of the Census and Production Estimates by the U. S. Department of Agriculture.

Surplus States*			Deficit States*		
Production exceeds consumption by: (million dozens)			*Consumption exceeds production by:* (million dozens)		
		cumulative total			cumulative total
1. Iowa	225		1. New York	320	
2. Georgia	145	370	2. Illinois	129	449
3. California	130	500	3. Michigan	109	558
4. Minnesota	125	625	4. Massachusetts	93	651
5. Arkansas	124	749	5. Ohio	75	726
6. Mississippi	108	857	6. Texas	70	796
7. South Dakota	89	946	7. Maryland	68	864
8. Alabama	80	1026	8. Pennsylvania	55	919
9. Nebraska	70	1096	9. Louisiana	49	968
10. North Carolina	59	1155	10. New Jersey	48	1016

* Calculated by assuming a uniform consumption of 314 eggs per capita, and adjusting total production downward by 7 per cent because of eggs sold for hatching and other non-food uses.

In 1960 there were 16 cities in the country with a total population of 600,000 or more. All but four of these were in the ten states having the largest deficits in egg production. The exceptions were Los Angeles, San Francisco, Milwaukee and Washington, D. C. The "egg stream" of the country continues to flow east just as it did thirty-five years ago. Georgia, Alabama, Mississippi and North Carolina are the only important surplus states east of the Mississippi River, while Texas and Louisiana are the most important deficit states west of the river.

Eggs or poultry from a single state or area may be widely distributed over the country, but the bulk of shipments often go to a single terminal market. In 1959 Maryland shipped 60 million

SUPPLY AND DISTRIBUTION
OF EGGS, 1959

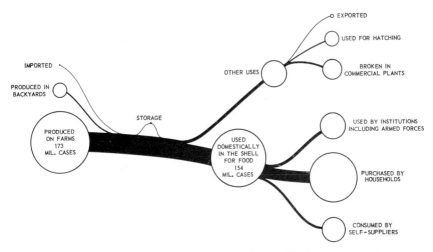

Fig. 12–1.—Supply and distribution of eggs, 1959, as estimated
by the U. S. Department of Agriculture.

pounds of processed poultry to the eight principal markets, but
50 million pounds of that total went to New York City. Of Ohio's
shipments of over a million cases of eggs in 1959, 57 per cent went
to Detroit and 39 per cent went to Pittsburgh.

The Maintenance of Quality

Because of the differences in geographical distribution of poultry
and human population, the matter of maintaining the quality of
poultry products during the time that elapses between their production and their delivery to the final consumer is of great importance.
Its successful accomplishment requires that every individual who
has anything to do with the marketing of eggs or poultry shall be
"quality conscious," and interested in reducing the loss of original
quality to a minimum. The advantage gained from strict attention
to production factors that affect quality may be quickly lost if the
products are not properly handled after they leave the farm.

Eggs are among the most delicate and perishable food products,
are subject to rapid deterioration, and are easily affected by unfavorable surroundings. In food value, flavor and general attractiveness,
they are better when first laid than at any later time. Because
consumers are quick to discriminate against poor eggs, it is important not only that the right kind of eggs be produced, but that
they be so handled as to reach the consumer with the least possible
loss of their original quality.

FIG. 12–2.—A convenient egg washer and sanitizer for farm use.
(J. C. Allen and Son Photo.)

Fig. 12–3.—A conveyor egg washer which spray washes and dries the eggs. Note the hand-operated vacuum lift. (Courtesy of Kuhl Poultry Equipment Company.)

Consumer Preferences

The consumer is the final judge of what constitutes quality in eggs and her measures or preferences do not always coincide with the measures used by the egg trade. Some consumers, for example, actually prefer eggs with medium or thin white over those with firm thick white. In general, consumers are not so much concerned with minor details representing egg quality as they are with size of the eggs and assurance of freshness.

With graded eggs available through retail outlets all over the country, most consumers obtain their needs from supermarkets or neighborhood grocery stores, although many patronize roadside stands and some buy eggs delivered by producers. A 1957 study in Rochester, New York, showed that 9 per cent of the 1029 families interviewed bought eggs at a farm, and 23 per cent had eggs delivered by a farmer, while 56 per cent bought from a supermarket or neighborhood grocery. The remaining 12 per cent obtained their eggs in other ways. Among these same families 44 per cent preferred eggs of AA quality, 21 per cent preferred A quality, while 15 and 20 per cent preferred B and C quality, respectively. About 40 per cent of these families preferred white eggs and 13 per cent preferred brown eggs, while 50 per cent had no preference as to shade of yolk color.

Tests of transparent plastic cartons have shown that consumers definitely prefer this type of package because they can see what they are getting. They also find the transparent cartons attractive and many feel that these cartons provide better protection for the eggs than is given by the regular carton. An opinion survey in six Maine cities showed that 70 per cent of consumers preferred the plastic carton. In actual test sales, about half of the customers chose the plastic carton, even though the price of eggs so packed was marked at 3 and 5 cents a dozen above eggs in regular cartons.

Measures of Egg Quality

Quality in eggs, with reference to food value or market desirability, is measured: (1) by external appearance; (2) by candling; and (3) by odor, flavor and physical character of the opened egg. For the most part, these measures give only a gross picture that is sufficient for trade purposes. Exact measures of quality, in the scientific sense, have been almost totally lacking, though considerable progress in that direction has recently been made.

External Appearance.—Under this heading may be mentioned size, shape, shell color and texture, cleanliness and uniformity of eggs within a given sample or lot. While small eggs of high interior quality may be worth more than large eggs of low quality, it is nevertheless true that size is a most important factor in determining the price received for eggs in any market. The standard size is 2 ounces each, or 24 ounces to the dozen, and it has become customary to refer to 22, 23, 24 or 26-ounce eggs when what is meant is the weight of a dozen. Eggs weighing up to 26 ounces to the dozen may sell at a premium over 24-ounce eggs, but extremely large eggs (30 ounces or more to the dozen) are not in great demand because of the greater danger of breakage when handled in ordinary containers, and the extra expense involved in handling them in special packages. These objections do not, of course, apply to a strictly local market where extra size may occasionally be made the basis of extra premiums. Eggs weighing less than 24 ounces to the dozen will have to be sold at a discount in most, if not all markets, during a large part of the year.

Workers at the Massachusetts Station studied the relation between egg quality and price in retail stores in Springfield, Worcester and Boston. The most definite and significant relationship found was that prices were directly related to weight under all conditions.

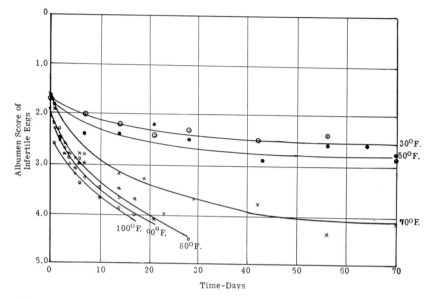

Fig. 12–4.—Showing the effect of temperature on change in egg quality as measured by the albumen score. (Courtesy of Missouri Agricultural Experiment Station.)

Weight was most important, both relatively and actually, in August, each additional ounce per dozen causing an increase of 4.5 cents a dozen in price. The corresponding figures for April and November were 2.4 cents and 3.2 cents, respectively.

Shape is not often of great importance, and in any event it is easily controlled by selection. It should be remembered, however, that short, round eggs do not make the best appearance in an ordinary case or carton, and that long eggs are much more likely to be broken during shipment than are eggs of normal shape.

Shell color is, in the main, a breed characteristic, though there is often wide variation among individual hens in a particular flock when all are of the same breed and variety. If white eggs are to sell at a good price in a competitive market, they must be chalk white. A few tinted or creamy eggs in a case of white ones will cause buyers to turn to other shipments that are more nearly uniform. With brown eggs there is more tolerance because of the natural variation in brown shell color, but it is nevertheless true that of two cases that are equal in other respects, the one that is most nearly uniform in shade of brown color will be likely to sell first. All of this simply means that uniformity of shell color gives the seller a price advantage. While there is no relation between shell color and interior quality, there is enough color preference in certain markets to warrant consideration by shippers. Thus New York City has long been known as a white-egg market.

Boston, on the other hand, has long been regarded as a brown-egg market.

Eggs with rough, thin, or uneven shells are always discriminated against, and should not be shipped to central markets. They should either be used at home or disposed of locally to customers who will appreciate the opportunity to get eggs of high interior quality at less than the regular market price. If the quantity of such eggs warrants, they may be broken out and sold as liquid eggs.

Stained or dirty eggs are unattractive in appearance and must always be sold at a discount. Furthermore, dirty eggs will spoil more quickly than clean eggs, and careless washing makes matters worse because it increases the chance of spoilage. For these reasons it becomes important to do everything possible to prevent the production of dirty eggs.

Studies at the Missouri Station have shown that the percentage of dirty eggs can be very materially reduced by following suitable management practices. When eggs were gathered only once daily, 31 per cent were either dirty or slightly dirty, but when gathered four times daily the percentage dropped to 15. During a six-months period 12.5 per cent of eggs laid in trapnests were soiled, while 29.4 per cent of those laid in open nests were dirty. In the Missouri tests White Leghorns gave more than twice as many dirty eggs on a percentage basis as did all other breeds combined. Many more dirty eggs were found among those laid before nine o'clock than among those laid later in the day. Perhaps the most significant finding in these tests was that more than 99 per cent of all eggs were clean at the moment of laying and before they came in contact with the nest.

Uniformity helps to sell any product, and eggs are no exception to the rule. A case of eggs weighing 23 ounces to the dozen, if all eggs in it are alike, will be much easier to sell than a heavier case in which there is wide variation in size, shape and color. It nearly always pays to sort eggs before sale or shipment in order to secure reasonable uniformity within each package.

Candling Quality.—External appearance is not an accurate indication of what is to be found inside the shell, and it is therefore customary to make use of the practice known as candling in order to measure interior quality. Accurate candling can best be done in a darkened room with some arrangement for passing the light from a lamp or an electric light bulb through the eggs to the observer. Many of the important differences in interior quality can then be plainly seen. Candling equipment may range from a simple home-made affair costing but a few cents, to an elaborate mechanical device, with which is combined an automatic grader (according to egg weight), costing several hundred dollars. Regardless of the type of equipment, each egg must be individually examined.

The characters used in measuring quality on the basis of candling appearance are shell, air cell, yolk, white and germ. Eggs that have thin, porous or cracked shells are easily detected. None but sound shells should be passed when candling eggs for shipment.

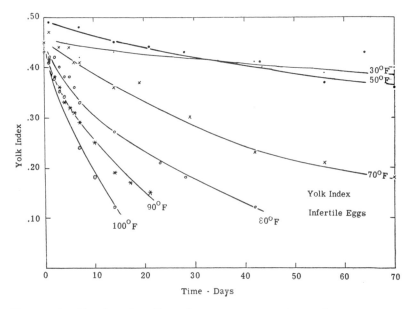

FIG. 12–5.—Showing the effect of temperature on change in egg quality as measured by the yolk index. (Courtesy of Missouri Agricultural Experiment Station.)

FIG. 12–6.—The so-called "black-lamp" candler does an excellent job of detecting certain low-quality eggs. (Courtesy of Poultry Processing and Marketing.)

The air space or air cell is usually at the large end of the egg, and can be plainly seen when the egg is candled. It develops between the two membranes that line the shell, and increases in size according to the amount of moisture evaporated from the egg. It should be fixed in position with no tendency to bubble or move about. A bubbly air cell is an indication of staleness and a weak shell membrane, or of rough handling, while an air cell that moves freely to any part of the egg is the result of a broken inner membrane.

Fig. 12–7.—Commercial egg processing plants are making increasing use of electronic equipment to detect eggs containing blood spots. (Courtesy of Poultry Tribune.)

When a strictly fresh egg is candled, the yolk cannot be seen except as a faint shadow. It should remain close to the center of the egg. In an egg of lower quality the yolk moves more freely and casts a darker shadow because it floats nearer to the shell. Much of this difference in appearance is really due to changes in the white, or albumen, rather than to changes in the yolk. In an egg of top quality the white is firm and clear, and so thick or viscous that the yolk does not move freely in it. Under usual holding conditions the egg-white gradually becomes thin, weak and watery in appearance so that the yolk is permitted to move about as the egg is turned. As a result of this condition, the yolk floats close to the shell where it casts a dark shadow and is therefore more plainly seen in candling.

High-grade eggs must not show any visible germ development. The greater the germ development the lower the quality. When it has reached the stage at which blood begins to show, the egg is considered unfit for food. This stage will be reached within forty-eight hours when fertile eggs are held at temperatures of 100° to 103° F. The best method of avoiding loss from this cause is to produce no fertile eggs except during the hatching season.

Although most eggs are of excellent interior quality when first laid, there are some faults that occasionally appear in eggs from flocks that are receiving the best of care in every way. Blood clots, bloody eggs, meat spots and body checks may be mentioned as examples. A blood clot is due to the rupture of a small blood

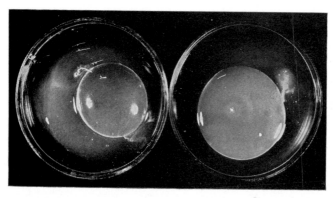

Fig. 12–8.—Heat is the principal cause of loss in egg quality. A firm yolk and a dense white (left) are quickly changed by heat. The egg shown at the right has been incubated for three days.

vessel while the yolk is being formed. The result is that a small clot of blood is enclosed within the egg, usually on the surface of the yolk. Less frequently the clot may be so large as to color most of the white and give it a pink appeaance before the candle. It is then referred to as a bloody egg and is unfit for food. Small blood clots can easily be removed after the egg is opened, so that the egg may be used, but such eggs should not be marketed.

Blood and meat spots present a serious problem for the industry, as shown by examination of samples from twenty different flocks in seven midwestern states made by the Illinois Station in May, 1944. Of 3600 eggs from ten Leghorn flocks, 12.5 per cent contained blood spots and 12.8 contained meat spots. Among 3600 eggs from ten commercial flocks of Plymouth Rocks, New Hampshires, and Rhode Island Reds, 36.7 per cent contained blood spots, and an additional 6.1 per cent contained meat spots.

More recently, workers at the Minnesota Station made a detailed examination of nearly 3000 eggs laid by 36 crossbred hens (Table 12–2). They found, as had other workers, that most of the meat

Table 12–2.—The Incidence, Size, Location and Color of Blood and Meat Spots in 2,761 Eggs from 36 Crossbred Hens.   Data of Helbacka and Swanson, 1958.

	Meat Spots Per cent	Blood Spots Per cent	Clear Eggs Per cent
Incidence	38.1	9.3	52.6
Size of spots:			
Pinpoint	13.9	33.9	
Up to $\frac{1}{8}$ inch	76.9	45.2	
$\frac{1}{8}$ to $\frac{3}{8}$ inch	8.9	12.8	
Over $\frac{3}{8}$ inch	0.3	8.1	
Location of spots:			
Albumen	58.6	Nearly	
Chalazae	29.1	100%	
Yolk	12.3	on yolk	
Color of spots:			
Dark	17.7		
Intermediate	26.8	All red	
Light	55.5		

FIG. 12–9.—A walk-in cooler for holding eggs.   (Courtesy of Poultry Tribune.)

spots from white eggs were white or very light in color, whereas 70 per cent of those from brown eggs were intermediate or dark brown in color. They also observed that meat spots from brown eggs would fluoresce under near ultraviolet light in a manner similar to the shell of such eggs. Blood spots and degenerated blood do not possess this quality. Spots similar to meat spots in eggs were found in the oviducts of autopsied hens, chiefly in the uterus, but their exact origin has not been determined.

A "body check" is an egg in which the shell appears to have been cracked while in the uterus or shell gland, presumably before all the shell material was formed. The break is then sealed by the deposition of additional shell material, so that after being laid it appears normal when given but casual inspection. The weak shell is easily detected by candling. Such eggs should not be shipped because of the greater likelihood of breakage.

The official United States standards for quality of individual eggs with clean unbroken shells are summarized in Table 12–3.

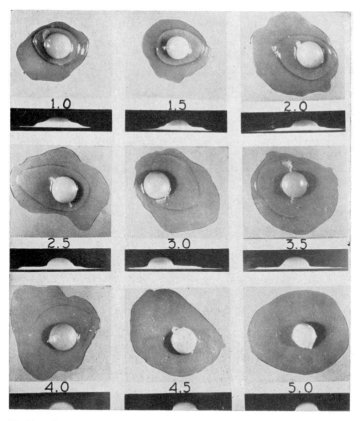

FIG. 12–10.—Successive stages in the "broken out" appearance of eggs. No. 1 is approximately equivalent to U. S. AA quality, No. 2 to U. S. A quality, No. 3 to U. S. B quality, and No. 4 to U. S. C quality. (Courtesy of Institute of American Poultry Industries.)

19

Table 12–3.—Summary of United States Standards for Quality of Individual Shell Eggs.

Specifications for Each Quality Factor

Quality Factor	AA Quality	A Quality	B Quality	C Quality
Shell	Clean. Unbroken. Practically normal.	Clean. Unbroken. Practically normal.	Clean; to very slightly stained. Unbroken. May be slightly abnormal.	Clean; to moderately stained. Unbroken. May be abnormal.
Air cell	$\frac{1}{8}$ inch or less in depth. Practically regular.	$\frac{3}{16}$ inch or less in depth. Practically regular.	$\frac{3}{8}$ inch or less in depth. May be free or bubbly.	May be over $\frac{3}{8}$ inch in depth. May be free or bubbly.
White	Clear. Firm. (72 Haugh units or higher.)	Clear. May be reasonably firm. (60 to 72 Haugh units.)	Clear. May be slightly weak. (31 to 60 Haugh units.)	May be weak and watery. Small blood clots or spots may be present.* (Less than 31 Haugh units.)

| Yolk | Outline slightly defined. Practically free from defects. | Outline may be fairly well defined. Practically free from defects. | Outline may be well defined. May be slightly enlarged and flattened. May show definite but not serious defects. | Outline may be plainly visible. May be enlarged and flattened. May show clearly visible germ development but no blood. May show other serious defects. |

For eggs with dirty or broken shells, the standards of quality provide three additional qualities:

Dirty	Check	Leaker
Unbroken May be dirty.	Checked or cracked but not leaking.	Broken so contents are leaking.

* If they are small (aggregating not more than $\frac{1}{8}$ inch in diameter).

(291)

Table 12–4.—Summary of U. S. Consumer Grades for Shell Eggs.

U. S. consumer grade	At least 80 per cent must be:	Tolerance permitted	
		Per cent	*Quality*
Grade AA or Fresh Fancy Quality	AA Quality	15 to 20 Not over 5	A B, C or Check
Grade A	A Quality or better	15 to 20 Not over 5	B C or Check
Grade B	B Quality or better	10 to 20 Not over 10	C Dirty or Check

Table 12–5.—Tolerance for an Individual Case or Carton Within a Lot of U. S. Consumer Grades of Eggs as Specified.

U. S. Consumer Grade	Case-minimum quality— (per cent)	Carton-minimum quality— (number of eggs)
Grade AA or Fancy Fresh Quality	70% AA 20% A 10% B, C or check	8 eggs AA 2 eggs A 2 eggs B, C or check
Grade A	70% A 20% B 10% C or check	8 eggs A 2 Eggs B 2 eggs C or check
Grade B	70% B 10% C 20% check or dirty	8 eggs B 2 eggs C 2 eggs check or dirty

Note: Individual states often specify lower tolerances than are permitted under U. S. minimums.

Table 12–6.—U. S. Weight Classes for Consumer Grades for Shell Eggs.

Size or weight class	Minimum net weight per dozen	Minimum net weight per 30 dozen	Minimum weight for individual eggs at rate per dozen
	Ounces	*Pounds*	*Ounces*
Jumbo	30	56	29
Extra Large	27	50½	26
Large	24	45	23
Medium	21	39½	20
Small	18	34	17
Peewee	15	28	—

Detailed definitions of terms used in describing eggs which conform to the various standards and grades may be obtained from the U. S. Department of Agriculture, Washington D. C. 20250.

Quality of Opened Eggs.—There are some characteristics of eggs that cannot be observed until the eggs are opened. These include odor, flavor and color of yolk. Since eggs will very quickly absorb odors of various sorts, it is important that they be handled at all times in such a way as to prevent contact with any materials that might cause an undesirable odor or flavor.

The differences, seen in candling, between an egg with a firm white and a well-centered, dimly visible yolk, and an egg with a watery white and prominent yolk, are even more pronounced when the eggs are opened. The yolk of the first egg will appear well rounded, while that of the second will be flattened and spread out. The white of the first egg will stand up well, suggesting the original shape of the unopened egg, while that of the second will be watery in appearance and quite without shape. Attempts to influence this condition by feeding have, as a rule, been unsuccessful. Although it has been shown that holding conditions affect the rate of change in viscosity of the white, it appears that the individual hen is a more important factor. The most promising means of bringing about improvement in this respect are selection and breeding, using hens that possess the desired characteristics, and sons of such hens.

One other measurement has found its way into the description of official standards of quality in the sense that specific numerical values have been assigned and recognized, namely, the measurement of egg white or albumen quality in Haugh units. It is a precise measurement, and one that is too refined for widespread use, but students who may have an interest in becoming official inspectors or graders should be familiar with it.

Curiously enough, it is not feasible to define a single Haugh unit because the scale of values is always used in a multiple sense with values ranging from 100 down to a practical minimum of 20 or slightly lower. Haugh units are found by determining the logarithm of albumen height, corrected to a standard egg weight of two ounces (24 ounces per dozen). The log values are then expressed in convenient whole numbers by multiplying by 100. Since albumen height is influenced by the pull of gravity, the gravitational constant 32.2 is introduced into the calculation. The original Haugh formula is:

$$HU = 100 \log\left[H - \frac{\sqrt{G(30W^{.37}-100)}}{100} + 1.9 \right]$$

HU = Haugh units
H = observed albumen height in millimeters
G = the gravitational constant, 32.2
W = observed weight of the egg in grams

For ease of calculation this can be simplified to:

$$HU = 100 \log(H + 7.57 - 1.7W^{.37})$$

Calculated Haugh unit values are shown in Table 12–7 for eggs of five different indicated weights from 21 to 27 ounces per dozen, and for albumen heights ranging from 10 to 2. The table also includes Haugh unit values of 100 to 20, by 10-unit intervals, with the corresponding albumen height measurements for eggs of the same five indicated weights. The relationship of Haugh units and of USDA Quality Scores to U. S. Standards of Quality of Individual Eggs is shown graphically in Figure 12–11. Note that each value in the scale of USDA Quality Scores covers a range of 8 Haugh units. This means that for most purposes, eggs differing by no more than 8 Haugh units are considered to be in good agreement. It is apparent also from a study of Table 12–7 that for eggs weighing from 1.75 to 2.25 ounces each (21 to 27 ounces per dozen), albumen height alone provides an adequate measure of egg white quality in trade channels.

Table 12–7.—Relationship Between Haugh Units and Albumen Height.

Haugh Units for Eggs of Indicated Weights

Albumen Height (millimeters)	49.6 grams (21 ounces per dozen)	53.2 grams (22.5 ounces per dozen)	56.7 grams (24 ounces per dozen)	60.2 grams (25.5 ounces per dozen)	63.8 grams (27 ounces per dozen)
10	102	101	100	99	98
9	97	96	95	95	94
8	92	91	90	89	88
7	87	86	84	83	82
6	80	79	78	77	75
5	73	71	70	68	67
4	64	62	60	58	56
3	53	50	48	45	42
2	37	34	30	26	22

Haugh Units	Albumen Height for Eggs of Indicated Weights				
100	9.6	9.8	10.0	10.2	10.3
90	7.6	7.8	7.9	8.1	8.3
80	5.9	6.1	6.5	6.5	6.7
70	4.6	4.8	5.0	5.2	5.4
60	3.6	3.8	4.0	4.2	4.3
50	2.8	3.0	3.2	3.3	3.5
40	2.2	2.3	2.5	2.7	2.8
30	1.6	1.8	2.0	2.2	2.3
20	1.2	1.4	1.6	1.8	1.9

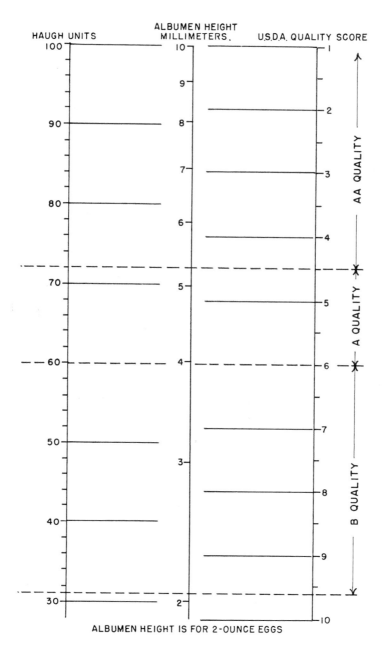

HAUGH UNITS

ALBUMEN HEIGHT
MILLIMETERS.

U.S.D.A. QUALITY SCORE

ALBUMEN HEIGHT IS FOR 2-OUNCE EGGS

Fɪɢ. 12–11.—Relationship between Haugh units, albumen height, and USDA Quality Score for 2-ounce eggs.

Other Measures of Quality.—Various attempts have been made to devise more exact measures of egg quality in order that careful scientific studies can be undertaken of the factors that influence quality. The yolk index is a measure of the standing-up quality of the yolk. It is obtained by dividing the height of the yolk by its average diameter. The measurements are made after the egg is broken out into a small plate. Average values for fresh eggs usually fall between 0.42 and 0.40. As the yolk becomes flattened the yolk index is lowered. When the value of the index is 0.25 or lower, the yolk is so weak that it is extremely difficult to handle it for measurement without breaking.

Deterioration in the eggs of individual hens has been measured by recording the percentage of thick and thin egg-white. As the yolk increased in weight due to absorption of water from the white, the percentage of thick white decreased. The rate of change in percentage of thick white, under uniform holding conditions, was a characteristic of individual hens, and there was considerable variation among hens in this respect. The concentration of water in thick white remained exactly equal to that in the associated thin white, regardless of losses to the yolk and to the atmosphere.

Albumen score has been used by workers at the Cornell Station, and is in many respects the simplest of all measures to apply. The scale of scores is illustrated in Figure 12–10.

Workers at the California Station have described a method for the study of eggshell porosity, and have suggested a set of standards tf comparison to be used with the method. The standards are ohown in Figure 12–12. These workers found that the initial porosity sn fresh eggs was normally low, that it was rather uniformly disiributed over the egg surface, and that it increased with holding time, more rapidly at higher temperatures. In eggs held for twenty-five days at room temperature the porosity increased from about Score 4 or 5 to Score 8 or 9.

Producer Control of Egg Quality

It has already been stated that eggs are highly perishable. A fact of equal significance is that no process has yet been found for improving an egg of poor quality. It is rather obvious, then, that in any successful marketing plan emphasis must be placed on those practices that will insure the production of high-quality eggs, and on handling methods that will preserve their original quality as long as possible. The importance of selection and breeding for desired egg characteristics, and of feeding and management looking toward high-quality eggs, have been discussed in previous chapters. Care and handling of eggs before they leave the farm is also important.

Care and Handling of Eggs on the Farm.—Except for those quality factors that are definitely controlled by inheritance and by feeding, the production of high-quality eggs is a matter of careful attention to a few details that do not require any elaborate buildings or equipment.

PLATE IV

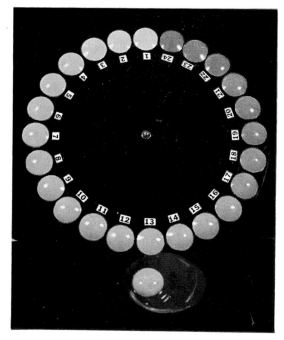

A

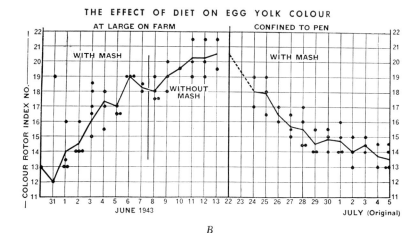

B

A, Heiman-Carver Yolk Color Rotor, a device for measuring yolk color by direct comparison.

B, Effect of feed on yolk color. Pullets which had been laying eggs with pale yolks (Rotor Nos. 12 to 14) when confined indoors, quickly produced darker yolks (Rotor Nos. 19 to 22) when turned out on range, especially when deprived of mash. When the pullets were returned to the original quarters and method of feeding, yolk color quickly became pale, as before. *(Courtesy of Ontario Department of Agriculture.)*

The first rule to remember is that fertile eggs should not be produced except for hatching purposes. As mentioned in connection with incubation, when a fertile egg is held at a temperature above 80° F., the germ begins to develop. In the early stages the development is referred to by market men as a "hatch spot," but in a very short time blood appears and thereafter the egg must be classed as inedible. A lower temperature at this stage will kill the tiny embryo and then decomposition will begin.

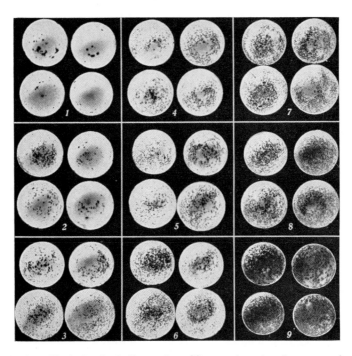

Fig. 12–12.—Variation in shell porosity. The numbers *1* to *9* represent increasing shell porosity as shown by the increasing number of small spots on the interior of the shells. Both halves of each shell are shown, with air-space ends to the left. (Courtesy of California Agricultural Experiment Station.)

Since dirty eggs must always be sold at a discount in a competitive market, it is now routine practice among commercial egg producers to wash eggs before they leave the farm. Several types of mechanical egg washers are available. The smaller ones depend on swirling wash water containing a detergent-sanitizer and maintained at a temperature which is 30° to 35° F. higher than the temperature of the eggs. Safe washing temperatures are in the range of 110° to 125° F. Larger installations include an in-line cooler through which the newly collected eggs are conveyed before going to the washer. From the spray-type washer, eggs pass to a drying unit before going to the candler and grader. Prompt drying after washing is important.

It is also important that the water used for egg washing contain no more than 3 ppm of iron. Even as much as 5 ppm can cause a serious egg spoilage problem because iron favors the development of *Pseudomonas* organisms that are responsible for a type of spoilage called "fluorescent sours."

If eggs are to be marketed locally without washing, they should be gathered frequently, cooled promptly, and held at a temperature of 35° to 40° F. until sold.

How Deterioration Occurs

Deterioration of eggs comes about in several ways, some of which have been mentioned briefly in connection with measures of egg quality. It will be profitable to inquire more fully into the specific processes by which deterioration is brought about.

Shrinkage.—Shrinkage is caused by the evaporation of moisture from within the egg. The amount of shrinkage is usually measured by the size of the air cell as seen in candling. The rapidity with which it progresses depends upon the temperature at which the egg is kept, the humidity of the surrounding air, the rate of ventilation and the porosity of the shell. In actual practice, temperature is the most important controlling factor. The vapor tension of water is about one-fifth as much at 30° F. as at 80° F., so that the lower the temperature of storage, at least down to near the freezing-point of eggs, the better will be the quality of the eggs at the end of the storage period. The favorable effect of low temperature is, of course, not due entirely to the reduced evaporation, but the fact remains that low temperatures constitute the most important practical means of controlling egg quality during the marketing process.

The increase in porosity of the shell which occurs in held eggs, a change that is more rapid at high than at low temperatures, is also an important factor in shrinkage. Since the increasing porosity leads to an increasing rate of evaporation, it is evident that eggs should be placed under conditions of low temperature at the earliest possible moment after being laid.

The overall importance of low temperatures in maintaining egg quality is readily shown by the fact that infertile eggs of AA quality will drop to C quality by the end of 3 days if held at 99° F. If held at 75° they drop to C quality in about 9 days, at 60° in about 25 days, and at 45° in 65 days. But if held at 37° they can be kept for 100 days before dropping to C quality.

Liquefaction.—Reference has been made to the increased visibility of yolk which results from a lowered viscosity of the white, permitting the yolk to float nearer to the shell and thus cast a darker shadow before the candle. The reasons for this liquefaction of the white, as it occurs under different sorts of conditions, are not yet fully explained, but some of the related facts are being brought to light. It has been shown, for example, that under the influence

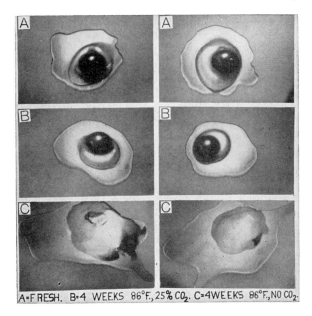

A=FRESH. B=4 WEEKS 86°F, 25% CO₂. C=4WEEKS 86°F, NO CO₂.

Fig. 12–13.—Showing the effect of carbon dioxide in preserving interior egg quality. *A*, the broken-out appearance of fresh eggs; *B*, eggs held four weeks at 86° F., in an atmosphere of 25 per cent CO_2; *C*, eggs held four weeks at 86° F., but without added CO_2. (Courtesy of P. F. Sharp.)

of osmotic pressure there is an actual passage of water from the white into the yolk. This may amount to as much as 2 grams per egg within a ten-day period with eggs held at 86° F. The vitelline membrane is compelled to stretch in order to make room for this incoming water, and is thereby weakened; and the substance of the yolk is made more fluid in character. These facts, together with the loss of mechanical support as a result of the disappearance of the thick white, explain the flattening of the yolk when such an egg is opened.

Shrinkage and liquefaction can be made to occur independently by imposing the right experimental conditions. If eggs are held in a desiccator over calcium chloride in an atmosphere maintained at 5 per cent carbon dioxide, water will be removed from the eggs at a rapid rate by the calcium chloride. But if eggs are stored in a desiccator over a 5 per cent solution of sodium hydroxide, a high humidity is maintained while carbon dioxide is rapidly removed from the air and, consequently, from the eggs. After twenty-six days all eggs subjected to the first treatment had air spaces from $\frac{1}{4}$ to $\frac{1}{2}$ inch in depth, showing extensive shrinkage, yet the interior quality as shown by white viscosity was excellent. Thick white made up 52 per cent of the total white. In the second lot there was very little shrinkage, but the eggs were badly liquefied, only

30 per cent of the white being thick white. In this case the watery eggs actually contained more water than did the eggs with viscous whites. In practice, on the other hand, it is usually true that the eggs with "watery" whites are those that have undergone considerable shrinkage, *i.e.*, an egg becomes more "watery" as it loses water by evaporation. The explanation is found in the fact that there is no necessary relation between these two processes. They simply happen to occur together. The loss of water which is so evident when a shrunken egg is candled is, after all, a relatively minor type of deterioration.

Gaseous Exchange.—Loss of carbon dioxide is not only something that can be made to occur under experimental conditions, but a process which occurs normally under usual holding conditions. Carbon dioxide is liberated from an infertile egg at a rate which decreases from the time the egg is laid, at first rapidly, and then more and more slowly over a period of at least one hundred days. Even after one hundred days at $10°$ C. ($50°$ F.) there is still an appreciable output amounting to 0.1 to 0.2 mg. of carbon dioxide per egg per day.

Hydrogen-ion Concentration.—The hydrogen-ion concentration of fresh egg white, expressed as pH, has been variously reported as from 7.6 to 8.2, whereas that of eggs held for some time may be low enough to give a pH value of 9.5, especially if they have been held in a well-ventilated room at a fairly high temperature. This results directly from the loss of carbon dioxide, and it makes egg white under these conditions one of the most alkaline of natural biological fluids. Such a change means an increase in alkalinity (hydroxyl-ion concentration) of about 80 times. It is significant that this change takes place less rapidly at low temperatures, which is another reason for holding market eggs at low temperatures from the time they are laid until they are ready to be consumed.

If eggs are held at room temperature it takes approximately 10 to 12 per cent of carbon dioxide in the atmosphere to hold the pH of the egg white down to 7.6, while at temperatures near freezing 3 per cent of carbon dioxide will have the same effect. If sufficient carbon dioxide is introduced to hold the pH down to near that of the fresh egg, the thick white becomes turbid, but this turbidity quickly disappears with the escape of carbon dioxide after the eggs are removed from the storage room.

The point of interest seems to be that the carbon dioxide tends to reach an equilibrium between the concentration in the egg white and that in the air in which the eggs are kept. If newly laid eggs are stored in a confined space, that is, in a room or other container that is full of eggs, and unventilated, the carbon dioxide concentration of the air surrounding them will soon be higher than that of normal outdoor air, and the equilibrium point will be reached at a pH value for the egg white that is intermediate between the 7.6 and 9.5 values previously mentioned. If more carbon dioxide is introduced into the surrounding air, some of it will be taken up

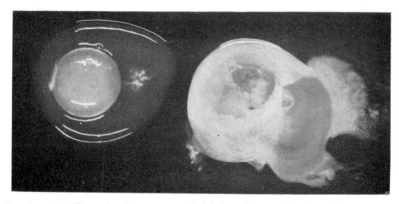

Fig. 12–14.—These fertile eggs were held four days at 100° F. The egg on the left was thermo-stabilized by dipping in hot water to prevent embryonic development and normal break-down of the thick white. (Courtesy of Missouri Agricultural Experiment Station.)

by the egg white and the pH will fall. Hence it may be said that the pH of the white of the egg is one of the controllable factors in the storage of eggs. Considerable practical use has already been made of this knowledge through the introduction of carbon dioxide into egg-storage rooms.

Bacterial Decomposition.—The contents of normal fresh eggs are, as a rule, sterile. As long as the shells are kept clean and dry, there is little danger of bacterial invasion. The soiling of shells, especially with fecal matter, favors the entrance of bacteria, as does the presence of moisture. The increase in shell porosity with age has already been mentioned, and this undoubtedly makes conditions more favorable for bacterial infection. Once bacteria are inside the shell, increased temperature will hasten decomposition.

Much of the bacterial spoilage in storage eggs is of the sour egg type caused by *Pseudomonas* organisms. These bacteria produce not only some of the substances which are responsible for the sour odor, but also a pigment which spreads through the white of the egg, and which has greenish fluorescence when illuminated with ultraviolet light. Workers at the California station found that ultraviolet light of the right wavelength and intensity will penetrate the shell of white eggs and cause those which are infected with *Pseudomonas* to fluoresce with a bright green glow. Commercial candling equipment using this long wave ultraviolet or "black" light have been widely used in the industry for the examination of eggs coming out of cold storage. The importance of keeping the iron content of egg wash water at a very low level has already been mentioned.

Certain other microorganisms, including molds, are found in eggs at times, and some of them develop at cold-storage temperatures. Certain of these organisms may also be involved in the breakdown or liquefaction of egg white during storage.

Table 12–8.—Annual Operating Costs per 30-dozen Case Related to Size of Firm and Volume of Eggs Handled—12 Companies, 1959, in Georgia, North Carolina and South Carolina.

	Number of firms			
	Small firms 5	Medium firms 4	Large firms 3	All firms 12
Average volume (cases/year)	13,136	32,175	104,000	42,200
Operating costs: Plant labor, utilities, incoming freight, repairs and maintenance	$ .608	$ .510	$ .460	$ .538
Management and office costs: Labor, telephone, audit, supplies, advertising	.239	.205	.140	.202
Overhead costs: Depreciation, taxes and licenses, interest, rent	.242	.190	.140	.201
Distribution costs: Labor, trucking, outgoing freight	.236	.218	.249	.236
Miscellaneous:	.016	.031	.017	.021
Total	$1.341	$1.154	$1.006	$1.198
Packaging supplies:				
For loose eggs	.476	.554	.487	.504
For cartoned eggs	.956	.939	.905	.937
Total of all costs:				
For loose eggs	$1.817	$1.708	$1.493	$1.702
For cartoned eggs	$2.297	$2.093	$1.911	$2.135

Preservation and Cold Storage

The uneven seasonal production of eggs results in a surplus during the spring months and a scarcity during the fall and winter months. For many years cold storage was about the only means of bringing about a balance between the seasonal changes in production and the much more nearly uniform rate of consumption. Now that seasonal variations in egg production have been greatly reduced by improved breeding and management methods, fewer eggs have to be stored. Total holdings on August 1 are about one-fifth of what they were twenty years ago.

Cold Storage.—The normal movement of eggs into storage begins in March, is most active during April and May, and reaches a peak, in terms of total holdings, about August 1. Prior to 1920, storage holdings consisted almost entirely of shell eggs, but the percentage of frozen eggs has increased steadily from 10 per cent in 1921–1925 to 90 per cent in 1961–1965. If this trend continues, as seems probable, storage holdings of shell eggs will soon become so small that they may not even be reported. Total into-storage movement of eggs, both shell and frozen, represented about 15 per cent of concurrent shell egg production during the storage season in 1945–1946, but by 1965 the figure had dropped to 2 per cent. Liquid eggs are being produced on a year-round basis and there is much less need for them to accumulate in storage.

Table 12–9.—Cold Storage Holdings of Eggs on August 1, by 5-Year Periods, 1916–1960, and Percentage of Total Holdings in Form of Frozen Eggs.

	Shell eggs, cases*	Frozen eggs		Total, case equivalent*	Per cent frozen
		Pounds*	Case equivalent*		
1916–1920	6.8	15	0.4	7.2	6
1921–1925	9.5	34	1.0	10.5	10
1926–1930	10.3	84	2.3	12.6	18
1931–1935	8.5	112	3.0	11.5	26
1936–1940	7.5	143	3.8	11.1	34
1941–1945	7.8	295	7.9	15.7	50
1946–1950	4.9	221	5.9	10.8	55
1951–1955	2.0	176	4.6	6.6	70
1956–1960	1.1	162	4.2	5.3	80
1961–1965	0.3	111	2.8	3.1	90

* Millions

Shell Protection.—Various methods of shell treatment designed to preserve interior quality have been tried from time to time. Some of these have been intended only for home use and others have been used commercially. Most "shell-protected" eggs are placed in cold storage if they are to be held for any length of time, the process of shell treatment being used to prevent evaporation rather than as a substitute for cold storage.

Large quantities of eggs have been treated by dipping in light-weight mineral oils which are colorless, odorless, and tasteless. Evaporation is retarded, and much of the original carbon dioxide is retained inside the eggs so treated.

Spray oiling is done in packing plants by automatic machines installed for the purpose. It may easily be done on a small scale by the use of small cans from which the oil spray is released under pressure.

Table 12–10.—States Shipping as Much as 500,000 Pounds of Frozen Eggs to Any One of the Indicated Cities in 1959. As Reported by the U. S. Department of Agriculture.

	Boston	Chicago	Detroit	New York	Philadelphia	Pittsburgh
			(Thousands of Pounds)			
Illinois	1,124	534	3,194	2,344	1,895	783
Indiana	—	470	—	1,054	662	774
Iowa	3,980	5,858	—	3,100	1,264	—
Kansas	—	—	—	518	—	—
Minnesota	770	4,067	—	570	1,870	—
Missouri	1,074	1,533	—	3,013	2,178	1,487
Nebraska	1,348	765	594	3,270	721	—
North Dakota	—	698	—	—	—	—
Ohio	—	—	499	1,784	1,003	—
South Dakota	—	2,741	—	—	1,711	—
Tennessee	—	—	2,160	—	—	—
Wisconsin	—	1,897	—	519	—	—
All other	870	519	1,117	1,456	1,318	1,360
Total	9,166	19,082	7,564	17,628	12,622	4,404

FIG. 12–15.—Automatic in-line egg cooler which handles up to 35 cases (1,050 dozens) per hour. (Courtesy of Seymour Foods, Inc.)

FIG. 12–16.—Automatic egg loader which transfers up to 35 cases of eggs per hour from filler flats to washer conveyor. (Courtesy of Seymour Foods, Inc.)

20

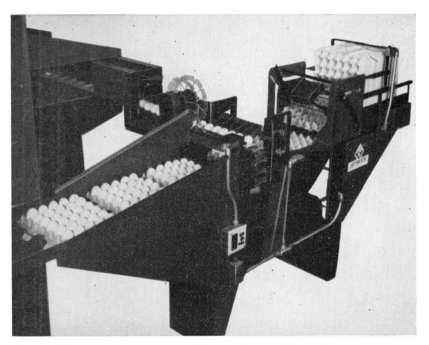

Fig. 12–17.—An automatic egg-packing machine which receives eggs in random fashion from a conveyor belt and automatically places them large end up in either cartons or filler flats. (Courtesy of Seymour Foods, Inc.)

Tests at the Missouri Station have shown that quality can be stabilized effectively by dipping eggs for ten to fifteen minutes in water heated to 130° to 140° F. Eggs treated by this process retained their fresh broken-out appearance, and therefore their commercial grade, much longer than untreated eggs. Embryonic development in fertile eggs was completely arrested.

The only disadvantages found were that the whites from thermo-stabilized eggs required more time for whipping, and the volume of foam was reduced. The incidence of stuck yolks during storage was increased, especially when lower grade eggs were thermostabilized.

Liquid Egg Production.—In 1949 there were nearly 500 egg-breaking plants in the United States, about 60 per cent of them in the North Central States. Currently the number of plants is about 250, and more than half of them are still in the North Central region, although there has been a substantial increase recently in South Atlantic States.

All the larger plants use mechanical equipment for automatic egg breaking and for separation of yolks and whites. A typical plant in the West North Central region may produce five million pounds of liquid egg annually. Total U. S. production of liquid eggs is currently in excess of 600 million pounds, representing about 10 per cent of annual farm egg production.

FIG. 12–18.—Spray oiling is an effective means of retarding the loss of quality in shell eggs. (Courtesy of Poultry Tribune.)

About 50 per cent of the total production is in the form of whole eggs, including some which have been fortified by the addition of egg yolk. The remaining 50 per cent, on a weight basis, is divided about 30 per cent albumen and 20 per cent yolk. Liquid yolks are further divided into plain yolk, sugared yolk and salted yolk, depending on ultimate use. All three products are normally frozen and held in this form until used.

Bakeries as a group are the largest users of frozen whole egg and albumen. Manufacturers of mayonnaise and salad dressings use large quantities of frozen salted yolks; ice cream makers use sugared yolks; and both noodle makers and processors of baby foods use plain yolks.

As of June 1, 1966, both Federal legislation and laws in some States require that all liquid eggs be pasteurized at 140° F. for three and one-half minutes. Prior to that date pasteurization was voluntary. The chief reason for the pasteurization requirement is the increased difficulty which has been experienced with contamination of egg products by organisms of the *Salmonella* group. More than 100 different types or strains of *Salmonella* organisms have been found at various times in poultry and poultry products. Growth of these organisms can be inhibited during storage by freezing liquid eggs and holding them at low temperatures, but the organisms can multiply rapidly after the eggs are removed from storage. Pasteurization is the only known method of control which will prevent the organisms from becoming a serious health hazard.

Pasteurization equipment is expensive, and a plant which is processing fewer than 300 cases a week may not be able to justify the $10,000 to $15,000 investment that is required. Some small processors may be able to expand, but others may have to discontinue operation. There are operating problems also because time and temperature must be accurately controlled so as to prevent overheating and the thickening of the product.

Dried Eggs.—Prior to 1941, less than 1 per cent of the eggs produced in the United States went to drying plants. Government purchases stimulated drying operations to such an extent that 45 million pounds were produced in 1941, 236 million in 1942, 262 million in 1943 and 321 million in 1944. The annual volume has since declined to less than 60 million pounds. A 30-dozen case of shell eggs will yield about 39.5 pounds of liquid whole egg or 10 pounds of a dried product containing 2.5 per cent of moisture.

The handling of shell eggs prior to drying is no different from the handling of eggs which are to be frozen. The liquid egg material is put through a clarifier to remove any bits of shell, and is then screened to remove the chalazae and vitelline membranes. Pasteurization is important, not only to control *Salmonella* infection, but also to preheat the liquid so as to insure a low-moisture powder that will not show any scorching.

The liquid egg is then pumped under pressure of 2,500 to 5,000 pounds per square inch to nozzles through which it is released into a large chamber where it comes immediately into contact with a stream of air which has been heated to temperatures of 250° to 350° F. This causes instantaneous evaporation of most of the moisture from the egg material, which falls to the floor as a fine powder while the moist air passes on out of the drying chamber at a temperature of 150° to 160° F.

Modern driers produce a powder in which the moisture content does not exceed 2 per cent. The temperature of the powder as it leaves the drier may be 150° F. or higher, and this must be reduced quickly to less than 85° F. if the product is to have good keeping qualities. Since the powder is extremely hygroscopic, the temperature must be reduced by contact cooling rather than by exposure to cold air. The powdered eggs are then packed immediately in sealed containers. Many of them are packed in carbon dioxide to remove the oxygen and lower the pH value in order to improve the keeping quality of the product.

Chief users of dried egg products are cake mix manufacturers, candy makers, and manufacturers of meringue powders. Some 5 million pounds are exported annually, chiefly to West Germany.

Methods of Marketing

The route traveled by eggs from producer to consumer in 1966 is, for the most part, completely different from what it was thirty years ago. No longer are eggs sold by farmers to a country store, picked

Fig. 12–19.—Liquid eggs are produced by the use of machines which automatically wash shell eggs, break them, and separate the yolks and whites. This equipment made by Seymour Foods, Inc. (Courtesy of Kansas Agricultural Experiment Station.)

up by a huckster and taken to a local assembling plant, candled, packed in wooden cases, and shipped to a city wholesale receiver, and resold to jobbers for grading and delivery to retail stores. Most of these intermediate handlers no longer exist. Eggs make the trip in much less time, and the retail purchaser therefore has a better chance of getting eggs of high quality.

If shell eggs only are considered, omitting those used for hatching and other non-food purposes, as well as those consumed on farms or used in the processing of liquid eggs and egg solids, it is probable that 9 out of 10 eggs go through chain-store warehouses on their way to supermarkets. The trend for several years has been for more and more eggs to make only this one stop on their way to the retail store.

Some producers, however, have built up a good local egg business by making regular deliveries to one or more independent retail stores. Others have found it profitable to set up small drive-in sales rooms—not adjacent to their farms, but at locations in small cities which are convenient for the motoring public. One such drive-in in Alabama offers eggs mostly in paper bags in dollar lots. Large eggs, for example, may be sold at $2\frac{1}{2}$ dozen for a dollar, mediums at 2 dozen and 9 eggs, and smalls at 3 dozen and 3 eggs for a dollar. This saves time in making change.

Fig. 12–20.—An installation of twelve automatic breaking and separating machines in a Chicago egg-breaking plant. Each machine handles 16 to 18 cases an hour. Eggs are automatically washed before being fed to the egg-breaking machine. (Courtesy of Seymour Foods, Inc.)

FIG. 12–21.—Eggs are often sold at retail in heavy paper bags. These are held in a refrigerator until time of sale. (Courtesy of Pacific Poultryman.)

FIG. 12–22.—This refrigerated egg vending machine is in operation twenty-four hours a day in San Jose, California. (Courtesy of Poultry Tribune.)

FIG. 12–23.—Miracle Egg Farm in Cullman County, Alabama, sells most of its eggs through small drive-in stores such as this. (Courtesy of Poultry Tribune.)

Fig. 12–24.—Clinton G. Park, Warrensburg, Illinois, delivers eggs to special outlets in nearby Decatur.   (J. C. Allen and Son photo.)

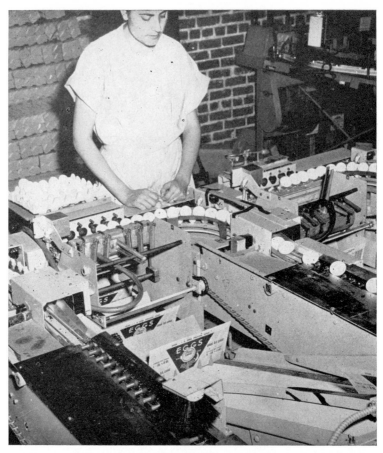

FIG. 12–25.—This equipment grades and cartons eggs at a rate of 7,200 eggs an hour. (Courtesy of Poultry Tribune.)

FIG. 12–26.—Weighing, shell-protecting and packaging are automatic in this plant at Modesto, California. (Courtesy of Poultry Processing and Marketing.)

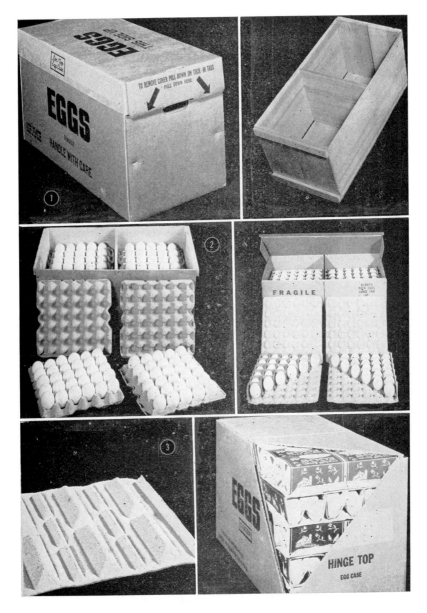

Fig. 12–27.—Examples of fiber and wood cases and filler flats in common use. Shown at the bottom, left, is a molded pulp flat designed to reduce breakage in cartoned eggs. (Courtesy of Poultry Processing and Marketing.)

FIG. 12–28.—This lightweight carton with a special locking feature is being used successfully in store sales of eggs in New York. (Courtesy of New York State College of Agriculture at Cornell University.)

FIG. 12–29.—This machine automatically wraps open-top egg cartons with polyolefin film. Heat tunnel at right shrinks the film tightly around each carton. Inset shows the finished wrap. (Courtesy of Hercules Incorporated, Wilmington, Delaware.)

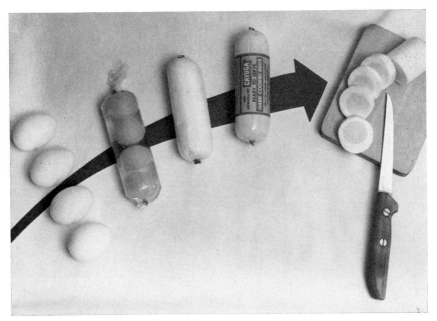

Fig. 12–30.—Hard-cooked egg roll proved acceptable in both retail and institutional sales in New York State. (Courtesy of New York State College of Agriculture at Cornell University.)

New Products

Egg consumption per capita reached a high of 402 in 1945 and has been declining since—to 314 in 1964, a decrease of 22 per cent. In the same period of time, total egg production in the United States has increased by 15 per cent, while population has gone up 49 per cent. If people were eating eggs today at the same rate they did in 1945, the Nation's egg farms would have had to produce nearly a third more total eggs than they actually did in 1965.

Consumption of broiler meat, by contrast, has increased from about 5 pounds per person (ready-to-cook basis) in 1945 to 27 pounds in 1964. Total chicken meat consumption was 22 pounds per person in 1945 and 31 pounds in 1964. This obviously meant a decrease in consumption of chicken other than broilers—mostly stewing hens—from 17 pounds per person in 1945 to about 4 pounds in 1964. Clearly, the housewife has accepted broilers as an economical and desirable food, but has used fewer and fewer eggs as well as much less stewing chicken. Since most of the Nation's 360 million layers are replaced every twelve to fourteen months, the industry is faced with the problem of disposing of some 300 million hens annually at very low prices. Many of them are used in the manufacture of chicken soup.

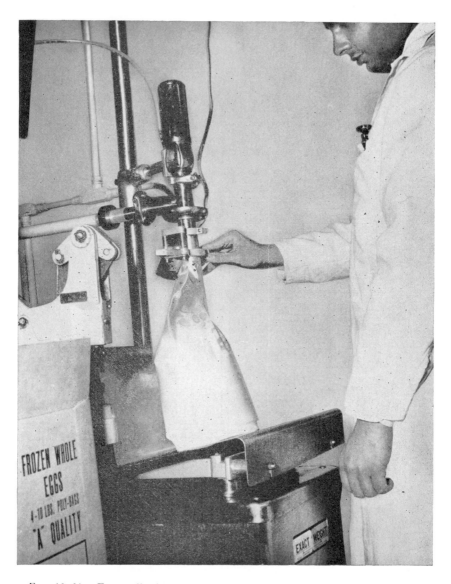

FIG. 12–31.—Frozen liquid eggs are being marketed in 10-pound plastic bags. In a period of two years, more than four million pounds of homogenized, whole frozen eggs were sold to state institutions in New York. (Courtesy of Poultry Tribune.)

Research workers have been cooperating with industry in developing, market testing, and promoting new egg and poultry products. Much of the research has been done at Cornell University and at the University of Connecticut. Among the new products finding their way into the market are chicken franks, bake-and-serve chicken loaf, baked chicken fillet, chicken hash, chicken burgers, hard-boiled egg roll, kidspak of small eggs, and liquid egg for scrambled eggs and omelet. Turkey products include frozen turkey roll, turkey sausage, chopped turkey steak, turkey and waffles, freeze-dried turkey, and a turkey dinner in a disposable bag. Frozen turkey and chicken dinners have been on the market for several years.

Frozen eggs for the restaurant and bakery trade have been packed for many years in 30-pound cans. Now, as a result of a new packaging system developed by the New York State Department of Agriculture in cooperation with the U. S. Department of Agriculture's Consumer and Marketing Service, they are available in 10-pound disposable polyethylene plastic bags. The 10-pound bag is equivalent to 100 shell eggs. Tests of the product for institutional use have shown that instead of taking an hour and forty-five minutes to scramble 1,800 shell eggs, the time can be cut to thirteen minutes by using the new package. In two years the program has marketed more than four million pounds of homogenized, whole frozen eggs, mostly to state institutions. Smaller packages could easily be developed for the retail trade.

Chapter 13

Marketing Poultry

UNTIL about 1950, most of the poultry marketed in this country came from farm flocks—essentially as a by-product of egg production, but with the great increase in commercial broiler growing and substantial increase in turkey production this is no longer true.

Commercial broiler production has developed most extensively in the southern and eastern states, and many millions of pounds of processed broilers are trucked long distances to market. Georgia, Arkansas and Alabama, the three leading states in broiler production in 1964, have only 5 per cent of the population, but produced 42 per cent of the commercial broilers.

Until a few years ago, over 40 per cent of total shipments of dressed poultry to the four principal markets, New York, Chicago, Philadelphia and Boston, were received during the three months of October, November and December. Today, the slaughter of young chickens—about 90 per cent of total poultry slaughter—is fairly well distributed throughout the year.

Other forms of poultry still show a distinctly seasonal marketing pattern. About 60 per cent of all turkeys are slaughtered during the three months of September to November, and 90 per cent of all geese during November and December. The season for duck slaughter is concentrated between May and September, while the bulk of mature poultry from farms is slaughtered from August through January.

Poultry slaughtered under the U. S. Department of Agriculture inspection service in 1965 totaled 9.5 billion pounds on a live-weight basis, as follows:

	Million Pounds
Young chickens, mostly broilers	7,176
Mature chickens	639
All turkeys	1,669
Ducks	67
Other poultry	6

Market Classes and Grades of Poultry

The U. S. Department of Agriculture has set up specifications for classes and grades of live poultry, dressed poultry, and ready-to-cook poultry. The following classes of chickens are specified:

Rock Cornish Game Hen or Cornish Game Hen.—A Rock Cornish game hen or Cornish game hen is a young immature chicken (usually five to seven weeks of age) weighing not more than 2 pounds ready-to-cook weight, which was prepared from a Cornish chicken or the progeny of a Cornish chicken crossed with another breed of chicken.

Broiler or Fryer.—A broiler or fryer is a young chicken (usually nine to twelve weeks of age), of either sex, that is tender-meated with soft, pliable, smooth-textured skin and flexible breastbone cartilage.

Roaster.—A roaster is a young chicken (usually three to five months of age), of either sex, that is tender-meated, with soft, pliable, smooth-textured skin and breastbone cartilage that may be somewhat less flexible than that of a broiler or fryer.

Capon.—A capon is a surgically unsexed male chicken (usually under eight months of age) that is tender-meated with soft, pliable, smooth-textured skin.

Stag.—A stag is a male chicken (usually under ten months of age) with coarse skin, somewhat toughened and darkened flesh, and considerable hardening of the breastbone cartilage. Stags show a condition of fleshing and a degree of maturity intermediate between that of a roaster and a cock or rooster.

Hen or Stewing Chicken or Fowl.—A hen or stewing chicken or fowl is a mature female chicken (usually more than ten months old) with meat less tender than that of a roaster, and non-flexible breastbone tip.

Cock or Rooster.—A cock or rooster is a mature male chicken with coarse skin, toughened and darkened meat, and hardened breastbone tip.

Standards of quality for live poultry on an individual bird basis are summarized in Table 13–1, and those for individual carcasses of dressed and ready-to-cook chickens in Table 13–2. Detailed specifications for the various grades are based on these standards of quality, and copies may be obtained from the U. S. Department of Agriculture, Washington D. C. 20250.

F IG. 13–1.—The wax method of plucking gives a clean, smooth appearance to the finished carcass. It is now used only for ducks and geese. (Courtesy of Institute of American Poultry Industries.)

21

Table 13-1.—Summary of Standards of Quality for Live Poultry of an Individual Bird Basis.

(Minimum Requirements and Maximum Defects Permitted)

Factor	A or No. 1 Quality	B or No. 2 Quality	C or No. 3 Quality
Health and vigor	Alert, bright eyes, healthy, vigorous	Good health and vigor	Lacking in vigor
Feathering	Well covered with feathers showing luster or sheen. Slight scattering of pin feathers	Fairly well covered with feathers. Moderate number of pin feathers	Complete lack of plumage feathers on back. Large number of pin feathers
Conformation:			
Breast bone	Normal	Practically normal	Abnormal
	Slight curve, $\frac{1}{2}''$ dent (chickens), $\frac{1}{4}''$ dent (turkeys)	Slightly crooked	Crooked
Back	Normal (except slight curve)	Moderately crooked	Crooked or hunched back
Legs and Wings	Normal	Slightly misshapen	Misshapen

Fleshing	Well fleshed, moderately broad and long breast	Fairly well fleshed	Poorly developed, narrow breast, thin covering of flesh]
Fat covering	Well covered, some fat under skin over entire carcass Chicken fryers and turkey fryers and young toms only moderate covering No excess abdominal fat	Enough fat on breast and legs to prevent a distinct appearance of flesh thru skin Hens or fowl may have excessive abdominal fat	Lacking in fat covering on back and thighs, small amount in feather tracks
Defects: Tears and broken bones	Slight Free	Moderate Free	Serious Free
Bruises, scratches and callouses	Slight skin bruises, scratches and callouses	Moderate (except only slight flesh bruises)	Unlimited to extent no part unfit for food
Shanks	Slightly scaly	Moderately scaly	Seriously scaly

Standards effective March 1, 1955

Table 13–2.—Summary of Specifications for Standards of Quality for Individual Carcasses of Ready-to-cook Poultry and Parts Therefrom.

(Minimum Requirements and Maximum Defects Permitted)

Factor	A Quality	B Quality	C Quality
Conformation:	Normal	Moderate deformities	Abnormal
Breastbone	Slight curve or dent	Moderately dented, curved or crooked	Seriously curved or crooked
Back	Normal (except slight curve)	Moderately crooked	Seriously crooked
Legs and Wings	Normal	Moderately misshapen	Misshapen
Fleshing:	Well fleshed, moderately long, deep and rounded breast	Moderately fleshed, considering kind, class and part	Poorly fleshed
Fat Covering:	Well covered—especially between heavy feather tracts on breast and considering kind, class and part	Sufficient fat on breast and legs to prevent distinct appearance of flesh through the skin	Lacking in fat covering over all parts of carcass
Pinfeathers:			
Non-protruding pins, and hair	Free	Few scattered	Scattering
Protruding pins	Free	Free	Free

Exposed Flesh:[1]

A Quality

Carcass Weight		Breast and Legs	Elsewhere	Part
Minimum	Maximum			
None	$1\frac{1}{4}$ lbs.	None	$\frac{3}{4}''$	Slight trim on edge
Over $1\frac{3}{4}$ lbs.	6 lbs.	None	$1\frac{1}{2}''$	

B Quality

Breast and Legs²	Elsewhere	Part
$\frac{3}{4}''$	$1\frac{1}{2}''$	Moderate amount of
$1\frac{1}{2}''$	$3''$	

C Quality: No limit

Factor	A Quality	B Quality	C Quality
Over 6 lbs.	None	2"	4"
Over 16 lbs.	None	3"	5" (the flesh normally covered)
Discolorations:³			
None — 1½ lbs.	¼", ½"	1", 2"	½" (No limit⁴)
Over 1½ lbs. — 6 lbs.	¼", 1"	2", 3"	1"
Over 6 lbs. — 16 lbs.	½", 1½"	2½", 4"	1½"
Over 16 lbs. — None	½", 2"	3", 5"	1½"
Disjointed bones	1	2 disjointed and no broken, or	No limit
Broken bones	None	1 disjointed and 1 non-protruding	No limit
Missing parts	Wing tips and tail⁵	Wing tips, 2nd wing joint and tail	Wing tips, wings and tail
Fleshing Defects: (When consumer packaged)	Slight darkening over the back and drumsticks. Few small ⅛" pockmarks for poultry weighing 6 lbs. or less and ¼" pockmarks for poultry weighing more than 6 lbs. Occasional small areas showing layer of clear or pinkish ice.	Moderate dried areas not in excess of ½" in diameter. May lack brightness. Moderate areas showing layer of clear, pinkish or colored ice.	Numerous pockmarks and large dried areas

[1] Total aggregate area of flesh exposed by all cuts and tears and missing skin.

[2] A carcass meeting the requirements of A quality for fleshing may be trimmed to remove skin and flesh defects, provided that no more than one-third of the flesh is exposed on any part and that meat yield is not appreciably affected.

[3] Flesh bruises and discolorations such as "blue back" are not permitted on breast and legs of A quality birds. Not more than one-half of total aggregate area of discolorations may be due to flesh bruises or "blue back" (when permitted) and skin bruises in any combination.

[4] No limit on size and number of areas of discolorations and flesh bruises if such areas do not render any part of the carcass unfit for food.

[5] In geese, the parts of the wing beyond the second joint may be removed, if removed at the joint and both wings are so treated.

Fig. 13–2.—An efficient mechanical picking machine called a Torq Featherator. Feathers are removed by spinning action of the small circular groups of fingers. (Courtesy of Gordon Johnson Company.)

Marketing Processed Poultry

Ready-to-cook poultry is available for purchase in supermarkets throughout the country, but only because there has been developed a highly commercialized operation for killing, dressing, eviscerating, cutting up and packaging chickens and transporting them over long distances. Poultry processing is no longer a farm operation but a highly specialized business. Furthermore, because of the speed and efficiency with which the various operations are carried out, most of this poultry reaches the market fresh chilled. Less than 10 per cent is frozen. Turkeys are still marketed on a highly seasonal basis and about 80 per cent of the crop has to be frozen for future consumption. The corresponding figure for ducks and geese is 40 per cent.

As of January 1, 1958, the number of commercial slaughter plants in the country—meaning those which slaughtered at least 30,000 pounds of poultry a week, live weight basis, was 594. Average weekly slaughter in these plants was 209,000 pounds. Large plants, slaughtering 300,000 pounds or more a week, made up 21 per cent of the plants and accounted for 51 per cent of the output. Twenty per cent of the large plants were located in the South Atlantic region and they accounted for 45 per cent of all slaughter in large plants.

Official Grading and Inspection

For many years the U. S. Department of Agriculture has offered the poultry industry official grading and inspection services on a voluntary basis. These services have been carried on under authority of Congressional acts which have provided that fees shall be charged users of the services to cover costs. Grading services are still permissive and are provided by the Department of Agriculture on a cost basis, but inspection service became compulsory with the enactment on August 28, 1957, of Public Law 85-172, known as the Poultry Products Inspection Act. It requires that all domesticated poultry slaughtered for human food which moves in interstate commerce be inspected for wholesomeness. The cost of such inspection service, except for necessary overtime and holiday work, is borne by the Government.

The sanitary provisions of the regulations are considered as the minimum requirements necessary to produce clean and sanitary poultry food products. They are adaptable to small as well as large poultry-processing operations. They require that processing operations be conducted in buildings that are capable of being kept clean and free from rodents, other vermin, dust, and other conditions that would contaminate food products. Floors and walls in processing rooms must be impervious to moisture, and be smooth and suitable for easy and thorough cleaning. The drainage and plumbing systems must be adequate to dispose of water and other wastes resulting from processing operations, be properly installed, and be equipped with approved traps to prevent the development of health hazards.

The equipment used in processing operations must be of metal or other impervious material and be constructed and so placed as to permit thorough cleaning. The operating procedures are designed so that they will be practicable and at the same time capable of producing clean, sanitary poultry under conditions that will conserve quality and prevent deterioration and contamination of the product.

The inspection procedures provide for both ante mortem and post mortem inspection of the birds and for disposal of birds or parts that are not acceptable for food. The inspector is responsible for the maintenance of sanitation throughout the official establishment. The preparation of food products which contain poultry and which are eligible to bear the inspection mark must be done under the supervision of the inspector.

About 85 per cent of all poultry meat sold by producers is Federally inspected. The percentage of condemnations is normally under three per cent, but there is some seasonal variation. Most of the condemnations among 586 million pounds of young chickens inspected in December, 1965, were for leukosis, septicemia and airsacculitis. Only a few were for bruises, overscalding, or other conditions resulting from improper handling and processing methods. A survey of 135 Delmarva broiler flocks in 1962 showed a decrease in condemnations with increasing market weight, but a corresponding increase in the percentage of undergrade broilers. The distribution was as follows:

Average weight (pounds)	Number of flocks	Average condemnations (per cent)	Average undergrades (per cent)
Under 3.30	21	5.27	6.52
3.30–3.49	37	3.43	7.13
3.50–3.69	36	3.02	8.91
3.70–3.89	27	2.20	10.17
3.90 or more	14	1.71	11.36
Total and average	135	2.92	8.74

Certain growers had consistently low condemnations, while others were consistently high. One grower, for example, had three flocks in succession in which the condemnations were 13.9 per cent, 35.5 per cent, and 8.0 per cent. Three flocks from a neighboring grower had an average condemnation of only 1.43 per cent. Good management is important in keeping the percentage of condemnations at a low figure.

Grades

The United States consumer grades for ready-to-cook poultry are applicable to chickens, turkeys, ducks, geese, guineas and pigeons conforming to the several classes such as Broiler or Fryer, Young Tom Turkey, etc., when each carcass or part has been graded by a grader on an individual basis. U. S. Grades A, B and C are described as follows:

Grade A.—A lot of ready-to-cook poultry or parts consisting of one or more ready-to-cook carcasses or parts of the same kind and class, each of which conforms to the requirements for A Quality, may be designated as U. S. Grade A.

Grade B.—A lot of ready-to-cook poultry or parts consisting of one or more ready-to-cook carcasses or parts of the same kind and class, each of which conforms to the requirements for B Quality or better, may be designated as U. S. Grade B.

Grade C.—A lot of ready-to-cook poultry or parts consisting of one or more ready-to-cook carcasses or parts of the same kind and class, each of which conforms to the requirements for C Quality or better, may be designated as U. S. Grade C.

Table 13-3.—Number and Distribution of Poultry Slaughter Plants, and Weekly Slaughter in 1957, as Reported by the U. S. Department of Agriculture. Reference, AMS-379, April, 1960.

| Region | Plants as of Jan 1, 1958 | | | | Weekly slaughter, 1957* | | | |
| | Small | Medium | Large | Total | Small | Medium | Large | All |
	(Number)				(1,000 pounds)			
New England	8	10	8	26	472	2,099	4,512	7,083
Middle Atlantic. . .	36	18	6	60	1,119	3,491	2,741	7,351
East North Central .	43	32	5	80	2,402	5,188	1,963	9,553
West North Central .	37	52	15	104	2,171	9,030	6,219	17,420
South Atlantic . . .	22	49	51	122	1,217	10,615	28,993	40,825
East South Central. .	13	21	18	52	765	4,346	8,720	13,831
West South Central .	19	49	10	78	1,024	9,083	4,425	14,532
Western	24	34	14	72	1,249	6,298	6,046	13,593
United States . . .	202	265	127	594	10,419	50,150	63,619	124,188

* Average weekly slaughter, live weight, while in operation. Small plants 30–99 thousand pounds; medium 100–299; and large over 300.

Fig. 13-3.—Ice chilling vats in a poultry processing plant. (Courtesy of Poultry Processing and Marketing.)

Fig. 13-4.—Frozen "turkey dinners" are being placed in cartons for shipment from this C. A. Swanson and Sons plant. (Courtesy of Poultry Processing and Marketing.)

Table 13–4.—Receipts of Processed Poultry at Four Markets, New York, Chicago, Philadelphia and Boston, from the Four Leading States, as a Per Cent of Total Receipts, 1934, 1944, 1949 and 1959. Calculated from Data Reported by the U. S. Department of Agriculture.

1934		1944		1949		1959	
State	*Per cent of total*	*State*	*Per cent of total*	*State*	*Per cent of total*	*State*	*Per cent of total*
Iowa	19.1	Iowa	17.0	Delaware	19.6	Georgia	23.5
Minnesota	14.1	Minnesota	15.6	Iowa	10.5	Maine	13.4
Illinois	8.8	Delaware	7.6	Maryland	9.6	Delaware	11.6
Kansas	8.6	Illinois	7.5	Minnesota	9.2	Maryland	11.3
Sum	51.0	Sum	47.7	Sum	48.9	Sum	59.8

FIG. 13–5.—Mechanical chilling equipment in a modern poultry processing plant. (Courtesy of Poultry Processing and Marketing.)

Table 13–5.—States Shipping as Much as Five Million Pounds of Processed Poultry (Not Including Turkeys) to Any One of the Indicated Cities, 1959. As Reported by the U.S. Department of Agriculture.

	Boston	Chicago	Detroit	Los Angeles (Millions of Pounds)	New York	Philadelphia	Pittsburgh	San Francisco
Alabama	—	17	18	35	—	—	—	—
Arkansas	—	6	—	30	—	—	—	6
California	—	—	—	—	—	—	—	8
Connecticut	9	—	—	—	12	—	—	—
Delaware	—	—	—	—	40	11	—	—
Georgia	—	105	42	—	12	—	9	—
Illinois	—	5	—	—	—	—	—	—
Indiana	—	12	—	—	—	—	—	—
Kentucky	—	11	—	—	—	—	—	—
Maine	29	—	—	—	39	—	—	—
Maryland	—	—	—	—	50	6	—	—
Massachusetts	5	—	—	—	—	—	—	—
Mississippi	—	6	5	35	—	—	—	5
Missouri	—	6	—	—	—	—	—	—
New York	—	—	—	—	9	—	—	—
North Carolina	—	—	—	—	18	16	9	—
Ohio	—	—	—	—	—	—	5	—
Pennsylvania	—	—	—	—	13	—	8	—
Tennessee	—	17	15	—	—	—	6	—
Texas	—	—	—	5	—	—	—	—
All other	16	16	12	5	21	11	8	4
Total	59	201	92	108	214	44	45	23

Table 13-6.—States Shipping as Much as Three Million Pounds of Processed Turkeys to Any One of the Indicated Cities, 1959.   As Reported by the U.S. Department of Agriculture.

	Boston	Chicago	Los Angeles	New York	Philadelphia	Pittsburgh	San Francisco
				(Millions of Pounds)			
California			43	9			8
Colorado				4			
Illinois		4			5		
Iowa	6	8		6	4		
Minnesota	4	25		9	5		
Missouri		3					
Nebraska				5			
Ohio						4	
Utah		6		10			
Virginia				4			
Wisconsin		8					
All other	12	10	—	11	10	7	—
Total	22	64	43	58	24	11	8

(333)

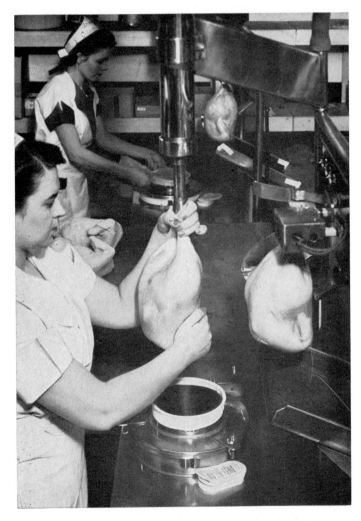

FIG. 13-6.—Carcasses of roasting chickens are commonly wrapped in plastic before freezing, for better preservation of quality. (Courtesy of U. S. Egg and Poultry Magazine.)

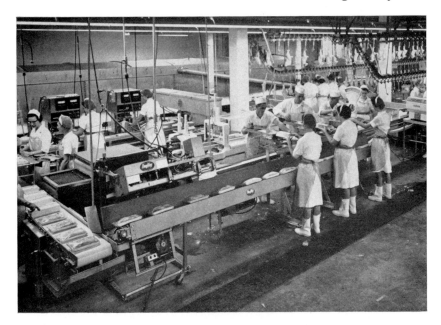

FIG. 13–7.—Chickens are cut up as they move along the line, extreme right, in this Collinswood Poultry Processing Plant, Collins, Mississippi. Cut-up chicken is then packaged, center and left. (Courtesy of Poultry Processing and Marketing.)

FIG. 13–8.—Refrigerated truck-trailers are used for long-distance hauling of processed poultry. (Courtesy of Poultry Processing and Marketing.)

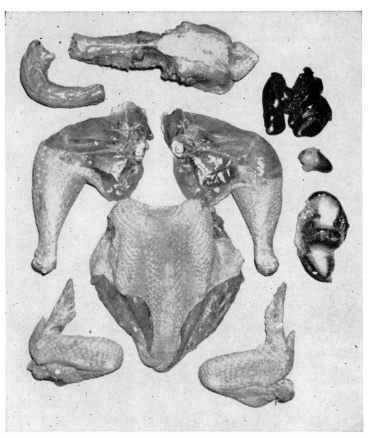

FIG. 13–9.—Cut-up chicken parts ready for wrapping. (Courtesy of Beacon Milling Company, a Division of Textron, Inc.)

FIG. 13–10.—Chicken parts packaged for sale at retail. (Courtesy of Poultry Processing and Marketing.)

FIG. 13–11.—Frozen chicken sticks developed at Cornell University were favorably received by customers at central New York super markets. Boned poultry meat was dipped in a batter containing corn-flakes crumbs. (Courtesy of New York State College of Agriculture at Cornell University.)

FIG. 13–12.—"Bake and Serve" chicken loaf is another new product developed at Cornell University and favorably received in market tests. (Courtesy of New York State College of Agriculture at Cornell University.)

22

Prompt chilling of the dressed or ready-to-cook carcasses is very important, and this is accomplished by immersion in vats containing water and crushed ice. If the water is agitated by compressed air, the total required chilling time is under two hours. New types of chilling equipment which are mechanically operated have reduced chilling time in some plants to less than thirty minutes.

Millions of pounds of broilers and fryers are prepared for market by being cut up and packaged, ready to cook. This has become possible with the widespread installation of refrigerated counters in retail stores and markets.

There are also many retail markets in which it is possible to buy half a chicken, one quarter of a turkey, or parts of a chicken such as breasts, legs, wings or giblets.

Killing, Dressing and Eviscerating Losses

Weight losses represented by inedible parts of the chicken are important to both producer and processor, because they are the basis upon which maximum paying prices should be adjusted in relation to the market price of the final product. They are also related to feeding practices just prior to killing.

Killing and dressing losses consist of feathers and blood. The amount of blood lost is close to 4 per cent of the live weight. This means a tenth of a pound for a $2\frac{1}{2}$-pound broiler and up to a fourth of a pound for a large roaster. The weight loss represented by feathers is more variable, but will average about 5 per cent of the live weight. It is higher for females than for males, and lower for short-feathered chickens such as Cornish than for the more heavily feathered breeds.

Records for twenty lots of 300 chickens each in the 1951 Maine Broiler Production Test, when all were killed and dressed at the same time, showed an average killing loss of 8.8 per cent. The average live weight of these chickens at time of slaughter was 4.94 pounds (cockerels and pullets combined). The lowest shrink for any lot was 6.0 per cent, and the highest 12.4 per cent. For a plant dressing 10,000 head daily, this difference, at 35 cents a pound, represents an extra processing cost of about $1,100 a day. The difference between 12.4 per cent and the average of 8.8 per cent, figured at the same price, is over $600 a day for such a plant. It is not surprising that dressing plant operators have definite preferences for certain types of poultry.

Killing and dressing losses are sometimes complicated by the amount of feed remaining in the crops but under ordinary conditions, when soft feed (as opposed to whole grain) is being fed, a fasting period of four hours prior to slaughter is sufficient. This will allow time for the crop to become empty, and for the intestinal contents to be reduced to a satisfactory point. About 60 per cent of the twenty-four-hour fasting loss of intestinal contents occurs in the first three or four hours.

Table 13-7.—Expected Yield in Pounds of Dressed Weight, Eviscerated Weight and Edible Meat Weight as Related to Live Weight. (Calculated from Data Published by the U.S. Department of Agriculture and Ohio State University.)

| Average live weight (pounds) | From 100 pounds live weight | | | | | From 100 pounds dressed weight | |
| | Dressed weight | | Eviscerated (with giblets) | | Edible meat (with giblets) | Eviscerated (with giblets) | Edible meat (with giblets) |
	(a)	(b)	(a)	(b)	(a)	(a)	(a)
2.0	83.2	87.8	65.6	71.7	55.7	78.9	67.0
2.5	84.4	88.4	67.1	72.0	56.7	79.5	67.2
3.0	85.2	88.9	68.1	72.0	57.4	80.0	67.4
3.5	85.7	89.3	68.8	72.1	57.9	80.3	67.5
4.0	86.2	89.5	69.4	72.2	58.2	80.5	67.5
4.5	86.5	89.8	69.8	72.3	58.5	80.6	67.6
5.0	86.8	89.9*	70.1	72.3*	58.7	80.7	67.6
5.5	87.1	90.0*	70.4	72.4*	58.9	80.8	67.6
6.0	87.2	90.1*	70.6	72.4*	59.0	80.9	67.7

(a) McNally and Spicknall, 1949 (chilled weight basis) battery-raised R. I. Red males slaughtered in groups of 25 at bi-weekly intervals.

(b) Jaap, Renard and Buckingham, 1950 (fresh dressed weight basis) over 1,600 males from 44 strains, all slaughtered at 12 weeks of age.

* These values are extrapolations beyond the 4.5-pound maximum live weight attained at twelve weeks of age by chickens used in the Ohio tests.

Eviscerating losses are influenced by the plumpness and degree of finish of the carcasses and, like dressing losses, they tend to be greater with small chickens than with large. Chickens which are grown to market weight on rations high enough in energy to produce a good covering of fat will show a lower eviscerating loss than will chickens which for any reason are somewhat thin or poorly finished.

Not too many reports have been published showing actual yields in terms of eviscerated weights or edible meat. Data from two tests, at Beltsville, Maryland, and Columbus, Ohio, are summarized in Table 13–7. More information of this sort is needed, especially as related to different degrees of finish.

Average percentage yields for cut-up parts from fryers, based on chilled, ready-to-cook weight, including giblets, are approximately as follows: Breast, 24 per cent; Legs, (drumsticks) 15 per cent; Thighs, 16 per cent; Wings, 13 per cent; Back, 17 per cent; Neck, $7\frac{1}{2}$ per cent and Giblets, $7\frac{1}{2}$ per cent.

FIG. 13–13.—For many years live poultry was shipped to the central markets in special railroad cars such as the one shown here, but by 1950 rail shipments had become negligible. (Courtesy of Institute of American Poultry Industries.)

Marketing Live Poultry

The live-poultry industry is one of considerable magnitude, with New York City as the principal market outlet. Until recent years, only about 20 per cent of the receipts of live poultry in that market came from nearby points. The balance was largely in the form of car-lot shipments from the western producing sections. Freight shipments into New York increased from about 2,000 cars a year in 1900–1905 to 12,000 cars in 1927, the highest year of record. From this high point, freight receipts have continued to decline. Only about 1,000 cars were received in 1944.

Truck receipts, on the other hand, have steadily increased. Truck and express receipts made up more than 80 per cent of the total at New York in 1943 and 1944. By 1949, over 99 per cent of the live poultry arrived by truck.

It is estimated that about 80 per cent of the live poultry that enters the metropolitan area of New York City is consumed by Jewish people, and the industry in this market is greatly influenced by Jewish customs and religion. For example, the orthodox Jewish church requires that poultry be kosher killed, that is, a deputy of the Jewish rabbi (shochet) must slaughter the bird.

Table 13–8.—Holidays That Affect the Demand for Poultry.

Holiday	Kinds of poultry particularly desired
New Year's Day	Turkeys, geese, fowls, capons
Purim	Fowls and hen turkeys
Pessach—First Days (Passover)	Heavy fowls, fat ducks, geese, turkeys
Pessach—Last Days (Last Passover)	Prime quality of all kinds
Shevuoth (Feast of Weeks)	Prime quality of all kinds
Rosh Hashanah (Jewish New Year)	Fat fowls, turkeys, ducks, geese
Yom Kippur (Day of Atonement)	All prime stock
Succoth—First Days (Feast of Tabernacles)	Ducks, geese, fat fowls
Succoth—Last Days* (Feast of Tabernacles)	Prime quality of all kinds
Thanksgiving Day	Turkeys, geese, fowls, capons
Hanukka (Feast of Dedication)	Prime quality of all kinds
Christmas Day	Turkeys, geese, fowls, capons

* The last, or ninth, day is also called Simchas-Torah (Feast of Law).

The Jewish feast and fast days greatly influence the demand for live poultry. The principal Jewish holidays come during the early fall and the early spring months, and at these times the quantity of poultry consumed is much greater than usual.

Fowls have long been the most important class of live poultry dealt in, making up 80 to 85 per cent of the total receipts. Development of the eastern broiler business in recent years has changed all this so that fowls now make up only a fraction of the total.

Shrinkage during shipment from farm to market represents a part of the marketing cost. It varies widely and is affected by such things as air temperature and humidity; age, weight and kind of chickens; the time chickens are on the road; and whether or not they have feed

and water available during the trip to market.   Records on 100
loads of poultry moving from eastern Connecticut to the New York
live poultry market, a distance of about 150 miles, showed shrinks
ranging from 8.5 per cent to as low as 1 per cent.

Table 13–9.—Dates of Certain Jewish Holidays, 1966–1975.

Year	Purim	First day of Pessach (Passover)	First day of Pentecost (Shevuoth)	Rosh Hashanah (New Year)
1966	Mar. 6	Apr. 5	May 25	Sept. 15
1967	Mar. 26	Apr. 25	June 14	Oct. 5
1968	Mar. 14	Apr. 13	June 2	Sept. 23
1969	Mar. 4	Apr. 3	May 23	Sept. 13
1970	Mar. 22	Apr. 21	June 10	Oct. 1
1971	Mar. 11	Apr. 10	May 30	Sept. 20
1972	Feb. 29	Mar. 30	May 19	Sept. 9
1973	Mar. 18	Apr. 17	June 6	Sept. 27
1974	Mar. 8	Apr. 7	May 27	Sept. 17
1975	Feb. 25	Mar. 27	May 16	Sept. 6

Year	Yom Kippur (Day of Atonement)	First day of Succoth (Feast of Tabernacles)	Simchas-Torah (Feast of Law)	Hanukka (Feast of Dedication)
1966	Sept. 24	Sept. 29	Oct. 7	Dec. 8
1967	Oct. 14	Oct. 19	Oct. 27	Dec. 27
1968	Oct. 2	Oct. 7	Oct. 15	Dec. 16
1969	Sept. 22	Sept. 27	Oct. 5	Dec. 5
1970	Oct. 10	Oct. 15	Oct. 23	Dec. 23
1971	Sept. 29	Oct. 4	Oct. 12	Dec. 13
1972	Sept. 18	Sept. 23	Oct. 1	Dec. 1
1973	Oct. 6	Oct. 11	Oct. 19	Dec. 20
1974	Sept. 26	Oct. 1	Oct. 9	Dec. 9
1975	Sept. 15	Sept. 20	Sept. 28	Nov. 29

Dates for other holidays and other years can be found in *The Centurial* by
Rev. E. M. Nyers, published by Bloch Publishing Company, New York.

Other Connecticut tests with fourteen-week-old broilers showed
shrinks of 5 to 7 per cent for chickens cooped without feed for
fourteen hours, compared with 7 to 8 per cent for similar chickens
trucked 300 miles during the same length of time.   Males showed
consistently greater amounts of shrink than did females.   Chickens
which had been fed high-energy rations fared better than did those
fed what had previously been considered standard mixtures.
Shrinkage could be estimated roughly as 1 per cent for each of the
first two hours plus $\frac{1}{2}$ per cent of the initial weight for each additonal
hour on the road.

Table 13–10.—States Shipping as Much as One Million Pounds of Live Poultry to Any One of the Indicated Cities, 1959. As Reported by the U.S. Department of Agriculture.

	Boston	Chicago	Detroit	New York*	Philadelphia	San Francisco
			(Thousands of Pounds)			
California	—	—	—		—	18,938
Connecticut	774	—	—		1,802	—
Delaware	—	3,086	—		—	—
Illinois	—	6,389	3,989		—	—
Indiana	—	1,146				—
Kentucky	1,457	—	—		—	—
Maine	7,040	—				—
Massachusetts . . .		—	4,811		—	—
Michigan	—	2,876			—	—
New Hampshire . . .	6,038	—	—		3,263	—
New Jersey	—	—	1,155		—	—
Ohio	—	—			3,627	—
Pennsylvania	—	1,156				—
Wisconsin	45	68	249		480	—
All other	15,314	14,721	10,204	58,450*	9,172	18,938
Total						

* Not available by State of origin.

(343)

Chapter 14

The Business of Poultry Keeping

THROUGHOUT the national economy it has become increasingly more profitable in recent years to employ capital than to employ labor. In the poultry business this has resulted in widespread use of such devices as bulk feed tanks, mechanical feeding and watering systems, medication by way of the water supply, egg collection belts, mechanical methods of cleaning houses, and manure disposal systems which involve hauling the material away in liquid form. Processors make use of automatic picking machines, mechanical chilling equipment, machines which grade, wash and package eggs mechanically, and high-capacity egg-breaking equipment. Liquid egg products are pasteurized by equipment which maintains automatic control of time and temperature.

These changes have accompanied the trend toward larger laying flocks and broiler plants, partly because only the larger operators could afford to install expensive equipment, but also because increasing labor costs of hand operations were making it nearly impossible for small flock owners to compete successfully in poultry meat and egg production. The once common farm flock of poultry has virtually disappeared in most sections of the country, along with the country

Table 14–1.—Prices of Eggs, Broilers and Poultry Feed, by Alternate Years, 1951 to 1965, as Reported by the U. S. Department of Agriculture.

Year	Eggs[1] (cents)	Broilers[2] (cents)	Laying feed[3]	Broiler grower[3]	Egg-feed ratio[4]	Broiler-feed ratio[5]
1951	47.7	28.5	$4.96	$5.36	9.6	5.3
1953	47.7	27.1	4.88	5.26	9.8	5.1
1955	39.5	25.2	4.58	5.00	8.6	5.0
1957	35.9	18.9	4.42	4.89	8.1	3.9
1959	31.4	16.1	4.44	4.84	7.1	3.3
1961	35.5	13.9	4.36	4.64	8.1	3.0
1963	34.4	14.6	4.48	4.80	7.7	3.0
1965	33.0	14.8	4.40	4.84	7.6	3.1

[1] Weighted average price per dozen.
[2] Weighted average price per pound.
[3] Average cost per 100 pounds.
[4] Pounds of laying feed one dozen eggs will buy.
[5] Pounds of broiler grower one pound of broiler will buy.

store and the local produce plant as outlets for eggs and chickens, and rail shipment of eggs and live poultry from local assembling plants to wholesale markets in a few large cities.

The long-time trend in poultry and egg prices has been downward, as shown in Table 14–1, and production has had to become increasingly efficient both in terms of feed conversion and in terms of management practices. If it takes 6 pounds of feed to produce a dozen eggs, there is little margin for profit if that dozen eggs can be exchanged for no more than 7 pounds of feed. Consequently, poultrymen have been striving for higher and higher egg yields, which mean better feed conversion, as well as for more efficient use of labor, and lower costs of housing.

The Effect of Location

For many years, farm prices of eggs, as reported by the U. S. Department of Agriculture, have been consistently higher in some parts of the country than in others. In 1963, for example, farm prices in New England were about 6 cents a dozen above those in the South Atlantic and South Central States, and about 20 cents above farm prices in the West North Central region. Corresponding differences in the cost of feed were much less, which gave New England producers an economic advantage. Table 14–2 shows the variation in 1965 for the several regions and for seven selected States.

Table 14–2.—Farm Prices of Eggs and Cost of Layer Feed, by Regions and for Seven Contiguous States—Nebraska to Connecticut —as Reported by the U. S. Department of Agriculture in 1965.

Region	Price per dozen (cents)	Value of 20 dozen	Cost of 90 pounds of layer feed	Difference
New England	47.4	$9.48	$3.59	$5.89
Middle Atlantic	36.7	7.34	3.95	3.59
East North Central	30.2	6.04	4.09	1.95
West North Central	24.7	4.94	4.01	.93
South Atlantic	39.0	7.80	4.27	3.33
East South Central	38.0	7.60	4.13	3.4,
West South Central	36.6	7.32	3.88	3.44
Mountain	33.8	6.76	4.10	2.66
Pacific	30.5	6.10	3.49	2.61
United States	33.4	$6.68	$3.97	$2.71
State				
Nebraska	23.3	4.66	4.00	.66
Iowa	24.4	4.88	4.28	.60
Illinois	27.8	5.56	4.40	1.16
Indiana	30.6	6.12	4.00	2.12
Ohio	32.0	6.40	4.15	2.25
New York	37.1	7.42	4.10	3.32
Connecticut	49.9	9.98	3.47	6.51

Higher egg prices in some regions can be explained in part by nearness to large centers of population with consequent strong demand for table eggs, and in part by more sales of eggs for hatching purposes, at prices somewhat above those for market eggs.

Concentration of broiler production in the southeast increased the local demand for hatching eggs, and large breeding farms were established to supply this demand. Although the number of farms reporting chickens on hand in the South Atlantic States declined by 42 per cent from 1954 to 1959, the total number of eggs sold annually in those states, as reported by the Census, doubled in the same five-year period.

COMMERCIAL EGG FARMING

Commercial egg production is a highly competitive business which involves a substantial investment of capital and a considerable element of risk. The demand for high quality eggs is growing along with the increase in population, but the total demand at any one time is inelastic so that relatively small changes in total egg production can cause sharp declines in the prices that independent producers receive for eggs. Vertical integration has served to distribute the financial risk, and large volume has enabled such operations to make a profit in spite of narrow margins between production costs and market prices.

During the years from 1915 to 1940, economic studies of poultry farming were concerned with enterprises in which the number of layers was usually under 1,000, and the total capital investment was around $10,000 or $12,000. Successful commercial poultry farms today are likely to have from 10,000 to 50,000 layers, and individual specialized farms often have 100,000 or more. This is the pattern in New England, in the South Atlantic States, in the South Central region and on the Pacific Coast. Commercial egg production has been growing in the Midwest also. In Illinois, for example, the total number of hens and pullets on farms declined from about 22 million in 1954 to 10 million in 1959. But commercial flocks have increased so that in 1965 there were 2.5 million hens in flocks of 10,000 or more, about 20 per cent of the state's total, and over 2 million hens in the state were kept in cages.

As pointed out in the opening chapter of this book, less than 3 per cent of all farms selling eggs in the United States in 1959 accounted for more than half of total egg sales in that year. The picture will probably be even more striking when data from the 1964 Census of Agriculture become available. Preliminary reports for the states of Indiana, Maine, Michigan, Ohio and Virginia show a 5-state total decrease of 57 per cent from 1959 to 1964 in the number of farms selling eggs, but a combined total increase of 31 per cent in the number of eggs sold.

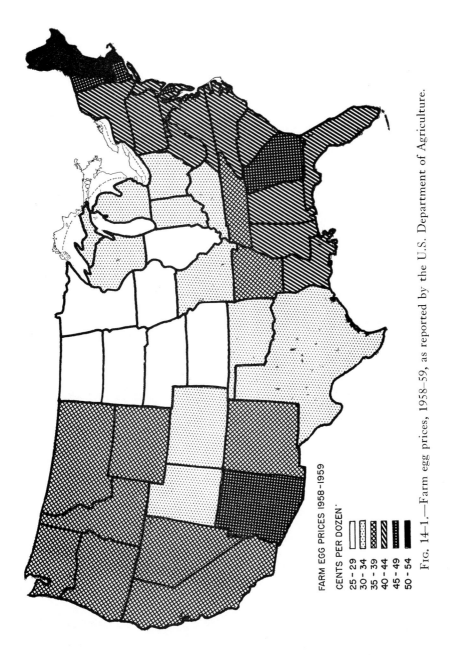

FARM EGG PRICES 1958-1959

CENTS PER DOZEN

25 - 29
30 - 34
35 - 39
40 - 44
45 - 49
50 - 54

Fig. 14-1.—Farm egg prices, 1958-59, as reported by the U.S. Department of Agriculture.

The Capital Investment

A farm flock of 400 or 500 hens may be kept in a relatively low-cost building, but when 10 to 50 times that number of layers is to be kept, a more expensive building is necessary. Furthermore, there must be much more equipment such as an efficient water system, bulk feed tanks, automatic feeders, and egg collection belts, as well as egg washing and grading equipment, and the like. And if the enterprise is to consist of 50,000 to 100,000 hens, the capital investment rises to a really substantial total.

Not too many records of actual plant investment have been published, and it is probably best to approach the problem from the hypothetical point of view, estimating the actual costs involved in setting up plants of varying capacity. This has been done by Dr. J. C. Headley for floor-managed flocks in Illinois, and some of his estimates will be used for illustration.

Fig. 14–2.—A flock of 15,000 layers in one half of this 400′ × 52′ four-story house in Middlesex, New York, averaged 262 eggs each in twelve months beginning July 1, 1959. Mortality was 11 per cent, and feed conversion 4.15 pounds of feed for each dozen eggs.

Fig. 14–3.—In an effort to reduce depreciation charges to a minimum, some poultrymen have turned to aluminum for construction of laying houses. This one is 500 feet long, 42 feet wide. (Courtesy of Poultry Tribune.)

FIG. 14–4.—Bulk tanks are an aid to keeping feed and labor costs low.   Park
Leghorn Farm, Warrensburg, Illinois.   (J. C. Allen and Son Photo.)

FIG. 14–5.—A cart like this saves labor in gathering eggs on the Frank Miller
ranch in Central California.   (Courtesy of Pacific Poultryman.)

Total capital investment in house and equipment varied from $4.14 per bird capacity for the 1,000-layer plant to $3.25 for the 100,000-layer establishment, but the division between house and equipment remained almost constant from 10,000 to 100,000—63 per cent house and 37 per cent equipment. The total house investment ranged from just under $3,000 for the 1,000-layer plant to $205,000 for the plant for 100,000 layers. Corresponding totals for equipment were $1,154 and $119,639. Converted to an annual basis, the non-feed costs for plants from 5,000 to 100,000 capacity are shown in Table 14–3.

It is significant that the percentage distribution of non-feed costs among various items—stock, labor, housing and equipment, and so forth—was almost identical for all plants from 10,000 to 100,000

Table 14–3.—Synthesized Annual Non-Feed Costs in Relation to Size of Plant. From University of Illinois, Department of Agricultural Economics Publication AERR-68, January, 1964.

	House Capacity (Number of Layers)				
	5,000	*10,000*	*25,000*	*50,000*	*100,000*
Depreciation:					
Housing (15-year life)	$773	$1,500	$3,467	$6,880	$13,667
Equipment (8-year life)	625	1,636	3,907	7,592	14,955
Interest (6% on average investment)	498	1,068	2,498	4,918	9,739
Manure removal (custom basis)	250	500	1,250	2,500	5,000
Utilities	90	280	600	1,200	2,400
Taxes	215	446	1,064	2,000	4,163
Supplies	700	1,400	3,000	6,000	12,000
Sub-total	$3,151	$6,830	$15,786	$31,189	$61,924
Stock depreciation (15% mortality)	8,515	16,630	41,075	81,150	161,300
Interest on stock investment	281	555	1,373	2,715	5,400
Labor ($1.50/hour)	3,285	2,190	5,213	9,600	18,600
Total non-feed costs	$15,232	$26,205	$63,447	$124,654	$247,224
Annual non-feed costs per layer	$3.04	$2.62	$2.54	$2.49	$2.47
	Percentage Distribution				
Stock charges	58	66	67	67	67
Labor	22	8	8	8	8
House and Equipment	12	16	16	16	16
Utilities, Taxes, Supplies	6	8	7	7	7
Manure removal	2	2	2	2	2
	100	100	100	100	100

capacity. This indicates that a 10,000 layer plant, large enough to warrant installation of an egg collection belt, can be efficient in terms of direct labor used in caring for the hens. The calculations also make clear the importance of operating any plant at full capacity   The annual non-feed costs per layer amounted to $2.53 for a 25,000-layer plant, but jumped to $2.85 in a 50,000-layer plant operated at half capacity.

Table 14–4.—California Poultry Management Study Averages for the Years 1962, 1963 and 1964. California Agricultural Extension Service.

	1962	1963	1964
Number of flock records	89	77	81
Average number of hens per flock	13,680	15,175	19,084
Eggs per hen, hen-day basis	239	238	237
Dozens sold per hen	20.0	19.8	19.7
Hen mortality, per cent	14	15	15
Culled or removed, per cent	70	62	69
Added as new layers, per cent	103	90	95
Pounds of feed per hen, including feed for replacement pullets	115	111	112
Hours of labor per hen	0.5	0.4	0.3
Average cost of feed per 100 pounds	$3.09	$3.18	$3.17
Average price of eggs per dozen	.287	.288	.285
Net cost per dozen eggs	.258	.251	.250
Management income per dozen	.029	.037	.035

Costs and Returns

Cost of production includes both cash and non-cash items, and although cash costs in the production of eggs are rather high when compared with the cash costs in some other enterprises, they make up only about two-thirds of the total cost. Feed purchased is by far the largest item in cash cost. Farm-grown feed represents about one-half cash cost and one-half non-cash cost. Among the non-cash costs would be included the labor of the operator and that of members of his family, together with interest and depreciation that may be charged against the business.

Major Cost Items.—The largest item of cost in the production of eggs is feed. It will normally make up from 50 to 60 per cent of the total cost, though in exceptional cases it may run as low as 45 per cent or as high as 65 per cent. With increased specialization, as on poultry breeding farms, many extra costs are introduced, so that the relative importance of feed becomes less. During periods of extremely high, or very low feed prices, the normal relationship may be temporarily disturbed.

Table 14–5.—Expense and Income Items—California Poultry Management Study, for the Years 1962, 1963 and 1964. Same Flocks as Table 14–4.

Item	1962	1963	1964
Income per hen:			
Egg sales	$5.73	$5.70	$5.63
Poultry sales	.16	.15	.14
Income from manure	.00	.01	.04
Increase in poultry stock inventory	.28	.12	.16
Total Income (A)	$6.17	$5.98	$5.97
Expense per hen:			
Total feed cost	$3.54	$3.54	$3.54
Poultry stock bought	.52	.41	.51
Miscellaneous costs	.42	.36	.31
Hired labor	.39	.31	.33
Depreciation	.27	.24	.21
Total cash and depreciation (B)	$5.14	$4.86	$4.90
Value of operator's labor	.22	.18	.17
Interest on investment	.23	.21	.21
Total—all costs (C)	$5.59	$5.25	$5.28
Management income per hen (A–C)	.58	.73	.69
Farm income per hen (A–B)	$1.03	$1.12	$1.07

Table 14–6.—Summary of Costs of Raising Pullets on New York Farms in 1958 and 1959. (Courtesy of C. D. Kearl, Dept. of Agr. Economics, Cornell University.)

Costs and returns per 100 chicks started:	1958	1959
Number of farms	6	7
Total number of chicks started	28,956	71,729
Mortality, per cent	4	3
Costs:		
Chicks—cost per 100 started	$ 38.41	$ 35.25
Feed (2,342 lbs. in 1958; 1,945 lbs. in 1959)	91.03	75.00
Labor (8 hours in 1958; 4 hours in 1959)	12.77	6.55
Auto, truck, tractor	3.25	1.18
Poultry equipment	2.91	6.41
Litter	.47	.38
Interest	3.17	2.39
Fuel and electricity	3.97	2.40
Medicine and disinfectants	1.59	.84
Buildings	10.76	6.42
All other	1.82	1.15
Total cost	$170.15	$137.97
Returns:		
Pullets for laying	$183.91	$164.64
Other returns	4.62	8.43
Total Returns	$188.53	$173.07
Gain	$ 18.38	$ 35.10

If flock size is below 10,000 layers, labor will usually be the second largest item of cost, but with larger flocks and fully automated equipment, labor cost per layer is much reduced and stock charges—pullet replacement and depreciation of layers—will move into second place. The distribution of costs as recorded for some 80 California flocks in 1962, 1963 and 1964 is shown in Table 14–5.

Feed is also the principal item of cost in raising pullets for flock replacement. A representative distribution of costs in this part of the egg farming business is shown for New York farms in Table 14–6, for smaller Iowa flocks in 1962 in Table 14–7, and for California ranches in 1964, in Table 14–8.

Table 14–7.—Cost of Raising Replacement Pullets—
Iowa, 1962.

	Range	Confinement	Total
Number of flocks	11	13	24
Average number of chicks started . . .	671	2,055	1,420
Average number of pullets raised . . .	620	1,945	1,330
Mortality, per cent	7.5	5.3	6.3
Pounds of feed per pullet raised . . .	18.6	18.1	18.4
Hours of labor per 100 pullets raised . .	16.4	9.6	11.3
Feed cost per 100 pounds	$ 3.54	$ 3.28	$ 3.40
Feed cost per pullet raised	.66	.60	.63
Chick cost per pullet raised	.49	.47	.48
Other costs, except labor	.14	.17	.15
Total cost per pullet, except labor . . .	$ 1.29	$ 1.24	$ 1.26
Valuation of pullets	1.68	1.68	1.68
Labor and management return per pullet	.39	.44	.42
Labor and management return per hour .	$ 2.92	$ 5.52	$ 4.54

Table 14–8.—Average Cost of Raising Replacement Pullets on Ten Ranches in Orange County, California, 1964. (Nine of the ten ranches raised all pullets on wire.)

	To Age:		
	16 weeks	20 weeks	24 weeks
Feed	46.2 cents	62.5 cents	78.1 cents
Chicks	31.8	32.4	33.1
Fuel	.6	.6	.6
Vaccine and medication	6.5	7.1	7.2
Labor	7.3	8.5	9.5
Miscellaneous . .	.4	.4	.4
Depreciation . . .	4.4	4.6	4.7
Interest	4.6	4.7	4.8
Totals . . .	$1.02	$1.21	$1.38
Feed per pullet (pounds)	12.8	17.8	22.7
Weight per pullet (pounds)	2.7	3.0	3.6
Mortality (per cent)	4.7	6.5	8.3

23

Sources of Income.—Just as feed accounts for the largest share of expense, so market eggs form the chief source of income on commercial egg farms.   Hatching eggs, cull hens, and young chickens sold for meat are of varying importance as sources of income on individual farms, but in the aggregate they are of only minor significance.   This is quite in contrast to the situation on general farms in earlier years, when the income from poultry meat often approached and occasionally exceeded that from market eggs. When a poultry business is being expanded, the increase in inventory value of the flock may represent a significant percentage of total yearly receipts.   Commercial broiler farms are discussed in a later section.

Major Factors Influencing Profits

Profits in egg production are influenced by many things, but the most important factors seem to be (1) size of business, (2) egg yield per hen and (3) efficiency in the use of labor.   The third factor is directly related to the first in that small flocks can rarely be handled as efficiently as large ones.   On the other hand, labor is not always efficiently utilized on large flocks.

Under certain conditions the rate of mortality and depreciation of flocks may outweigh everything else, and again the price received for market eggs, though not often under the control of the operator, may have much to do with the profit on the enterprise.

Size of Business.—Many poultry businesses are less profitable than they might be because they are too small.   A small flock can never make a very large profit, nor can it ever cause the owner a very large loss.   One who is trying to make a living from poultry must keep a rather large flock, and must assume the risk of a possible large loss in order to have the opportunity of making a reasonably large total net income.   Economic studies of poultry farming have shown, without exception, that net income increases almost in direct proportion to the increase in size of flock.   Within the limits of flock size that have come under careful study and observation, there has been little evidence of the application of the law of diminishing returns.   It seems clear that if one intends to stay in the business of producing market eggs he should plan to maintain a flock that is larger than the average in most, if not all sections of the country.

Not many recent records are available from which to show the effect of flock size on costs and returns per hen, but the data in Table 14–9, based on 63 New York farms for 1954–55 indicate the relationships.   Returns in that year were low because of low egg prices—the U. S. egg-feed ratio at the time was 9.4 as compared with an average of 11.7 for the ten-year period from 1944 to 1954— but this did not greatly affect the distribution of cost items.   The 19 farms with flocks averaging 7,066 hens had an average total cost per layer of $7.80 as compared with $8.40 per layer for the 22 farms on which flock size averaged 2,380 hens.

Table 14–9.—Effect of Flock Size on Costs and Related Items, 63 New York Poultry Farms, 1954–55.   Cornell Agr. Exp. Station A. E. 1052.

Item	Size of flock			
	Under 3000	3000–5000	Over 5000	All flocks
Number of farms . . .	22	22	19	63
Average number of layers . .	2,380	3,944	7,066	4,340
Eggs per layer	191	191	196	193
Per cent mortality	23	21	22	22
Pounds of feed per layer . .	105	106	107	106
Hours of labor per layer . .	1.3	1.1	1.0	1.1
Pounds of feed per dozen eggs .	6.8	6.7	6.7	6.7
Dozens of eggs sold per farm .	37,505	62,943	115,580	69,661
Dozens of eggs sold per hour of labor	12.1	14.5	16.4	14.6
Cost per layer:				
Feed	$4.15	$4.14	$4.04	$4.11
Labor	1.69	1.33	1.11	1.39
Depreciation	1.36	1.35	1.39	1.37
Building and equipment . .	.76	.78	.79	.78
Other	.44	.42	.47	.43
Return per hour of labor . .	−.10	.16	.41	.12

Egg Yield.—Productive livestock has long been recognized as one of the essentials of good farming, and poultry farming is no exception to the rule. High egg yields nearly always mean high costs per hen, but they usually result in low costs per dozen eggs, and of course they mean high gross returns per hen when comparison is made with low-producing flocks. The net result is that egg yield is one of the most important factors in determining the profits to be realized from a poultry farm business.

Data for 135 New York farms in 1946–47, given in Table 14–10, show the relation of egg yield to costs and returns at that time. Because of better breeding, feeding and management, most commercial egg flocks today are laying as well as the best flocks of a few years ago, and the net effect of a small increase in average egg yield is not so apparent as it was formerly, but the differences are still important. A 1959 egg cost study for San Diego County, California, provides a good example.

Among the 40 cooperators with an average of 7,177 layers per ranch and an average yield of 243 eggs per hen, there were 31 flocks with 4,000 or more hens. The top 9 flocks in this latter group had an average yield of 248 or more eggs per hen. Their net cost averaged 26.5 cents a dozen. At the low production end were 9 flocks with average yields of 237 eggs or less, and their average net cost was 29.5 cents a dozen. The unweighted average egg production for the two groups was 254 and 230 eggs, respectively, enough of a spread to account for a difference of three cents a dozen in net cost. All of these layers were housed in cages, the most common practice in southern California.

A comparable study in 1964 included 28 flocks averaging 25,111 layers, all in cages, and again with an average yield of 243 eggs. There were five flocks above 250 eggs a year, averaging 253; and five other flocks below 230 eggs a year, averaging 227. Total cost per dozen for the two groups was 25.1 and 32.1 cents, respectively. The first group consumed 4.4 pounds of feed for each dozen eggs, compared with 5.0 pounds for the second group. The average price received for market eggs from all flocks was 27.9 cents a dozen.

Table 14–10.—Relation of Eggs per Layer to Costs and Returns per Dozen Eggs on 135 Farms in New York State, 1946–47. (Cornell Agr. Exp. Sta. Bulletin 864.)

	Light breeds			Heavy breeds		
	Low	Medium	High	Low	Medium	High
Number of farms	28	27	27	18	18	17
Average number of layers	1,252	1,022	1,006	604	609	629
Eggs per layer	152	178	203	137	188	218
Per cent mortality	13	17	15	21	13	15
Labor per dozen eggs (minutes)	9.3	8.1	7.2	6.8	7.8	9.0
Feed per dozen eggs (pounds)	8.3	7.2	6.8	9.6	7.6	6.7
	Cents	Cents	Cents	Cents	Cents	Cents
Cost per dozen eggs:						
Feed	34.8	29.9	28.3	39.8	31.3	27.3
Labor	9.2	8.9	7.7	11.9	8.4	9.1
Buildings and equipment	3.8	3.6	2.8	3.6	4.2	3.5
Depreciation	6.9	6.1	6.9	2.3	2.9	2.3
Other	2.8	2.9	2.6	4.2	3.6	3.5
Total	57.5	51.4	48.3	61.8	50.4	45.7
Returns per dozen eggs:						
Eggs	54.7	54.4	55.7	51.1	51.4	51.2
Other	0.2	0.4	0.3	0.6	0.6	0.5
Total	54.9	54.8	56.0	51.9	52.0	51.7
Profit per dozen eggs	−2.6	3.4	7.7	−10.1	1.6	6.0

One important reason why high egg yields are profitable is that the feed required for maintenance is constant for hens of any given weight, and bears no relation to the number of eggs laid. The amount of feed consumed for each dozen eggs produced is therefore much less in the case of high-producing hens or flocks than it is for low producers. With the high-energy rations currently in use, a 5-pound hen laying 4 eggs every ten days will eat 6.7 pounds of total feed for each dozen eggs; whereas a hen of the same size laying 7 eggs every ten days will eat only 4.3 pounds of feed for each dozen. A 4-pound hen, because of her lower maintenance requirement, will do even better, eating 5.8 pounds and 3.8 pounds of feed for each dozen eggs, respectively, at the two rates of production. At 4 cents a pound for feed, the respective feed costs of a dozen eggs would be 27 and 17 cents for the 5-pound hen, and 23 and 15 cents for the 4-pound hen.

Labor Efficiency.—Efficient use of labor is important on poultry farms because, as has already been stated, the number of hens kept has a great deal to do with the size of the farm income. For maximum labor efficiency it is necessary also to have good stock, because a high egg yield per hen makes possible the production of a large number of eggs per man. Eggs produced per hour of man labor, or per man employed per year, can be used as an index of labor efficiency.

A common cause of low efficiency in the use of labor is the route of travel in doing the necessary daily chores connected with the poultry enterprise. In a study made in Oregon, it was found that the long-distance men on measured chore routes traveled seven to fourteen times as far as the short-distance men. Time saved in chore-route travel can be better expended in taking care of more hens or in finding additional ways to cut costs or increase market returns.

In a study of labor saving on Pennsylvania poultry farms it was found that installation of automatic watering systems saved nearly one-half hour of chore time daily per 1,000 layers. Substantial savings in chore time and travel were effected by such changes as removing partitions and rearranging nests.

Table 14–11.—Average Results of California Poultry Management Studies, 1958 to 1964. California Agricultural Extension Service

Year	Average flock size	Eggs per hen	Price received for eggs	Feed cost per 100 pounds	Hours of labor per hen	Dozens of eggs per man hour
1958	4,899	233	37.5c	$3.38	0.8	24.2
1959	5,892	235	30.2	3.29	0.7	28.0
1960	7,051	237	34.0	3.07	0.6	32.8
1961	10,187	239	31.3	3.08	0.5	39.8
1962	13,680	239	28.7	3.09	0.5	40.0
1963	15,575	238	28.8	3.18	0.4	49.5
1964	19,084	237	28.5	3.17	0.3	65.7

Year	Total income per hen	Total expense per hen	Net cost per dozen	Management income per hen	Management income per dozen	Total farm income
1958	$7.92	$6.60	30.7c	$1.32	6.8c	$10,582
1959	6.33	6.25	29.8	.08	0.4	5,067
1960	7.12	5.86	27.5	1.26	6.5	13,890
1961	6.60	5.66	26.6	.94	4.7	15,077
1962	6.17	5.59	25.8	.58	2.9	14,090
1963	5.98	5.25	25.1	.73	3.7	16,996
1964	5.97	5.28	25.0	.69	3.5	20,420

Fig. 14–6.—Eggs roll gently out of this wire-floor nest onto a belt which serves two rows of nests back to back. Each nest is 12 × 18 inches. See Figure 14–7 for a view of the automatic egg gatherer. (Photograph by Eleanor Gilman.)

Fig. 14–7.—Eggs from three floors are gathered by conveyor belts moving at 6 feet a minute. Picture shows how eggs are picked up by the vertical conveyor and taken to the grader on the second floor. Coll's Poultry Farm, East Jaffrey, N.H. (Photograph by Eleanor Gilman.)

In a 1957 Illinois report the time required for hand feeding 1,000 hens averaged 25 to 30 minutes a day, compared with 10 to 12 minutes a day when self-feeders were used, and 6 minutes a day with mechanical feeders.

Competition has forced poultrymen to find ways of caring for more layers per man, or selling more dozens of eggs per man, or both, in order to get the cost per dozen down low enough to leave a margin of profit with current low market egg prices. The data in Table 14–11 show the trends in six California counties from 1958 through 1964. The records for 1964 covered 1.5 million hens, or about $4\frac{1}{2}$ per cent of all hens in the state. Egg yield remained nearly constant throughout the seven years, but nearly everything else changed. The market price of eggs, and consequently the total income per hen, decreased by about one-fourth, but total farm income doubled.

Average flock size nearly quadrupled and, partly because of this, hours of labor per hen dropped from 0.8 to 0.3. Fifteen years earlier when flock size was about 2,000 hens, labor per hen had been 1.5 hours. This change in labor efficiency brought about an increase in dozens of eggs sold per man-hour expended on the flock from 24 dozens in 1958 to 66 dozens in 1964.

Large commercial egg operations are using bulk delivery of feed, automatic feeders to distribute feed to the laying pens, automatic egg washing and grading equipment, and in many cases mechanical belts for gathering eggs—all with the primary objective of saving labor and reducing the cost of each dozen eggs. Even on a well-equipped egg ranch, about half of all labor will be used in egg handling, including gathering, washing and grading. The total time required for these operations cannot often be reduced below thirty minutes for each 30-dozen case of eggs sold. Attempts to increase speed much beyond this may involve the risk of more breakage which can easily offset the saving in labor cost.

Mortality and Flock Depreciation.—One of the most serious problems confronting poultrymen in many sections of the country is the mortality among laying pullets, and to a less extent among older hens. Methods of sanitation, as previously pointed out, have enabled flock owners to bring the mortality of young growing chickens reasonably well under control, but the problem of reducing or preventing excessive mortality of laying stock is not yet completely solved. It appears that the most promising method of attack is through breeding and selection for highly resistant strains, but until the vital significance of the problem is fully appreciated, progress is likely to be rather slow.

Mortality among laying flocks not only causes a direct monetary loss amounting to the value of the birds that die, but it results in further indirect losses that may be even more costly in spite of the fact that they are less apparent. Houses, equipment and labor sufficient to care for 1,200 hens will be used with decreasing efficiency as the death loss mounts during the year. This is partly obscured by the common practice of making calculations, such as average egg yield, on the basis of the average number of layers in the flock during the year, or on the hen-day basis. A flock that has lost 50 per cent of the original number by death may thus show an average yield well above 200 eggs. If all such calculations were made on the basis of the number of hens and pullets at the beginning of the laying year the picture would often be quite different.

The mortality among commercial flocks observed in some of the economic studies of poultry farming made during the last 45 years was 7 per cent in New Jersey in 1915–1916; 13 per cent in Oregon in 1926–1928; 17 per cent in New Hampshire in 1929–1930; 20 per cent in Utah in 1929–1931, 25 per cent in New York in 1940–1941, and 13 per cent in California in 1956–57–58.

Fortunately there has been substantial improvement in this respect in recent years, and many commercial farms now experience a death loss of no more than 10 per cent. If this is distributed uniformly through the year, the effect on the cost of producing eggs is small, especially with Leghorns or other light breeds with relatively small market value when sold for meat. The difference between the inevitable depreciation and total loss by death is not very great.

Even if the pullets all lived through the first twelve months in the laying house, they would be worth less after a year of production than at the beginning. As potential egg-producers they are worth more when about six months old and ready to lay than at any other time. The normal expectation is that they will continue to be worth less and less as they get older, until their egg-laying value is equal to their meat value. This does not take into account the possible breeding value of certain individuals, but is concerned only with their value as egg layers.

The difference between the value of a pullet at the beginning of the year, and the value of the same individual at the end of the year, is depreciation, and is one of the important costs in commercial egg production. If a pullet is worth $2.00 at the beginning of the year, and will bring but 50 cents after twelve months of laying, it has clearly cost the poultryman $1.50 just to own her for a year, without considering any expense for feed, labor, housing, interest, and the like. Whether one likes it or not, depreciation is just as much a part of the cost of producing eggs as it is a part of the cost of owning an automobile.

In cost accounting work, depreciation is usually determined by adding together the value of layers at the beginning inventory, the value of any pullets raised and later added to the laying flock, and the value of any pullets purchased, and subtracting from this total the sum of the ending inventory and the value of any layers sold or eaten. With equal death losses, depreciation is higher in Leghorn flocks than in flocks of heavy breeds because of the greater meat value of the latter. For the same reason, death losses are more serious, as measured in dollars, in flocks of heavy breeds.

Price of Market Eggs.—Although price is less completely under the control of the farm operator than the other factors that have been discussed, it is nevertheless true that the average price received for eggs is one of the most important factors in determining the labor income on a poultry farm. A high average price is the result of securing a large proportion of the yearly egg production during the high-price months, or of marketing eggs at premium prices, or both. If one can obtain a premium of one cent a dozen on market eggs when selling 20 dozen eggs per layer annually, the difference in income will amount to $800 a year on a flock of 4,000 layers. Going after a price premium may be a very profitable way for a poultryman to spend part of his time.

Table 14–12.—Data for 31 New York State Poultry Farms, 1959. Department of Agr. Economics, Cornell University, A. E. Ext. 90.

Item	15 High Labor Income Farms	16 Low Labor Income Farms
Average farm inventory	$39,633	$41,289
Total receipts	37,596	34,053
Total expenses	31,537	33,643
Farm income	$ 6,032	$ 410
Interest on capital @ 5%	1,982	2,064
Labor income per farm	$ 4,050	$–1,654
Average number of layers	4,657	4,539
Eggs produced per layer	221	201
Layer mortality, per cent	11	13
Man equivalent	1.8	1.9
Dozens of eggs sold per man . . .	44,764	38,765
Price received per dozen (cents) . .	37.1	34.4
Feed per dozen eggs produced (pounds)	4.8	5.6

Although several other factors were involved, the data for 31 New York poultry farms shown in Table 14–12 suggest that the price received for eggs was important in determining labor income. If the 73,653 dozens of eggs sold from each of the low-labor-income farms could have been sold at the price received by the high-labor-income group it would have meant an extra $1989 in cash receipts, or enough to change the negative labor income of $1654 to a plus labor income of $335 per farm

As an extreme example, consider the California flock records shown in Table 14–11. At 1964 costs and income per hen, with eggs selling at 28.5 cents a dozen, a 1958-size flock would have yielded a farm income of only $5,242 instead of $10,582; while at 1958 costs and income, with eggs selling at 37.5 cents, the farm income from a 1964-size flock would have increased from $20,420 to $41,221.

The Replacement Cycle

On most large commercial egg farms today chicks to be grown out as replacement pullets are started two to five times a year instead of only once in the spring. This is important in order to be able to maintain a fairly uniform weekly or monthly egg production all through the year. It also simplifies the problem of labor distribution, and keeps brooding and rearing equipment, as well as laying houses, filled to near capacity most of the year.

It is more profitable to replace layers when they are seventeen to twenty months of age than to keep them longer. Young birds lay at a higher rate and produce eggs of better shell quality than do older hens. To maintain a laying flock of 8,000 pullets, it will be necessary to start about 8,000 pullet chicks in batches of 2,000 four times a year. This will allow for normal mortality and some slight culling.

When the pullets are two to two and one-half months old, they can be moved to a growing-laying house that has been emptied and cleaned. Here they will be kept for about fifteen months until they are removed to make room for a new lot of pullets. Obviously they should be kept as long as they are profitable because income on such a farm or ranch can come only from egg sales. As each group of layers approaches seventeen months of age, both their performance and the current market situation should be studied before deciding on the exact age at which to sell them. Since brooding and rearing are on a year-round basis, it is sometimes better to skip a hatch and carry a good flock of layers for an extra three months than to replace them arbitrarily. This is one way of keeping the cost of eggs low when conditions warrant.

The program suggested for a flock averaging 8,000 layers would require a brooder house and five growing-laying houses. This is to avoid mixing of two lots at any time or having chickens of more than one age in any one house. If any one lot is carried to a full twenty-one months of age, it may be desirable to double the size of one hatch in anticipation of the replacement of two groups at one time. Under the old-style program of hatching once a year, no such adjustment was possible. In any event, the brooder house is normally in use for eight to ten months out of the year, and the five growing-laying houses are filled except at the normal recurring clean-up time.

An alternative procedure followed by many producers in some parts of the country is to buy started pullets from a dependable source instead of raising their own.

Poultry Farm Organization

Perhaps the most significant, and at the same time the most encouraging fact growing out of the various analyses that have been made of poultry farm records is that whether the labor income is high or low depends almost exclusively on the operator himself. The possibilities seem to be limited only by the extent to which he will adopt profitable practices and a profitable farm organization.

Aside from the necessary physical qualifications, the operator of a specialized commercial egg enterprise should have more or less natural aptitude for attention to details. Permanent success in specialized poultry farming is, to a considerable degree, a matter of constant and sharp attention to a great many details, the neglect of any one of which may lead to serious losses. Men who do not like to bother with too much detail are not naturally well fitted for success in specialized poultry farming. Persistent attention and genuine interest in details are necessary qualifications for the poultry business.

The accumulation of a reserve fund for tiding over an occasional bad year is a prime essential of permanent success in any type of specialized farming. Every enterprise has a bad year occasionally, sometimes owing to circumstances beyond the operator's control. The large cash expenditures required for feed make it especially necessary for the specialized poultry farm to have a reserve fund.

From a dollars viewpoint, the requirements for a successful egg-farming business can be simply stated. They are about as follows:

1. Have productive stock. This means hens with the genetic makeup and the physical stamina necessary for high annual egg production. High production is essential if the feed cost of each dozen eggs is to be kept at a profitable level.

2. Keep enough hens—as many as one can care for. This is necessary in order to make possible a reasonably large gross income, and to be able to reduce the man labor requirement below twenty minutes per layer per year.

3. Provide comfortable housing, so as to permit year-round production. This means protection from extremes of both heat and cold, along with the necessary safeguards to flock health.

4. Feed a well-balanced ration. A close corollary is found in doing everything possible to encourage maximum feed consumption.

5. Practice quantity buying of feed and other supplies so as to permit maximum savings in costs. Bulk delivery of feed is an example.

6. Find and maintain a market outlet which pays a premium price for high quality eggs.

BROILER PRODUCTION

The proportion of the total chicken meat supply furnished by commercial broilers has risen steadily from about 5 per cent in 1935 to nearly 50 per cent in 1951 and then to 84 per cent in 1959. The average price received by producers in 1935–39 was about 20 cents a pound, live weight. It rose to a high of 36 cents in 1948 and since then has declined almost steadily to 29 cents in 1952, 20 cents in 1956, and finally to 14 cents in 1964. To a large extent this is the result of year-round production and availability of fresh ready-to-cook broilers.

There are well-defined broiler-producing areas in Delmarva, northern Georgia, northwest Arkansas, Texas, North Carolina, Alabama, Mississippi, and in parts of New England, and similar if less extensive areas in several other states. Since most commercial producers depend on hatcheries for their supply of chicks, and since they can change sources promptly if performance is not satisfactory, there are many hatcheries and breeding farms which specialize in the production and sale of broiler chicks.

Total placements of broiler-type chicks in 1964–65 (the last ten weeks of 1964 and the first forty-two weeks of 1965) were 2,260 million. More than half of these (56 per cent) went into the four states of Georgia, Arkansas, Alabama and North Carolina, and an additional 29 per cent went into Mississippi, Maryland, Texas, Delaware and Maine. New lots of broilers are started in large numbers every week in the year. The seasonal index of broiler chick placements for thirteen important broiler areas, based on the five years 1952 through 1956, dropped as low as 90 in only ten weeks, with the actual minimum at 84 during the first week in September, and reached a level of 110 in only ten weeks, with the maximum at 115 during the first week in March.

The Broiler Business

Many broiler farms have lost money—sometimes because of disease, more often because of inefficient management, and at times simply because the market price of broilers at the time of sale was too low in proportion to the cost of feed which had gone into their production. The total production of broilers is enormous, and the business is well established in many areas, but it is nevertheless true that only the more efficient operators are in a position to make substantial profits.

The broiler business requires a relatively large investment in short-term capital. From 40 to 50 per cent of the total capital may be invested in chicks, feed, fuel, labor and other cash costs. Furthermore, the amount of such capital increases rapidly as each lot of broilers approaches market age or weight. This is because feed represents about 60 per cent of the total cost of production. It takes about 40 tons of feed to raise a lot of 10,000 broilers to market weight. They may eat only three-fourths of a ton during the first week, but will require seven or eight tons during the final week, depending on the type of ration used, how well they have grown and the weight at which they are sold.

Fig. 14–8.—Inside view of a 48′ × 230′ broiler house in Mississippi. (Courtesy of Broiler Business.)

Fig. 14–9.—Wooden blocks make it easy to adjust feed troughs to any desired height in this broiler house. (Courtesy of Broiler Business.)

Efficiency of feed utilization in the production of broilers has been increasing steadily for a number of years, partly because of the selection and breeding of chickens capable of rapid growth, and partly because of improved rations.   Better management, which has resulted in lower mortality, is also responsible for part of the improvement.   The following data for selected years of the Maine Broiler Test are typical:

Year	Days required to reach 3.5 pounds	Pounds of feed for each pound of gain
1952	74	3.13
1955	65	2.66
1958	60	2.18
1961	53	2.07
1964	49	1.87

Commercial broiler growers have made similar progress in improving feed conversion and in marketing broilers at younger ages. The following data, made available through the courtesy of Lipman Research Center, Augusta, Maine, provide an excellent example.

Year	Market age (days)	Market weight (pounds)	Feed Conversion (pounds of feed per pound of weight)
1952	80	3.35	3.17
1953	78	3.20	3.12
1954	76	3.30	3.06
1955	74	3.35	2.87
1956	71	3.40	2.71
1957	71	3.45	2.56
1958	68	3.44	2.37
1959	70	3.65	2.43
1960	66	3.66	2.27
1961	67	3.80	2.24
1962	65	3.76	2.15
1963	63	3.85	2.15
1964	60	3.81	2.07
1965*	58	3.75	2.05

* Averages through July.

Since feed consumption increases with a decrease in environmental temperature, broiler growers are faced with the very practical question of whether it is cheaper to provide some artificial heat in order to keep feed consumption at a minimum, than to keep the broilers in unheated houses where they are certain to consume more feed. Workers at the University of Connecticut undertook to find an answer to this question.   They found that with 2-pound broilers, as the temperature dropped below 75° F., feed consumption increased by 0.6 pound of feed per 1,000 broilers per day for each drop of one degree in temperature. Simultaneously, feed conversion became less efficient at the rate of 0.1 pound of feed per pound of gain, with each decrease of one degree in environmental temperature. The nomogram shown in Figure 14–11 was constructed from their data. It shows for the specified conditions the fuel requirement in gallons per 1,000 broilers per day to maintain any desired difference in temperature between inside and outside air for three different ventilation rates expressed as cubic feet of air per minute per bird.

Fig. 14–10.—Automatic feeders save labor and reduce feed wastage, especially in broiler plants. A 40-foot house requires two loops to provide ample feeding capacity. (Courtesy of U.S. Egg and Poultry Magazine.)

Rate of Feed Conversion

Since feed is the largest single item of cost in broiler production, it follows that the rate at which feed is converted into poultry meat is an important measure of efficiency. In Table 14–13 are shown data for 456 lots of broilers grown in Maine between July 1, 1959 and June 30, 1960, and marketed at seventy-seven days of age or less. Records of the 456 lots were sorted according to rate of feed conversion. It is clear that as the amount of feed required per pound of broiler increased, the total cost per pound of finished broiler also increased. When the sort is made on this basis there is relatively little change in either age or weight at time of sale.

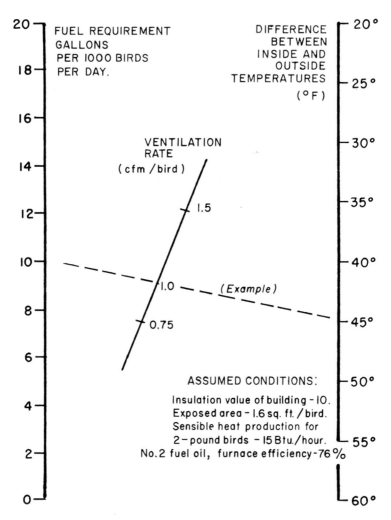

FIG. 14–11.—Fuel required to maintain indicated temperature differences in a broiler house, with three different specified ventilation rates. Based on data of Prince, Irish and Potter, University of Connecticut.

Table 14–13.—Feed Conversion as Related to Costs in Broiler Production. (Unpublished Data, Maine Agr. Exp. Sta., Courtesy of R. F. Saunders.)

Feed conversion	Number of lots	Average age when processed (days)	Average weight (pounds)	Total cost per pound (cents)
Under 2.40	41	67.0	3.56	17.91
2.40–2.49	101	70.5	3.71	18.11
2.50–2.59	145	71.8	3.76	18.66
2.60–2.69	86	72.4	3.75	19.18
2.70–2.79	57	71.9	3.67	19.93
2.80–2.89	18	73.2	3.62	20.87
Above 2.90	8	73.4	3.59	22.01
All	456	72.2	3.71	18.88

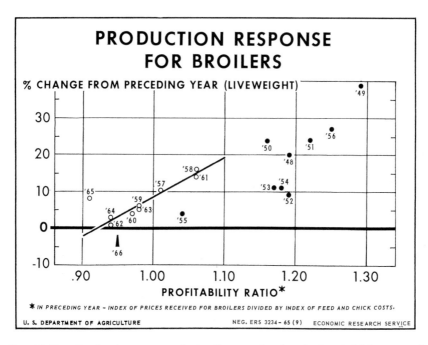

FIG. 14–12.—Production response for broilers as related to feed and chick costs and the selling price of broilers. (U. S. Department of Agriculture.)

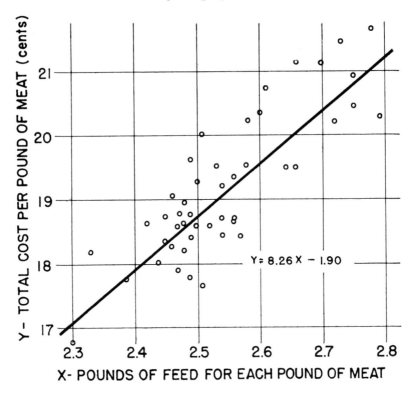

FIG. 14–13.—The rate of feed conversion is an important factor in determining costs and returns in broiler growing. Plotted points are for 47 different lots of broilers in 1959–60. All lots contained the same kind of chicks; all were fed the same brand of feed; and all were marketed at 69 days of age. (Original data supplied by Dr. R. F. Saunders, Maine Agr. Exp. Station.)

Another analysis of the effect of feed conversion on costs is shown in Figure 14–13. It is based on 47 lots, about 10 per cent of the total, which were sold at 69 days of age. As shown by the equation of the straight line, an improvement of 0.1 pound in feed conversion accounted for a reduction of slightly more than 0.8 cent in total cost per pound of broiler meat. Since these lots averaged slightly above 15,000 broilers and were sold at an average weight of 3.56 pounds, a gain in feed efficiency of one tenth of a pound was worth about $440 four times a year. This explains why successful operators have learned to purchase the kind of chicks that will grow rapidly, to use efficient rations, and to keep both feed wastage and mortality at a minimum.

Broiler growers must also make decisions as to the age or weight at which to sell their flocks. In Tables 14–14 and 14–15 the records of the same lots of Maine broilers have been sorted according to age and weight at time of sale. As age at time of sale increased from about nine to about eleven weeks, average weight increased sharply, while rate of feed conversion and cost per pound were only slightly affected. But as weight at time of sale increased—the sort being made on that basis in constructing Table 14–15—cost per pound of broiler decreased steadily, with almost no change in the rate of feed conversion. This clearly suggests that in a market which pays as

Table 14–14.—Age at Processing as Related to Costs in Broiler Production. (Unpublished Data, Maine Agr. Exp. Station, Courtesy of R. F. Saunders.)

Age when sold (Days)	Number of lots	Average weight (pounds)	Feed conversion	Total cost per pound (cents)
Under 66	21	3.33	2.34	18.39
66–68	68	3.44	2.51	19.14
69–71	151	3.64	2.56	19.02
72–74	141	3.81	2.59	18.87
75–77	75	4.01	2.61	18.49
All	456	3.71	2.56	18.88

Table 14–15.—Weight at Processing as Related to Costs in Broiler Production. (Unpublished Data, Maine Agr. Exp. Station, Courtesy of R. F. Saunders.)

Weight when processed (pounds)	Number of lots	Feed conversion	Age when sold (days)	Total cost per pound (cents)
Under 3.20	13	2.50	65.9	20.35
3.20–3.39	48	2.58	68.4	19.84
3.40–3.59	106	2.56	69.4	19.32
3.60–3.79	107	2.55	71.0	18.77
3.80–3.99	107	2.58	73.2	18.61
4.00–4.19	54	2.55	74.2	17.97
4.20 and over	21	2.56	75.1	17.74
All	456	2.56	72.2	18.88

well for heavy as for light broilers, many growers could increase their returns by carrying broilers to heavier weights than is current practice in the industry.

As further evidence of this, some Maine growers are actually producing roasters at an average cost per pound of live weight only 1.4 cents above the average cost of producing broilers. Data for 306 lots of over 15,000 roasters each, processed at 15 weeks of age when they weighed $6\frac{1}{2}$ pounds each, showed a feed conversion of 3.12 pounds and a production cost of 20.23 cents a pound. These roasters were grown between July 1, 1959, and June 30, 1960.

Actually, the broiler industry has been moving slowly toward heavier average weights for the past ten years, but this has more often been the result of improved growth potential and better feed conversion than of definite planning.   There have been some exceptions when individual operators found the heavier broilers more profitable.   And there have been well-defined area differences. Growers in Maine have consistently marketed broilers at heavier weights than the average for the country, while growers in Arkansas, Mississippi, Texas and Virginia have usually marketed at lighter weights.

Table 14–16.—Broiler Production, Average Live Weight, and Average Price per Pound, as Reported by the U. S. Dept. of Agriculture.

Year	Million pounds produced	Average weight (pounds)	Price per pound (cents)
48 States:			
1954	3,236	3.1	23.1
1955	3,350	3.1	25.2
1956	4,270	3.2	19.6
1957	4,683	3.2	18.9
1958	5,431	3.3	18.5
1959	5,763	3.3	16.1
1960	6,017	3.4	16.9
50 States:			
1961	6,841	3.4	13.9
1962	6,917	3.4	15.2
1963	7,284	3.5	14.6
1964	7,524	3.5	14.2
1965	8,106	3.5	15.0

Table 14–17.—Growth and Feed Consumption Data for Cockerels Only.   Based on Records Obtained at the Maine Broiler Test, Monmouth, Maine.   Figures for Odd-Numbered Weeks are Interpolations.

Age in weeks	Average weight (pounds)	Cumulative feed consumption (pounds)	Feed conversion to attained age (pounds)	Lots per year*
6	3.10	5.40	1.80	7.43
7	3.80	7.03	1.90	6.50
8	4.60	9.00	2.00	5.78
9	5.45	11.34	2.12	5.20
10	6.20	13.79	2.26	4.73
11	6.90	16.46	2.42	4.33
12	7.40	18.98	2.60	4.00

* One week interval between lots for cleanup.

Sorts of the kind just mentioned are helpful in showing what happens to different groups of growers, but they still do not explain why the differences occurred, and they may sometimes lead broiler operators to make wrong decisions or to adopt unprofitable practices.

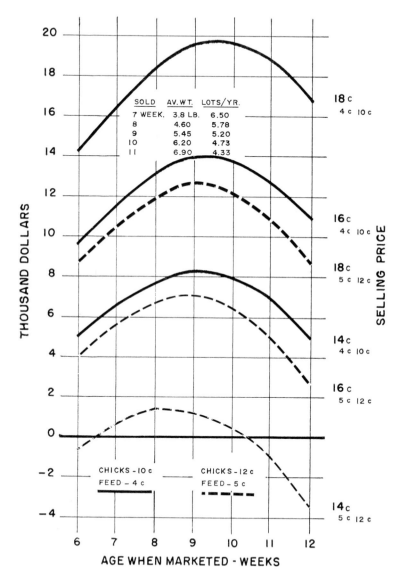

SOLD	AV.WT.	LOTS/YR.
7 WEEK.	3.8 LB.	6.50
8	4.60	5.78
9	5.45	5.20
10	6.20	4.73
11	6.90	4.33

18 c
4 c 10 c

16 c
4 c 10 c

18 c
5 c 12 c

14 c
4 c 10 c

16 c
5 c 12 c

14 c
5 c 12 c

THOUSAND DOLLARS

SELLING PRICE

CHICKS - 10 c   CHICKS - 12 c
FEED - 4 c   FEED - 5 c

AGE WHEN MARKETED - WEEKS

FIG. 14–14.—Yearly returns from a continuous broiler operation, 10,000 broilers per lot, with an interval of one week between lots. Based on data for cockerels in Maine Broiler Test (*see* Table 14–17).

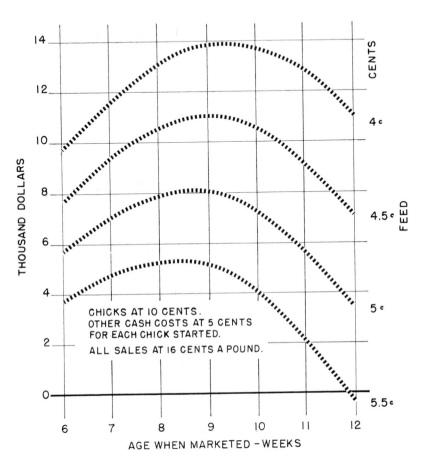

CHICKS AT 10 CENTS.
OTHER CASH COSTS AT 5 CENTS
FOR EACH CHICK STARTED.

ALL SALES AT 16 CENTS A POUND.

FIG. 14–15.—Showing the effect of feed cost on yearly returns from a continuous broiler operation, 10,000 broilers per lot, with an interval of one week between lots.

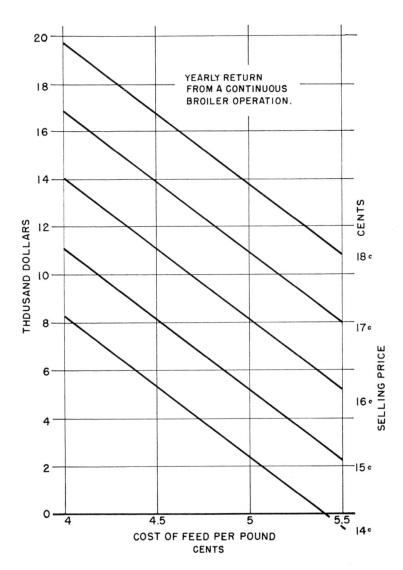

FIG. 14–16.—Combined effect of feed cost and selling price on yearly returns from a continuous broiler operation, 10,000 broilers per lot, with an interval of one week between lots.

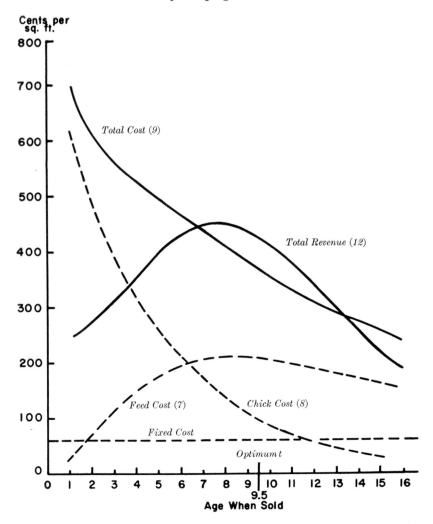

Fig. 14–17.—Relationship between broiler costs, returns, and age at sale, when calculated per square foot of available broiler house space. (After Hoepner and Freund in Virginia Agr. Exp. Station Technical Bulletin 170.)

What is needed is a breakdown which will show how the accumulated cost is changing from week to week, or with each added fraction of weight, so that an individual producer can have a reasonable basis for deciding when to sell. Not many data of this kind are available, but Table 14–18 will serve as an example.

As shown in Table 14–18, the higher the cost of feed, the earlier broilers must be sold if the grower is to obtain the maximum margin over feed cost. On the other hand, high fixed or initial costs, such as a high price paid for chicks, make it necessary to sell at a later time (in terms of age or weight) in order to distribute these costs

Table 14–18.—Effect of Chick Cost and Feed Cost on the Cost of 100 Pounds of Broilers, for a Single Lot Marketed at Different Ages. Growth and Feed Consumption Shown in Table 14–17.

Feed cost *per pound*	*Age at Market (Weeks)*						
	6	*7*	*8*	*9*	*10*	*11*	*12*
	Feed cost per 100 pounds of broilers						
4¢	$6.97	$7.40	$7.83	$8.32	$8.90	$9.54	$10.26
4½¢	7.84	8.32	8.80	9.37	10.01	10.73	11.54
5¢	8.71	9.25	9.78	10.40	11.12	11.93	13.12
5½¢	9.58	10.17	10.76	11.44	12.23	13.12	14.11
Chick cost *(day-old)*	*Chick cost per 100 pounds of broilers*						
10¢	$3.23	$2.63	$2.13	$1.84	$1.61	$1.45	$1.35
12¢	3.87	3.16	2.57	2.20	1.94	1.74	1.62
14¢	4.52	3.68	3.04	2.57	2.26	2.03	1.89
16¢	5.16	4.21	3.48	2.94	2.58	2.32	2.16

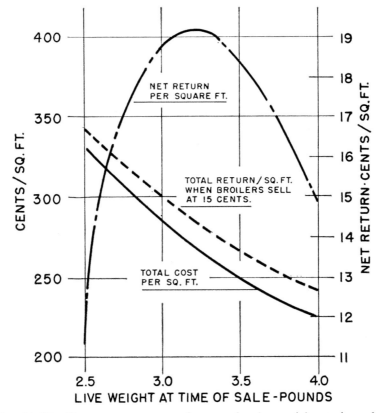

FIG. 14–18.—Net return per square foot as related to weight at time of sale. The scale for net return is purposely exaggerated. (Prepared from data of R. K. Noles, University of Georgia.)

over more pounds of broiler and thus obtain a maximum margin. One set of costs increases, and the other decreases, the longer the chickens are kept, and the broiler grower is faced with the nice problem of deciding for each lot he raises when the combination of the two is at a minimum. The whole problem is often further complicated by the prospect of a declining market.

One way to estimate the best selling time is to keep a careful record of feed consumption and cost so that these can be related to broiler selling prices. If a given lot of broilers has grown according to the data shown in Table 14–17, they will have reached an average weight of 4.6 pounds at eight weeks of age and will have consumed 9 pounds of feed each. This is 1.96 pounds of feed for each pound of broiler. If feed has cost 4.8 cents a pound, the feed cost of each pound of broiler will be 9.4 cents. Assume that the owner's records show him that feed accounts for 55 per cent of his total costs. The necessary selling price in order for him to recover all costs, including his own labor, will then be (9.4/.55 =) 17.1 cents a pound.

It is important to remember that within the range of marketable weights each additional pound of gain will require more feed than the preceding pound. The records on which all the foregoing calculations have been based show that a pound of gain between six and seven weeks of age required 2.33 pounds of feed. During succeeding weeks up to twelve, the amounts were 2.54, 2.75, 3.27, 3.81 and 5.05 respectively. Obviously, if broilers are selling at 15 cents and feed is costing 5 cents a pound, an owner cannot even get back his additional feed costs after the flock has reached the point at which it takes 3.27 pounds of feed for a pound of gain. Even though feed conversion up to that point may have been exceptional, it is time to take a close look at costs and probable returns before deciding to hold the broilers any longer.

In the language of the economist, this approach represents an analysis of input-output relationships in order to maximize returns from the broiler enterprise in terms of the margin between the total cost per pound of broiler sold and the current selling price. It involves the whole concept of marginal cost and marginal revenue. More complete data than are now available are needed on weight gains and feed consumption, by both cockerels and pullets, over the entire range of increasing marketable weights, so that broiler growers and processors can be provided with background material as an aid to making correct decisions.

Delaware research workers, during the summer of 1961, obtained data on 788 flocks, including more than six million broilers, going through processing plants on the Delmarva Peninsula. When actual in-plant value of dressed birds was related to buyers' estimates of the value of live broilers, it was found that buyers in the field (commonly called spotters) tend consistently to underestimate the value of high-quality flocks and to overestimate the value of low-quality flocks. Estimates were often as much as 0.4 cent a pound under or over the actual in-plant values. If processors do not obtain yield data on individual flocks, they have no accurate check on field buyers, and this may easily mean that, in effect, good producers in the area are subsidizing poor producers.

Labor Efficiency

Efficient use of labor is an important means of increasing profits in the broiler business, because more broilers raised per man means more total dollar income per man. Size of business is therefore the most important contributing factor in labor efficiency. If only a few broilers are grown, one cannot afford to install expensive labor-saving equipment, but if the flock size warrants, there are many devices which will simplify chore work and reduce the number of hours required for each 1,000 broilers raised. Automatic watering systems alone may cut the chore labor in half, and the use of feed carriers or automatic feeding equipment will produce additional savings.

Maximizing Annual Returns

The foregoing discussion has emphasized returns per pound of broiler for a single lot. Assuming that there is no appreciable price discount for broilers sold at the heavier weights, it has been shown that as the price of feed decreases, or the price of broilers increases, flocks should be carried to heavier weights. Many growers are tempted to do just the opposite—sell at lighter weights in order to take advantage of a good market. The charts and tables in the preceding section should help them to analyze the current situation and to make the right decision.

It is always a mistake to top out or "cream" a flock of broilers. The birds that are doing best are not the ones to sell first. Neither should cockerels be sold before pullets. Greater returns can usually be realized by selling pullets as much as a week younger than cockerels when both are ready for market at about the same time.

For growers who are following a system of continuous year-round production, there is another important question to be answered. Will the total annual returns be greater if individual lots are sold just enough short of the point of maximum returns to permit growing out an extra lot each year? This, too, will be influenced somewhat by the cost of feed and the price received for each pound of broiler.

Figures 14–14, 14–15 and 14–16, and Tables 14–19 and 14–20 present an analysis of this problem using growth and feed consumption data from the Maine Broiler Test, as given in Table 14–17, and the indicated feed and chick costs and broiler selling prices. Actual results would vary with other sets of conditions, but the principles would be no different.

It is easy to see from the curves that broilers may be sold either too early or too late for maximum returns in a continuous operation, and that the age or weight at which to sell for maximum yearly returns is earlier when feed costs are high than when they are low. Similarly, the optimum selling time is earlier when broiler prices are low than when they are high.

Table 14–19.—Effect of Various Factors on the Return per 1,000 Broilers in a Continuous Operation

Age at market (weeks)	Av. weight (pounds)	Av. feed consumption (pounds)	2-cent change in price of chicks		½-cent change in cost of feed per pound		1-cent change in selling price of broilers	
			(a)	(b)	(a)	(b)	(a)	(b)
6	3.10	5.40	$149	$130	$204	$178	$187	$211
7	3.80	7.03	130	116	236	210	208	231
8	4.60	9.00	118	104	263	236	227	250
9	5.45	11.34	104	95	298	266	245	267
10	6.20	13.79	95	87	317	290	255	276
11	6.90	16.46	87	80	333	311	257	277
12	7.40	18.98	80	75	357	331	254	272

Growth and feed consumption from Maine Broiler Test Results.
Calculations based on cockerels only.
(a) One-week interval between lots.
(b) Two-week interval between lots.

Table 14–20.—Effect of Time Allowed for Cleanup Between Lots in a Continuous Broiler Operation—10,000 Broilers per Lot.

Age at market (weeks)	Time Allowed Between Lots				Av. weight* (pounds)
	7 days	10 days	14 days	21 days	
	Number of lots per year				
6	7.43	7.02	6.50	5.78	3.10
7	6.50	6.19	5.78	5.20	3.80
8	5.78	5.53	5.20	4.73	4.60
9	5.20	5.00	4.73	4.33	5.45
10	4.73	4.56	4.33	4.00	6.20
11	4.33	4.20	4.00	3.71	6.90
12	4.00	3.88	3.71	3.47	7.40
					Effect of one day
	Annual Gross Income When All Sales Are @ 16¢ a Pound				
6	$36,853	$34,853	$32,240	$28,669	$584
7	39,520	37,635	35,142	31,616	569
8	42,491	40,701	38,272	34,813	548
9	45,340	43,600	41,246	37,758	542
10	46,922	45,235	42,954	39,680	517
11	47,803	46,368	44,160	40,958	489
12	47,360	45,939	43,926	41,085	449

* Cockerels only, based on Maine Broiler Test Results.

The specific dollar effect of changes in the cost of chicks or feed, or in the selling price of broilers, is shown in Table 14–19. The effect of varying the interval or cleanup time between lots is shown in Table 14–20.

In a completely integrated operation there are other variables to consider, such as costs in producing hatching eggs or in the hatching of the required number of chicks, the costs in feed milling, and the costs in processing the finished broilers. Under some conditions it may be more important to relate costs and returns to available space in broiler houses. In such cases it is convenient to reduce all figures to "cents per square foot" as shown in Figure 14–17. Note particularly the shape of the Feed Cost, Chick Cost and Fixed Cost lines, and the curve of Total Revenue. The Total Cost curve is simply the sum of the other three cost curves.

Since July, 1963, research workers at West Virginia have been studying another method designed to increase total annual returns in a continuous broiler operation. They used a windowless, insulated broiler house 32 × 72 feet in size, divided into three pens—a starting pen 32 × 12 feet, an intermediate pen 32 × 20 feet, and a finishing pen 32 × 40 feet. These pens provide 0.3, 0.5, and 1 square foot per broiler, respectively, when each lot contains 1,200 birds. Broilers are shifted from the starting pen to the intermediate pen at the end of three weeks, and to the finishing pen at the end of six weeks. At the end of nine weeks they are sold.

As each pen is emptied, it is cleaned, washed thoroughly, and left idle for one week. Air-tight partitions separate the pens and entrance to each pen is from the outside only, except when chicks are transferred from one pen to another through a panel opening.

With three weeks in each pen and a one-week interval between lots, 13 lots a year can be grown in a continuous operation, for a total of 15,600 broilers. Under the conventional system, the house would accommodate 2,304 broilers at 1 square foot per bird and, assuming the same one-week interval between lots, 5.2 lots could be grown in a year, for a total of 11,980 broilers. The difference works out as an increase of 30 per cent for the new system. In the first year, the gain would be only 10 per cent because it would take eight weeks to get the house up to full capacity.

The new system makes more efficient use of brooding equipment as only two-thirds as much is necessary, and fuel costs would be less per lot because a smaller volume of space would have to be heated. In northern parts of the country some heat would be needed in the entire house even under the new system. Annual fuel costs would of course be greater because more chicks would be brooded. With a lot of broilers going to market every twenty-eight days, work loads would be evened out; chicks, feed and supplies would arrive at shorter intervals, and the grower would be receiving a regular income every twenty-eight days.

Most broiler growers buy straight-run chicks and sell on the same basis. Sex separation is an accepted practice in the turkey industry, but few people have seriously considered the idea for broilers in spite of its inherent advantages. Cockerels grow faster than pullets and have a slightly better feed conversion rate. They will reach a weight of 3.5 pounds about a week ahead of pullets grown under the same conditions and fed the same ration. In the 1965 Maine Broiler Test, for example, cockerels from the first three hatches gained 1.61 pounds each between six and eight weeks of age, compared with .94 pound for pullets.

To obtain maximum margins, when cockerels and pullets are bought at the same price as day-old chicks, pullets should be sold earlier than cockerels, usually by about a week, just as flocks of slower-growing straight-run broilers—because they are less efficient feed converters—should be sold earlier than rapidly growing, efficient flocks. Of course if cockerel chicks are bought at a low price, and pullets at a high price, it is possible that the most profitable selling times might be reversed.

Sex separation may also have advantages for the processor. Recent tests at the University of Maryland have shown that over the usual range of market weights, from seven to ten weeks of age, the total cost of broiler meat per pound—including both production and processing costs—is eight per cent higher for pullets than for cockerels, but that the lowest total cost for pullets occurs about a week earlier than the corresponding lowest cost for cockerels. If the two sexes were grown separately, and delivered separately, many details of processing could be adjusted more precisely than when mixed sexes and weights are processed at the same time. These include scald water time and temperature, height adjustment of mechanical pickers, chill time in a continuous chiller, ease of uniform packaging, and mechanical sizing of parts.

Lipman Research Center, Augusta, Maine, kindly furnished the following data on their broiler operations for the complete years 1964 and 1965—for all broilers marketed at less than ten weeks of age.

	1964	1965
Total number of chicks started	12,317,838	13,633,012
Average farm capacity (for one lot)	18,500	20,000
Average when processed (days)	60	59
Average live weight when processed (pounds) .	3.8	3.8
Feed conversion (feed per pound of broiler) . .	2.1	2.0
Mortality (per cent)	2.0	2.9
Cost per pound of broiler:	cents	cents
Feed	11.14	11.37
Chicks	3.58	3.59
Fuel	0.35	0.33
Litter	0.15	0.15
Medication	0.36	0.39
Miscellaneous	2.27	2.18
Total	17.85	18.01

Grower payment is based on a set guarantee, plus an incentive related to flock performance. Average grower income in 1965 amounted to about $450 for each 1,000 broilers raised. For a plant with 20,000 capacity this meant $9,000 for the year, or about $175 a week. For this return, the grower raised five flocks, supplying buildings, equipment and labor.

A Pennsylvania operation in 1965, involving 523,000 broilers marketed at about 65 days of age at an average weight of 3.7 pounds, had summarized results as follows:

Feed conversion	2.4
Mortality (per cent)	4.5
Condemnations (per cent)	2.5
Cost per pound of saleable meat:	
Chicks	3.2¢
Feed	10.5
Labor	0.5
Other	2.3
Total	16.5¢

An Arkansas operator with 132 lots averaging 21,042 broilers per lot in September, 1965, had the following results:

Age when processed (days)	67
Average weight (pounds)	3.4
Feed conversion	2.4
Mortality (per cent)	4.4
Cost per pound live weight:	
Chicks	3.7¢
Feed	9.4
Medication	0.4
Grower payment	1.5
Other	0.1
Total	15.1¢

Finally, in Table 14–21 are given production information and cost data for over 29 million broilers grown out during the 1959–60 year in five different broiler areas. They will serve as background information.

Table 14–21.—Cost Data and Selected Production Information for Commercial Broilers Grown in Five Different Areas, 1959–60.

Item	Maine	New York and Northern Pennsylvania	Del-Mar-Va Peninsula	Shenandoah Valley Virginia	Arkansas
Number of lots	494	553	774	1,538	83
Av. number started per lot	15,984	8,904	11,766	3,840	16,577
Age when processed (days)	72	67	68	63	70
Weight when processed (pounds)	3.76	3.70	3.48	3.29	3.20
Feed conversion	2.57	2.35	2.48	2.25	2.48
Mortality (per cent)	2.3	2.0	5.0	1.5	2.9
Cost per pound live weight					
Feed	11.89¢	10.49¢	11.48¢	10.64¢	12.34¢
Chicks	3.42	3.04	3.31	3.68	4.78
Fuel	.43	.62	.56	.57	.07
Litter	.12	.25	.22	.19	.10
Medication	.12	.07	.08	.07	.49
Grower payment and flock supervision	2.77	2.61	2.16	2.08	2.28
Total cost	18.82¢	17.08¢	17.81¢	17.23¢	20.06¢

Note: All operations covered a full year, except Arkansas, which was for September, 1960 only.

The Future of the Poultry Business

Whenever there is temporary overproduction of poultry and eggs, the question of the future prospects for the business comes uppermost in the minds of many producers. In a business that is nationwide, every producer comes into more or less direct competition with producers in many other sections of the country. Certain sections have a price advantage in the selling of eggs and poultry, while others have an advantage in the way of low costs of production.

In the long run, the producer who will best be able to meet competition, and to survive recurring periods of depression in the industry, will be the one whose cost of production is lower than that of his competitors, and who is able through individual initiative or collective organization to receive a premium price for high quality products.

The poultry business has become firmly established as a part of the agricultural production of this country. If it is to maintain and improve its position in the national economy, continued improvement in the quality of poultry and eggs which reach the consumer's table is essential.

Index

Chicks, hover space for, 141
sex of day-old, 49, 70
Chilling, effects of, on chicks, 136
Chlorine, 207, 208, 224
as a disinfectant, 275
Cholera, 265
Choline, 205
Chorion, 114
Chromosomes, 68, 69
sex, 68
Chronic respiratory disease, 262
Classes of market poultry, 320 ff
Cloaca, 37
Clutch, defined, 76
size, 58, 78
effect on production rate, 77
Coccidiosis, 256
Coccidiostats, 256
Cocks, defined, 321
Coefficient of heat transfer, 172
Cold, storage of eggs, 303
Colds, 265
Comb, changes in, with egg laying, 98
characters, transmission of, 66, 67
types, inheritance of, 66
Combining ability, 83
general, defined, 82
selection for, 83
specific, defined, 83
Commercial egg farming, 346 ff
Composition of feed ingredients, 217, 218
tables, nutrient, 216, 217, 218
Condemnations, broiler, 328
Consumer buying habits, 281 ff
preferences for eggs, 281 ff
Cooling dressed poultry, 330, 331
eggs during incubation, 124
limits of, 123
Copulatory organ, rudimentary, 49
Corn, 219
Coryza, 265
Cost of egg production itemized, 352
Costs, labor, 352
major items, 351
Cottonseed meal, 222
and egg quality, 222
gossypol in, 222
Counties, leading, in production, 9
Crazy chick disease, 200
Cresol solutions, 276
Critical periods of incubation, 118
temperature, 154, 159
and heat production, 154, 228
Crop, 35

Crossbreeding, 81
Crosses for sex identification, 70
Crossing of inbred lines, 82
Crude fiber, digestion of, 210
Cull, how often to, 102
Culling, defined, 95
Curled-toe paralysis, 202
Cuticle, shell, 64
Cystine, 193, 194, 200, 218, 232

D

Dampness in brooders, 137
in poultry house, 155 ff
Dead germs, incubator, 129
Deaminization, 214
Death losses, 245
in commercial flocks, 359
Debeaking, to prevent cannibalism, 268
Deficiency diseases, 197 ff
Defluorinated phosphate, 224
Depreciation, cost of egg production and, 360
of poultry flocks, 359
Diathesis, exudative, 200
Dicalcium phosphate as a source of phosphorus, 224
Digestion, 209 ff
defined, 209
mechanical processes in, 209
of carbohydrates, 210
of fats, 210
of fiber, 210
of proteins, 210
of starch, 210
process of, 209
Digestive changes in nutrients, 209 ff
system, 35 ff
diagram of, 36
relative length, 35
Dirty eggs, 284
Disease, causes of, 246
control of, 245 ff
diagnosis, 251
how to recognize, 250
Marek's, 259
nature of, 245
prevention, 246
spread of, 247
Diseases, of chicks, 253 ff
of hens, 258
Disinfectants, 275
Distillers' solubles, 224
Dressed poultry, marketing of, 326 ff
Dried eggs, 308

G